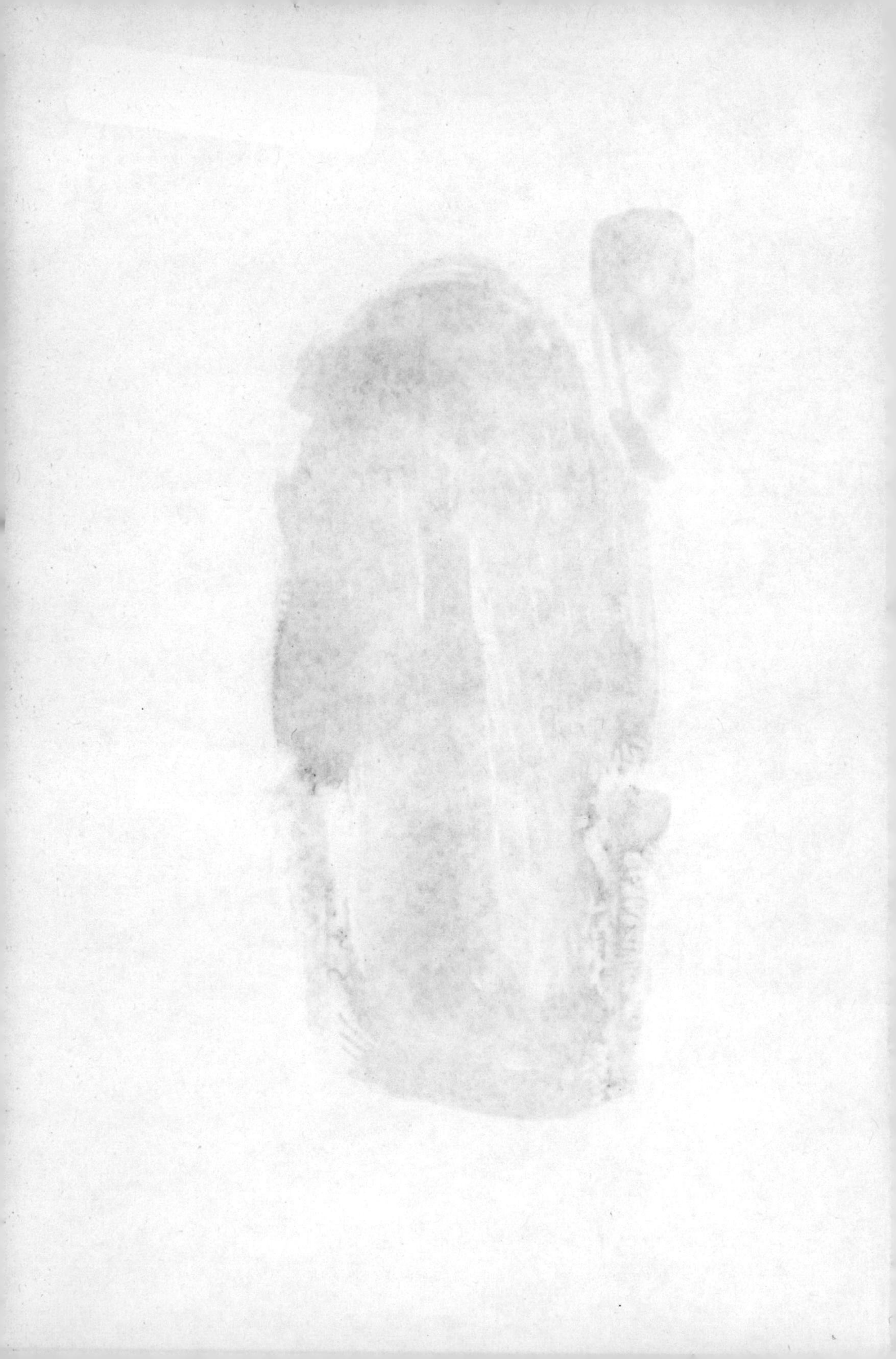

VENOMOUS AND POISONOUS ANIMALS AND NOXIOUS PLANTS OF THE PACIFIC REGION

A

VENOMOUS AND POISONOUS ANIMALS AND NOXIOUS PLANTS OF THE PACIFIC REGION

A collection of Papers based on a symposium in the Public Health and Medical Science Division at the Tenth Pacific Science Congress

Edited by

HUGH L. KEEGAN

Lieutenant Colonel, MSC, USA, Chief, Entomology Branch
Department of Preventive Medicine, Medical Field Service School
Brooke Army Medical Center, Fort Sam Houston, Texas, USA

and

W. V. MACFARLANE

Professorial Fellow of Physiology, The John Curtin School of Medical Research, Australian National University, Canberra

SYMPOSIUM PUBLICATIONS DIVISION

PERGAMON PRESS

OXFORD · LONDON · NEW YORK · PARIS

1963

A*

PERGAMON PRESS LTD.

Headington Hill Hall, Oxford
4 & 5 *Fitzroy Square, London, W.*1

PERGAMON PRESS INC.

122 *East* 55*th Street, New York* 22, *N.Y.*

GAUTHIER-VILLARS ED.

55 *Quai des Grands Augustius, Paris* 6

PERGAMON PRESS G.m.b.H.

Kaisserstrasse 75, *Frankfurt am Main*

Distributed in the Western Hemisphere by
THE MACMILLAN COMPANY · NEW YORK
pursuant to a special arrangement with
PERGAMON PRESS INC.
New York, N.Y.

Library of Congress Card No. 63-14518

Printed in Great Britain by METCALFE & COOPER LTD., London

PREFACE

THE First International Conference on Venoms, held at Berkeley, California, in December 1954, attracted participants from many countries and gave evidence of the widespread interest in this field of research. All indications are that this interest, perhaps stimulated by the Berkeley conference, has continued to grow. Since much of the most recent research on venomous and poisonous animals and noxious plants has been accomplished by scientists working in the Pacific area, it was thought fitting that a symposium for discussion of these subjects should be included in the program of the Public Health and Medical Sciences Division at the Tenth Pacific Science Congress of the Pacific Science Association, held at the University of Hawaii, 21 August to 6 September 1961, and sponsored by the National Academy of Sciences, Bernice Pauahi Bishop Museum and the University of Hawaii. This book is a collection of papers based on that symposium. Some of the papers presented could not be included here, but it has been possible to add some authoritative material not delivered at the time.

HUGH L. KEEGAN
Medical Field Service School
Brooke Army Medical Center
Fort Sam Houston, Texas

W. V. MACFARLANE
Department of Physiology
The John Curtin School of
Medical Research
Canberra

ACKNOWLEDGMENTS

THE editors would like to express their appreciation for the advice and other assistance given by Drs. K. F. Meyer and J. R. Audy, organizers of the Division of Public Health and Medical Sciences of the Tenth Pacific Science Congress. We are also deeply grateful to Dr. Harold J. Coolidge, Secretary-General of the Congress, for his efforts on behalf of this symposium, and particularly for his help in expediting travel of delegates to Honolulu. Artists of the 406th Medical Laboratory (U.S. Army Medical Command, Japan) under direction of Major Gordon Field, M.S.C., prepared illustrations for several of the papers. Lastly, we deeply appreciate the help given by Mrs. Marjorie A. Obie, who gave efficient and cheerful assistance in processing the manuscripts submitted for inclusion in this volume.

Financial support for preparation of illustrations at the 406th Medical General Laboratory and for travel of one of the editors (H.L.K.) to the Tenth Pacific Science Congress was given by the U.S. Army Medical Research and Development Command, Office of the Surgeon-General, Washington, D.C.

CONTENTS

Section I. Plants

Section II. Coelenterates and other Marine Invertebrates

Section III. Leeches

Section IV. Arthropods

Section IV. Arthropods (*continued*)

Section V. Fishes

Section VI. Snakes

Section VI. Snakes (*continued*)

Section I

PLANTS

THE POISONOUS AND URTICATING PLANTS OF AUSTRALIA

J. B. CLELAND* and D. J. LEE†

INTRODUCTION

The following account deals only with plants indigenous to Australia. Introduced plants, as for example castor oil seeds, belladonna, poison ivy (*Rhus*), and angels' trumpet (*Brugmansia*), naturalized or in gardens, have been responsible occasionally for injurious effects. References to the recorded Australian cases of injury to man by plants will be found in the references. Many Australian and introduced plants have been held responsible, often on very slender grounds, for poisoning stock, but only human cases are considered here. Poisoning by agarics, favism, lathyrism, occupational dermatoses among timber workers, and hay fever plants are not dealt with.

Unlike other parts of the world with ancient civilizations and long experience with native vegetation, the European occupation of Australia has a history of little more than 170 years. Nevertheless, it seems unlikely that many more, if any, injurious plants of importance will be encountered in the future. The search for alkaloids, some of which may be dangerous, may reveal their presence in various species, but it is unlikely that these would be naturally ingested. Only a slight amount of information has been obtained from the native population; Webb (1960) summarized the information available concerning Queensland plants.

PLANTS INJURIOUS ON INGESTION

Family Cycadaceae

Effects similar to those caused by *Macrozamia* (see under Zamiaceae) befell Captain Cook's men in 1770 at Endeavour River. Hearty attacks of vomiting occurred after eating the fruits of *Cycas media* R. Br. Macrozamin was recovered from *C. media* by Riggs (1954).

*Emeritus Professor, University of Adelaide.
†School of Public Health and Tropical Medicine, University of Sydney.

Family Zamiaceae

There are several species of the genus *Macrozamia* in Australia; their cones contain large seeds which, if not thoroughly washed or treated, may cause vomiting if eaten. Cattle develop " wobbles " or " rickets "—not true rickets but a form of paralysis—from eating the fronds.

Particularly important are *M. communis* L. Johnson, the Burrawang of the east coast of Australia, and *M. riedlei* (Fisch. ex Gaudich.) C. A. Gardner of south-western Australia. In 1697 the Dutchman Willen de Vlamingh ate five or six of the nuts, and he, as well as five others, 3 hr later began to

FIG. 1. The Burrawang, *Macrozamia communis* L. Johnson. (Reproduced by permission of the Linnean Society of New South Wales.)

vomit so violently that they were as dead men. La Perouse's seamen in 1788 had a similar experience at Botany Bay with *Macrozamia* as did Mr. Thistle and others of Flinders' complement at Lucky Bay near Esperance in 1802. Sir George Grey's men in western Australia in 1839 were similarly affected. In 1860 some of McDouall Stuart's party vomited violently after eating the nuts of *M. macdonnellii* (F. Muell. ex Miq.); one vomited 2 hr after eating the lower sweet end of one of the leaves.

The seeds of *Macrozamia*, although a conspicuous orange and attractive to look at, are now well known to be poisonous, and episodes such as the above have not been reported in the present century.

Cooper (1940) showed macrozamin to be the toxic principle of *M. communis* (then, as in all other early references, referred to as *M. spiralis* Miq., but see

Johnson, 1959). Macrozamin has also been demonstrated in *M. riedlei* by Lythgoe and Riggs (1949) and *M. miquelii* (f. Muell.) by Riggs (1954). Its chemistry has been further studied by Langley, Lythgoe and Riggs (1951).

Although macrozamin is accepted as the toxic principle of these plants it is not clear whether this pseudo-cyanogenetic compound is responsible for the emetic action.

Family Araceae

Known as the cungevoi, the arum *Alocasia macrorrhizos* (L.) G. Don is a native of the east coast of New South Wales and Queensland; it is often grown as a pot plant. The leaves contain an acrid juice which causes swelling of the mouth and throat if chewed. Parents have been warned of the danger of this pot plant if there are young children in the home.

There is a record of a child of 22 months whose lips and tongue became very red and swollen with large amounts of saliva pouring into the open mouth after chewing leaves of the plant. Another child died from eating the rhizome. In this case, although crystals of calcium oxalate were found, death was attributed to some other unknown ingredient.

Family Papilionaceae

The seeds of the prayer-bean (*Abrus precatorius* L.) are highly poisonous. Although the seed coat is very hard there have been cases of human poisoning; Webb (1948) recorded a fatality in a child.

Abrin, the active principle, is very highly toxic and is a toxalbumin resembling ricin in its action.

Seeds of the Moreton Bay chestnut, *Castanospermum australe* A. Cunn., which have been soaked and roasted are eaten by aborigines. Europeans who have eaten these seeds have suffered diarrhoea and griping pains which were often severe. Such effects have also been recorded even after ingestion of roasted seeds.

Family Thymelœaceœ

There is a record of two small children who ate the leaves of *Pimelea dichotoma* Schl. (originally reported as *P. flava*) and suffered vomiting and passed watery motions to such a degree that they were quite exhausted. No analysis has been made of this plant.

Family Myrtaceae

The fruit of the Queensland plant, *Rhodomyrtus macrocarpa* Benth., called " finger cherry " or " native loquat ", was reported many years ago as causing " comparatively sudden blindness " when eaten by some persons or at certain times. Dr. D. A. Herbert (Q'ld Poison Plants Committee Minutes, 12 October 1937) stated that at times it had been found to contain enormous quantities of saponin and at other times no trace of saponin could be found.

The danger from it was considered so serious that the Queensland Department of Education, in 1915, issued illustrations and descriptions of the plant to be displayed in all schools throughout North Queensland. Since then no Australian cases have been reported but the *Courier Mail* of Brisbane (27 December 1945) reported 27 cases of permanent blindness in soldiers in New Guinea from eating fruits of this plant. Arthur Dombrain (1944) examined the eyes of a coal-miner who had eaten the fruits many years ago and had no central vision, and found both optic discs pale. Flecker (1944) discussed the circumstantial evidence for blindness resulting from the eating of finger cherries, but notes that there is still no satisfactory explanation.

FIG. 2. Tobacco bush, *Nicotiana velutina* Wheeler. (Reproduced by permission of the Director of Animal Industry, Northern Territory Administration, Australia.)

Family Solanaceae

Though not in the ordinary sense poisonous plants, the species of *Nicotiana* in Australia may be mentioned on account of the interest associated with them. The genus occurs only in the Americas (with over 30 species in South America), Australia (with at least 15 species), and in some South Pacific islands between these. Quite independently the native inhabitants of America and of Australia discovered the pleasurable narcotic effects of the leaves. In Australia this was confined to chewing them after the quid had been rubbed in the burnt ash of an *Acacia* to liberate the nicotine.

The Australian natives are known to have used *Nicotiana benthamiana* Domin, *N. excelsior* Black, *N. ingulba* Black, *N. goodspeedii* Wheeler, *N. gossei* Domin, and when short of better species, *N. velutina* Wheeler.

The natives also chewed the leaves and small stems of another solanaceous plant, *Duboisia hopwoodii* F. Muell, which the aborigines of Cooper's Creek called " pituri ". Hicks and Le Mesurier (1935) reported that this plant contains d-nor-nicotine. The dried material was traded extensively, and in

FIG. 3. The Pituri, *Duboisea hopwoodii* F. Muell. (Reproduced by permission of the Director of Animal Industry, Northern Territory Administration, Australia.)

places where *Nicotiana* was available *Duboisia* was there used for stupefying emus by casting the branches into rockholes. It was dreaded by explorers as a camel poison.

There are no records of ill effects following the deliberate chewing of either *Nicotiana* or *Duboisia*, but when it was found that the latter was used by the natives, Dr. Joseph Bancroft turned his attention to *Duboisia myoporoides* R. Br. of the eastern coast of Australia and found it to contain a mydriatic which he called " duboisine ". Recent work reported by Hurst (1942) has shown that the leaves contain from 0·62 to 3·13 per cent of alkaloids, chiefly hyoscine and hyoscyamine.

Accidental poisoning by *D. myoporoides* has been recorded. One small child became acutely delirious with symptoms like those of atropine poisoning and another died after eating the leaves.

A child of five who chewed the leaves of *Anthocercis littorea* Labill. also had symptoms like those from belladonna (muttering delirium, dryness of the mouth and throat, dilated pupils, aimless throwing about of the arms and legs and incoherent talking).

FIG. 4. The Rock Isotome, *Isotoma petraea* F. Muell. (Reproduced by permission of the Director of Animal Industry, Northern Territory Administration, Australia.)

Family Lobeliaceae

Isotoma petraea Muell. has a bad reputation with the natives of Central Australia who speak of it as " cheeky bugger " ; this, in pidgin-English, means very dangerous. It may be used by them sparingly mixed with dried *Nicotiana* leaves when the latter are scarce. There are no records of the ill effects caused by it. In collecting plants for chemical investigation, Higginson (1957) found that a burning sensation with lachrymation occurred in the eyes from the pungent vapour (or dust) when travelling in a closed motor vehicle containing sacks full of the plants. The throat also became dry.

This was followed by fits of coughing. Professor Badger of Adelaide, who has been carrying out a chemical investigation, informed us that extraction of the ground material has yielded the known triterpene ursolic acid and three alkaloids all of the lobelia type. One has been identified as sedamine, previously obtained from *Sedum acre* L. The others are structurally very closely related but appear to be new.

PLANTS INJURIOUS ON CONTACT (URTICATING AND VESICATING PLANTS)

Family Urticaceae

Three species of nettle trees or stinging trees, *Laportea gigas* Wedd., *L. photinophylla* Wedd., and *L. moroides* Wedd., occur along the eastern part of Queensland, the two former extending into the coastal brush forests of New South Wales.

FIG. 5. The Finger Cherry, *Rhodomyrtus macrocarpa* Benth. (From Hooker, *Icon. pl.* (T. 1043), 3rd ser., vol. 1, 1867–71.)

The urtication from accidental contact with the hollow siliceous hairs on the leaves and green stems is very severe and may be felt for days and occasionally weeks afterwards. There is first a slight itch, followed in less than a minute by a severe pricking effect which quickly becomes an intense pain. The pain has a background of tingling on which is superimposed an intermittent stabbing pain with sharp radiations passing in all directions. In about 10 min the stabs of sharper pain decrease in intensity and in frequency and the background increases to a diffuse pain. Referred pain may be experienced within 5 min in the thorax, chin, forehead and opposite limb. The duller aspect of pain may last for several days and may be later revived if the part is exposed to rubbing or to cold but not to warm water. Simultaneously with the pain the nettled areas become covered with dark red spots about a millimetre in size which fuse to form a zone of swelling and erythema, which may reach a size of 4 cm from a 1 cm focus. Piloerection and sweating also occur. Rubbing may slightly reduce the pain, but there is no satisfactory antagonist.

Robertson and Macfarlane (1957) gave a brief introductory summary, from which the above is taken, of injuries to man and animals from the stings from the three species of *Laportea* that grow in Queensland. These authors also mentioned a human fatality following the sting of the New Guinea species *L. cordata* Warb. They found that " a stable, non-dialysable substance, resistant to heat, neutral in reaction, unattacked by proteolytic enzymes appears to be the essential pain-producing material. It also induces sweating, piloerection and arteriolar dilation ".

The Australian native nettle, *Urtica incisa* Poir., is widely distributed in moist places and stings at least as severely as the introduced *U. urens* L. It is of interest historically, in as much as Mulholland, one of Captain Sturt's party in 1829, was severely stung by these nettles on the river flat during the crossing of the Murrumbidgee in the interior of New South Wales. This man was naked at the time.

Family Proteaceae

The woody follicles of *Grevillea viscidula* Gardner and *G. pyramidalis* Cunn. ex R. Br. are covered with a viscous secretion which rapidly causes painful blistering if it accidentally comes in contact with the skin. Symptoms may be particularly severe if the area of contact is rubbed. It is even dangerous to sit under a tree from which the secretion may drop.

Dr. Ludwig Leichhardt, the explorer, in 1845 near the Macarthur River, which runs into the Gulf of Carpentaria, met with a drooping *Grevillea*, evidently one of the two mentioned, with a glutinous secretion on the seed vessels. His dramatic account of the vesicating effect of this secretion emphasizes its severity.

> John Murphy, having no pockets in his trousers, put the seeds . . . into his bosom, close to the skin . . . upon arriving at the camp, he felt great pain, and, on examining the place, he saw, to his greatest horror, that the whole of the skin of the epigastric region was coloured black, and raised into a great number of

painful blisters. . . . Brown . . . merely touched the skin of his arm with the matter, when blisters immediately rose . . . the discolouration of the skin was like the effects of nitrate of silver.

FIG. 6. *Grevillea viscidula* C. A. Gardner. Taken at Sir Graham Moore Island, N.W. Australia. (By permission C.S.I.R.O., Division of Fisheries and Oceanography.)

Family Ranunculaceae

Handling the leaves of *Clematis microphylla* may cause inflammation. Poultices of the crushed leaves have been used as a counter-irritant for rheumatic joints. One poultice left on for 7 min instead of 3 resulted in the formation of blisters 12 hr after application.

Family Lauraceae

Webb (1948) reported that a man handling the bark and coming in contact with the sap of *Cryptocarya pleurosparma* White and Francis developed an itchy rash within 24 hr, along with reddening on the backs of the hands, wrists and around the mouth. The irritation and blistering persisted for about 2 weeks, but scars were persistent for about 2 years.

Lande (1948) recovered an alkaloid, crytopleurine, from the sap and bark of this plant. Cryptopleurine is a powerful skin irritant and vesicant and is highly toxic to mammals and fish. Persons handling the bark of the plant may be severely affected. It has been found necessary to use respirators in the laboratory when dealing with finely ground material. A single application in cotton wool of very small amounts of 0·1 to 0·3 per cent solutions in chloroform of the alkaloid is capable of producing, after a latent period of 1 to 3 days, an erythema followed by honeycomb vesication. The vesicles become confluent to form blisters. Desquamation follows drying up of the blisters. In one volunteer the reaction was most intense between 7 and 14 days after the application. No ulceration or secondary infection occurred, but accidental transference led to a reaction about the lips and under the eyes.

The physiological properties of cryptopleurine have been studied by Lande (1948), Barnard (1949), Cleland (1950), and Hoffman (1952) and its chemistry by Gellert and Riggs (1954).

Family Rutaceae

A western Australian blister plant, *Phebalium argentenum* Sm., causes vesication if the leaves are handled. The personal experience of one of the authors (J.B.C.) with this or an allied species showed that 24 hr after some leaves had been rubbed vigorously over an area on the back of the hand, a red blush appeared followed by vesication which was complete in 48 hr. On healing, a de-pigmented patch remained for many years.

Family Euphorbiaceae

Excoecaria agallocha L., the "milky mangrove", "river poison tree" or " blind-your-eyes ", and *E. parvifolia* J. Muell. possess a volatile sap which is very irritating. A single drop getting into the eye causes severe inflammation and temporary blindness. Queensland children sometimes use the sap of the Moreton Bay fig and other figs as chewing gum. They have used the sap of the milky mangrove in mistake once or twice, with fatal results.

DISCUSSION

The discoverers and explorers of Australia have in the main been responsible for revealing the relatively few poisonous plants occurring indigenously in this country. Their experiences, though largely forgotten, have become incorporated in the lore of the Australian people and incidents of similar poisoning are rarely met with nowadays. The cases of accidental poisoning and urtication which are recorded from time to time usually involve cultivated, introduced plants.

ACKNOWLEDGEMENT

The assistance of the botanists of the National Herbarium, Sydney, in checking all botanical citations is gratefully acknowledged.

REFERENCES

Barnard, C. 1949. The C-mitotic activity of cryptopleurine. *Aust. J. Sci.* **12**, 30.

Bottomley, W. and White, D. E. 1951. The chemistry of western Australian plants. IV. *Duboisia hopwoodii. Aust. J. Sci. Res.*, Ser. A, **4**, 107.

Chippendale, G. and Murray, L. R. 1957–60. Poisonous plants of the northern territory. Northern Territory Administration, Animal Industry Branch. Extension Article No. 2, Parts I–III.

Cleland, J. B. 1914. Plants, including fungi, poisonous or otherwise injurious to man in Australia. *Aust. Med. Gaz.* **35**, 541.

Cleland, J. B. 1925. Plants, including fungi, poisonous or otherwise injurious to man in Australia. *Med. J. Aust.* **2**, 443.

Cleland, J. B. 1931. Plants, including fungi, poisonous or otherwise injurious to man in Australia. Series III. *Med. J. Aust.* **2**, 775.

Cleland, J. B. 1943. Plants, including fungi, poisonous or otherwise injurious to man in Australia. Series IV. *Med. J. Aust.* **2**, 161.

Cleland, J. B. 1957. Plants, including fungi, poisonous or otherwise injurious to man in Australia. Series V. Parts I and II. *South Aust. Nat.* **31**, 36, 53.

Cleland, K. W. 1950. Effect of cryptopleurine on cell division. *Aust. J. Sci.* **12**, 144.

Cooper, J. M. 1940. Isolation of a toxic principle from the seeds of *Macrozamia spiralis. J. Roy. Soc. N.S.W.* **74**, 450.

Dombrain, A. 1944. Sudden blindness after eating finger cherries (*Rhodomyrtus macrocarpa*). *Med. J. Aust.* **2**, 263.

Flecker, H. 1944. Sudden blindness after eating finger cherries. *Med. J. Aust.* **2**, 183.

Gardner, C. A. and Bennetts, H. W. 1956. The toxic plants of western Australia. West. Aust. Newspapers, Ltd.

Gellert, E. and Riggs, N. V. 1954. Cryptopleurine: An alkaloid of *Cryptocarya pleurosperma* White and Francis. *Aust. J. Chem.* **7**, 113.

Hicks, C. S. and Le Mesurier, H. 1935. Preliminary observations on the chemistry and pharmacology of the alkaloids of *Duboisia hopwoodii. Aust. J. Exp. Biol. and Med. Sci.* **13**, 175.

Higginson, A. R. R. 1957. Further notes on plants injurious to man. *South Aust. Nat.* **32**, 26.

Hoffman, H. 1952. Acceleration and retardation of the process of axon-sprouting in partially denervated muscles. *Aust. J. Exp. Biol. and Med. Sci.* **30**, 541.

Hurst, E. 1942. The poison plants of New South Wales. Poison Plants Committee (University of Sydney and N.S.W. Dept. of Agriculture).

Johnson, L. A. S. 1959. The families of cycads and the zamiaceae of Australia. *Proc. Linn. Soc. N.S.W.* **84**, 64.

Lande, I. S. de la. 1948. The alkaloids of *Cryptocarya pleurosperma. Aust. J. Exp. Biol. and Med. Sci.* **26**, 181.

Langley, B. W., Lythgoe, B., and Riggs, N. V. 1951. Macrozamin, II. The aliphatic azoxy structure of the aglycon part. *J. Chem. Soc.* **1951**, 2309.

Lythgoe, B. and Riggs, N. V. 1949. Macrozamin. Part I. The identity of the carbohydrate component. *J. Chem. Soc.* **1949**, 2716.

Riggs, N. V. 1954. The occurrence of macrozamin in the seeds of cycads. *Aust. J. Chem.* **7**, 123.

Robertson, P. A. and Macfarlane, W. V. 1957. Pain-producing substances from the stinging bush *Laportea moroides. Aust. J. Exp. Biol. and Med. Sci.* **35**, 381.

WEBB, L. J. 1948. Guide to the medicinal and poisonous plants of Queensland. *C.S.I.R. Bull.* **232**.

WEBB, L. J. 1960. Some new records of medicinal plants used by the Aborigines of tropical Queensland and New Guinea. *Proc. Roy. Soc. Q'ld.* **71**, 103.

POISONOUS PLANTS ON GUAM

PAUL SOUDER*

ALTHOUGH Guam has many plants with poisonous or irritating characteristics, knowledge of these characteristics, and ability to recognize them, can make tenure in tropical flora safe. Anyone exercising reasonable caution need have no fear of being poisoned.

Certain families of plants are characterized by distinct poisonous properties. The Aroid, the Spurge, the Agave, the Nettle, the *Umbellifera*, the Strychnine, the Dogbane, the Milkweed, and the Nightshade families all have poisonous properties. Poisonous plants differ in degree of harmfulness. Properties are sometimes affected by local conditions of soil, climate and cultivation. They may vary according to season. Certain parts may be highly poisonous, while others are harmless. Any plant which contains a milky juice should be treated with caution, until more is known about it.

The known poisonous plants of Guam are listed here alphabetically by their botanical names under family name headings which are arranged according to a system designed to group related plants together.

CYCADACEAE—CYCAD FAMILY

1. *Cycas circinalis* — Native
   Vern. names: fadang, federico, cycad.
   Fruit (nut) cyanogenic.

GRAMINEAE—GRASS FAMILY

2. *Sorghum bicolor* — Planted
   Vern. name: sorghum.
   Cyanogenic—contains glucoside yielding hydrocyanic acid on hydrolysis.
3. *Sorghum halepense* — Naturalized
   Vern. name: Johnson grass.
   Cyanogenic—contains glucoside yielding hydrocyanic acid on hydrolysis.

*P.O. Box 1651 Agana, Territory of Guam.

PALMAE—PALM FAMILY

4. *Areca catechu* Naturalized
   Vern. name: pugua, betel nut.
   Fruit (nut) contains arecoline.
   Anthelmintic.

5. *Arenga pinnata* Planted
   Vern. name: cabo negro, sugar palm.
   Fruit (nut) contains microscopic stinging crystals.

6. *Caryota urens* Planted
   Vern. name: fishtail palm.
   Fruit (nut) contains microscopic stinging crystals.

ARACEAE—ARUM FAMILY

The Aroids, which follow, all contain microscopic stinging crystals of calcium oxalate that are intensely irritating when brought in contact with mucuous membranes of mouth, nose and throat, even in contact with tender skin. Application of heat breaks down crystals, and thorough cooking makes leaves edible. Crystals are not poisonous—just irritating.

7. *Aglaonema commutatum* Planted

8. *Aglaonema modestum* Planted

9. *Alocasia indica* Naturalized
   Vern. name: piga. Juice blisters skin.

10. *Alocasia macrorrhiza* Naturalized
    Vern. names: papao apaca, piga, elephant ear.

11. *Alocasia sanderiana* Planted
    Vern. name: Philippine taro.

12. *Caladium bicolor* Planted
    Vern. names: corazon de Santa Maria, elephant ear.

13. *Anthurium andraenum* Planted
    Vern. name: Anthurium.

14. *Colocasia esculenta* Planted
    Vern. names: suni, taro dasheen.

15. *Crytosperma chamissonis* Planted
    Vern. names: baba, giant taro.

16. *Dieffenbachia picta* Planted
    Vern. name: dumb cane.
    Swallowing chewed material may paralyse throat and cause temporary loss of speech.

17. *Monstera deliciosa* — Planted
18. *Monstera schleichtleinii* — Planted
19. *Philodendron bipinnatifidum* — Planted
20. *Philodendron hastatum* — Planted
21. *Philodendron* var. *Jaluit* — Planted
22. *Philodendron selloum* — Planted
23. *Scindapsus aureus* — Planted
    Vern. name: taro vine.
24. *Spathiphyllum kochii* var. *clevelandii* — Planted
25. *Syngonium podaphyllum* — Planted
26. *Typhonium cuspidatum* — Planted
    Vern. name: pantake.
27. *Xanthosoma sagittifolium* — Planted
    Vern. name: yantia.
28. *Xanthosoma violacium* — Planted
    Vern. name: sunin honolulu.

AGAVACEAE—AGAVE OR CENTURY PLANT FAMILY

Agaves contain saponin and minute stinging crystals of calcium oxalate.

29. *Agave americana* — Planted
    Vern. name: maguey, century plant.
30. *Agave fourcroydes* — Planted
    Vern. name: henequen.
31. *Agave vivipara* — Established
    Vern. name: lirio de palo.
32. *Cordyline stricta* — Planted
    Vern. name: dracnea.
33. *Cordyline terminalis* — Naturalized
    Vern. name: baston de Jose.
34. *Furcraea gigantia*—green oloe — Planted
35. *Phorium tenax*—New Zealand flax — Planted
36. *Polianthes tuberosus* — Planted
    Vern. name: tuberose.
37. *Sanseviera cylindrica* — Planted
38. *Sanseviera hahnii* — Planted
    Vern. name: dwarf snake plant.

39. *Sanseviera roxburghiana* Planted, locally established
    Vern. names: tigre, bowstring hemp.
40. *Sanseviera trifasiata* var. *laurenti* Planted, locally established
    Vern. name: Yellow leaf mother-in-laws tongue.
41. *Yucca gloriosa* Planted
    Vern. name: Spanish bayonet.

AMARYLLIDACEAE—AMARYLLIS FAMILY

42. *Crinum asiaticum* Planted
    Vern. names: piga-palayi, crinum lily.
    Bulb used as an antidote for snake and arrow poison, for earache and other infections, and after eating poison fish.
43. *Hymenocallis littoralis* Planted
    Vern. name: spider lily.
    Bulb poisonous.
44. *Zephranthes atamasco* Planted
    Vern. name: white rain lily.
    Bulb is poisonous.

DIOSCOREACEAE—YAM FAMILY

45. *Dioscorea bulbifera* Native
    Vern. names: magnaheugo, wild yam.
    Poison tuber.

URTICACEAE—NETTLE FAMILY

Nettles have hollow siliceous stinging hairs containing powerful irritant substances. Their action is really not primarily mechanical.

46. *Fleurya interrupta* Native
    Vern. name: palilalia.
47. *Laportea latifolia* Native

NYCTAGINACEAE—FOUR O'CLOCK FAMILY

48. *Mirabilis jalapa* Naturalized
    Vern. names: maravilla, four o'clock.
    Roots and seeds are poisonous.

ANNONACEAE—CUSTARD APPLE FAMILY

49. *Annona muricata* Planted and naturalized
    Vern. names: laguana, laguanaha, anonas, soursop.
    Root is a fish poison, leaves are anthelmintic.

50. *Annona squamosa* Planted
    Vern. names: atis, sugar apple, sweetsop.
    Seeds, leaves and unripe fruits are insecticidal.

HERNANDIACEAE

51. *Hernandia sonora* Native
    Vern. name: Jack-in-the-box.
    Bark, seed and young leaves purgative. Leaf juice dipilatory.

PAPAVERACEAE—POPPY FAMILY

52. *Argemone mexicana* Naturalized
    Vern. name: prickly poppy.
    It has emetic, carthetic, anoydyne and narcotic properties.

LEGUMINOSAE—BEAN FAMILY

Certain beans of legumes with pink or brown shells are poisonous until cooked.

53. *Abrus precatorius* Native
    Vern. name: kolales halumtano, black-eyed susan.
    Acrid poison " abrin " is present in red seed covering, and is fatal if injected into blood stream.

54. *Canavolia ensiformis* Planted
    Vern. name: Jack bean.
    Mature seed pods are poisonous, but edible if boiled.

55. *Cassia alata* Planted
    Vern. name: acapulco, andadoce, take biha, candle bush.
    All parts of plant poisonous.

56. *Cassia fistula* Planted
    Vern. name: canafistula, golden shower.
    Fruit is purgative.

57. *Cassia occidentalis* Naturalized
    Vern. name: coffee senna.
    Poisonous to livestock.

58. *Clitoria ternatea* Naturalized

Vern. name: paokeke, capa de la reina, butterfly pea.

Seeds and roots are cathartic.

59. *Crotalaria spectabilis* Naturalized

Vern. name: rattlebox, rattlepod.

Contains alkaloid monocrotoline. Present in leaves, stem root and seed.

60. *Derris trifoliata* Native

Vern. name: bagin.

Sap root and bark poison, insecticidal.

Poisons fish but not mammals. Used as a stimulant, anti-spasmodic and counter-irritant.

61. *Dolichos lablab* Naturalized

Vern. name: hyacinth bean.

Seeds contain poisonous glucoside, destroyed by heat.

62. *Entada pursaetha* Native

Vern. name: bagogo, bayogon dangkulo, lodusong, snuff-box bean.

Crushed leaves used to stupify fish.

63. *Erythrina variegata* var. *orientalis* Native

Vern. name: gaogao, gabgab, coral tree.

Juice of leaves anthelmintic. All parts of tree poisonous.

64. *Gliricidia sepium* Established

Vern. name: madre de cacao.

Powdered seed, bark, and leaves are used as a rat poison.

65. *Indigofera endecephylla* Introduced

Vern. name: prostrate indigo.

Leaves poisonous to cattle. Contains 3-nitropropionic acid.

66. *Leucaena glauca* Naturalized

Vern. name: tangantangan, koa haole.

When eaten by horses tail hair falls.

67. *Mucuna gigantea* Native

Vern. name: gaye tan, bayoga dikiki, dikiki gaogao, bayogon dailaili.

Seeds strong purgative—the trichomes produce itching through the action of the enzyme mucunain or some other histamine liberator.

68. *Mucuna urens*

Vern. name: cow itch.

The trichomes produce itching through the action of the enzyme mucunain or some other histamine liberator.

69. *Pachyrrhizus erosus* Naturalized

Vern. name: hikamas, yam bean.

Seeds stupify fish. Leaves contain glucoside, pachyrrhizid.

70. *Phaseolus lunatus* — Planted
Vern. name: lima bean.
Mature seeds contain hydrocyanic acid.

71. *Pongamia pinnata* — Native
Fish poison from seeds and root. Contains hydrocyanic acid.

72. *Sesbania grandiflora* — Planted
Vern. name: katurai.
Flower and pod have laxative.

73. *Sophora tomentosa* — Native
Vern. name: silver bush.
All parts of plant bitter. Contain alkaloid " Sophorine ".

74. *Tamarindus indicus*
Vern. name: kamalindo, tamarind.
Laxative.

75. *Tephrosia hookeriana*
Fish poison.

ZYGOPHYLLACEAE—CALTROPS FAMILY

76. *Guaiacum officinale* — Planted
Vern. name: lignum vitae.
Poisonous wood and seeds.

MELIACEAE—CHINABERRY FAMILY

77. *Melia azederach* — Naturalized
Vern. name: paraiso, china-berry, Pride of India.
Contains alkaloid " Saponin ". Anthelmintic, insecticide, cathartic, and fish narcotic.

EUPHORBIACEAE—SPURGE FAMILY

Members of this family contain a milky white latex or sap which causes an acute skin dermatitis on contact.

78. *Acalpha hispida* — Planted
Vern. name: chenile plant.

79. *Acalypha indica* — Naturalized
Vern. name: hierba del cancer.
Cathartic.

80. *Acalypha wilkesiana* — Planted
Vern. name: Beef steak plant.

81. *Aleurites moluccana* Planted
Vern. name: lumbang, candlenut.
Cathartic. Contains saponin.

82. *Aleurites trisperma* Planted
Vern. name: soft lumbang.

83. *Antidesma bunius* Planted
Vern. name: bignay.

84. *Claoxylon marianum* Native
Vern. name: panao, cator.

85. *Codiaeum variegatum* Planted
Vern. name: San Francisco, Buena Vista, lestun puyitos, croton.
Leaves and roots have medicinal properties.

86. *Endospermum moluccanum* Planted
Vern. name: Moon tree.

87. *Euphorbia antiquorum* Planted
Vern. name: malayan spurge.
Acrid juice poisonous. Causes blindness on contact with eyes.

88. *Euphorbia chamissonis* Native
Vern. name: beach spurge.

89. *Euphorbia cyathophora* Naturalized
Vern. name: dwarf poinsettia.

90. *Euphorbia guadichaudii* Native

91. *Euphorbia gomerifera* Naturalized

92. *Euphorbia hirta* Naturalized
Vern. name: golondrina, hairy spurge.

93. *Euphorbia neriifolia* Naturalized
Vern. name: Lengua i baca, hila i baca. Planted

94. *Euphorbia prostrata* Naturalized

95. *Euphorbia pulcherrima* Planted
Vern. name: poinsettia.
Sap poisonous, causes skin dermatitis. Internal poison.

96. *Euphorbia ramosissima* Native

97. *Euphorbia serrulata* Native

98. *Euphorbia splendens* Planted
Vern. name: Crown of Thorns.
Toxic if eaten.

99. *Euphorbia thymifolia* Naturalized

100. *Euphorbia tirucalli* Planted
 Vern. name: milk bush, stick plant.
 Toxic if eaten. Sap is skin vessicant.

101. *Euphorbia trigona* Planted

102. *Excoecaria agallocha* L. Native
 Vern. name: poison mangrove.
 Skin blisters and sap causes painful irritation and blindness if it gets in the eye. Smoke from burning wood is very irritating.

103. *Glochidion marianum* Native
 Vern. name: chosgo.

104. *Heavea brasiliensis* Planted
 Vern. name: Para rubber.

105. *Jatropha curcas* Planted and naturalized
 Vern. name: tuba tuba, physic nut.
 Seeds poisonous and purgative.

106. *Jatropha gossypifolia* Planted and established

107. *Jathropha multifida* Planted
 Vern. name: Santa Ana, coral plant.
 Seeds poisonous.

108. *Jatropha podagarica* Planted
 Vern. name: gout stick.
 Seeds poisonous.

109. *Macaranga thomsonii* Native
 Vern. name: pengua.

110. *Manihot esculenta* Planted
 Vern. name: medioka, cassava, tapioca.
 Contains " amygdalin ", a poison alkaloid, and hydrocyanic acid.

111. *Manihot glaziovii* Planted
 Vern. name: ceara rubber.

112. *Melanolepis multiglandulosa* var. *glabrata* Native
 Vern. name: alom.

113. *Pedilanthus tithymaloides* Planted
 Vern. name: slipper flower.

114. *Phyllanthus acidus* Planted
 Vern. name: otaheite gooseberry.

115. *Phyllanthus amarus* Naturalized
 Vern. name: maigo lalo.

116. *Phyllanthus debilis* Naturalized

117. *Phyllanthus marianus* Native
Vern. name: gaogao uchan.

118. *Phyllanthus nivosus* Planted

119. *Phyllanthus saffordii* Native

120. *Phyllanthus simplex* Native

121. *Phyllanthus urinaria* Naturalized

122. *Ricinus communis* Naturalized
Vern. name: agaliya, castor bean.
Toxic seed contains " ricin ", ricinoleic acid, and oleic acid.

ANACARDIACEAE—CASHEW FAMILY

Members of this family contain a toxic albumin which causes skin dermatitis.

123. *Anacardium occidentale* Planted
Vern. name: kasoy, kasue, cashew.
Juice from seed shell burns skin.

124. *Mangifera indica* Planted and naturalized
Vern. name: mango, mangga.

125. *Mangifera odorata* Naturalized
Vern. name: Saipan mango.

126. *Maytenus thompsonii* Native
Vern. name: luluhut.

127. *Rhus taitensis* Native
Vern. name: lemayo, sumac.

128. *Schinus terebinthifolia* Planted
Vern. name: Christmas berry tree.

MALVACEAE—MALLOW FAMILY

129. *Abutilon indicum* Naturalized
Vern. name: malbas.
Seeds are laxative.

GUTTIFERAE—MANGOSTEEN FAMILY

130. *Calophyllum inophyllum* Native
Vern. name: daog, palo maria, kamani, Alexandrian laurel.
Fruits, seeds and leaves poisonous. Used as fish poison.

FLACOURTIACEAE—FLACOURTIA FAMILY

131. *Pangium edule* Naturalized
Vern. name: raual, lasret.
Leaves poisonous, contain hydrocyanic acid.

CARICACEAE—PAPAYA FAMILY

132. *Carica papaya* Planted and naturalized
Vern. name: papaya.
Sap causes skin dermatitis.

PASSIFLORACEAE—PASSION FLOWER FAMILY

133. *Passiflora edulis* var. *flavicarpa* Planted
Vern. name: passion fruit vine.
Stem and roots are poisonous containing hydrocyanic acid.

CURCURBITACEAE—MELON FAMILY

133. *Lagenaria siceraria* Planted
Vern. name: gourd.
Fruit is a purgative and laxative.

THYMELEACEAE—DAPHNE FAMILY

134. *Wikstroemia elliptica* Native
Vern. name: gapit atayake.
Fish narcotic. Not poisonous to mammals.

LECYTHIDACEAE—BRAZIL-NUT FAMILY

135. *Barringtonia asiatica* Native
Vern. name: puting.
Seeds fish narcotic when green.

136. *Barringtonia racemosa* Native
Vern. name: langasat, langassag.
Seeds fish narcotic.

UMBELLIEFERAE

137. *Apium guaveolens* Planted
Vern. name: celery.

138. *Apium petroselinum* — Planted
Vern. name: parsley.

139. *Centella asiatica* — Native

140. *Foeniculum vulgare* — Planted, naturalized
Vern. name: anis hinoho, fennel.

LOGANIACEAE—STRYCHNINE FAMILY

Every part of plant is poisonous.

141. *Buddleja asiatica* — Naturalized

142. *Geniostoma micranthum* — Native
Vern. name: majlocjayo, anasser.

APOCYNACEAE—DOGBANE FAMILY

143. *Allamanda cathartica* L. — Planted
Vern. name: allamanda.
Cathartic.

144 *Allamanda cathartica* var. *hendersonii* — Planted
Vern. name: allamanda.
Cathartic.

145. *Alyxia torresiana* — Native
Vern. name: nanago, loduson lahe.
Poison juice.

146. *Bleekeria mariannensis* — Native
Vern. name: langiti.

147. *Carissa arduina* — Planted
Vern. name: hedge thorn.

148. *Carissa grandiflora* — Planted
Vern. name: natal plum.

149. *Catharanthus roseus* — Planted and naturalized
Vern. name: chichirica, madagascar periwinkle.
Poisonous to cattle.

150. *Cerbera dilatata* — Native
Vern. name: chiute.
Poison seed. Fish poison.

151. *Ligustrum japonicum* — Planted

152. *Ligustrum lucidum* — Planted
Vern. name: glossy privet.
Toxic if eaten.

153. *Ligustrum sinense* Planted

154. *Nerium indicum* Planted
Vern. name: adelfa, oleander.
Every part of plant poisonous. Contains " Oleandrin " a glycoside which on hydrolysis yields gitoxigenin.

155. *Nerium oleander* Planted
Vern. name: adelfa, rosa laurel, oleander.
Every part of plant poisonous—contains " Oleandrin ".

156. *Ochrosia oppositifolia* Native
Vern. name: fago.
Poison fruit. Fish poison antidote.

157. *Plumeria rubra* Planted
Vern. name: plumeria, frangipani.
Poisonous.

158. *Tabernaemontana divaricata* Planted
Vern. name: cape jasmine, paper gardenia.
Roots contain poison.

159. *Thevetia peruviana* Planted
Vern. name: bestill tree, yellow oleander.

ASCLEPIADACEAE—MILKWEED FAMILY

160. *Asclepias curassavica* L. Naturalized
Vern. name: asuncion, milkweed.
Juice is anthelmintic.

161. *Dischidia puberula* Native

162. *Telosma cordata* Planted
Vern. name: mil-leguas.

VERBENACEAE—VERBENA FAMILY

162. *Lantana camera* Naturalized
Vern. name: lantana.
Causes photosensitivity on cattle when eaten.

SOLANACEAE—NIGHTSHADE FAMILY

163. *Capsicum annuum* Planted
Vern. name: doni, pepper.

163. *Capisum annuum* var. *cerasiforme* Planted
Vern. name: cherry pepper.

164. *Capsicum annuum* var. *grossum* Planted
Vern. name: doni, bell pepper.

165. *Capsicum frutescens* Planted, naturalized
Vern. name: doni sali, doni halen tano, chili pepper.

166. *Cestrum diurnum* Naturalized
Vern. name: tintan-China, Chinese-inkberry.

167. *Cestrum nocturnum* Planted
Vern. name: dama de noche, lady of the night.

168. *Cyphomandra betacea* Planted
Vern. name: tree tomato.

169. *Datura metel* Planted
Vern. name: jimson weed, thorn apple.
All poisonous. Contains alkaloides hyoscyamine, scopolamine and atropine.

170. *Nicotiana tabacum* Planted, persisting
Vern. name: chupa, tobacco.

171. *Physalis angulata* Naturalized
Vern. name: tomates chaka, ground cherry.

172. *Physalis lanceifolia* Naturalized
Vern. name: tomates caputi, ground cherry.

173. *Solanum grandifolium* Planted
Vern. name: contains " Solannine " and related gluco-alkaloides.

174. *Solanum guamense* Native
Vern. name: berenghenas halomtano.

175. *Solanum lycopersicum* Planted
Vern. name: tomate, tomato.

176. *Solanum lycopersicum* var. *cerasiforme* Naturalized
Vern. name: tomates, kaputi, ubas, cherry tomato.

177. *Solanum lycopersicum* Naturalized
Vern. name: tomates, tomates halen tano.

178. *Solanum melongena* Planted
Vern. name: Berenghenas, egg plant.

179. *Solanum nigrum* L. Naturalized
Vern. name: nightshade.
Leaves and unripe berries poisonous, caused by Solanine and related gluco-alkaloides.

CAMPANULACEAE—BELL FLOWER FAMILY, LOBELIA FAMILY

180. *Hippobroma longiflora* Established
Vern. name: Star of Bethlehem.
A drop of sap in eyes can cause blindness.

CAMPOSITAE—SUNFLOWER FAMILY

181. *Artemisia vulgaris* Naturalized
Vern. name: wormwood.
Very poisonous to livestock.

REFERENCES

KUMADA, TOSHIO. 1940. *Poisonous Fishes and Plants in the Tropics.* Translated by K. Nusya. Published by the U.S. Geological Survey in Tokyo, Japan.

MACMILLAN, H. H. 1956. 5th ed. *Tropical Planting and Gardening.* Macmillan, London, England.

MERRILL, E. D. 1943. Emergency Food Plants and Poisonous Plants of the Islands, of the Pacific. Tech. Manual TM 10–420, War Dept., G.P.O., Wash., D.C.

NEAL, M. C. 1948. In Gardens of Hawaii, *Bishop Museum Bulletin* No. 40, Honolulu. Hawaii.

SAFFORD, W. E. 1905. *The Useful Plants of Guam.* U.S. National Herbariums Volume IX, Washington, D.C.

WEST, E. I. 1960. *Poisonous Plants around the Home.* Bull. 175 Agri. Ext. Serv., Gainesville, Florida.

WEST, E. and EMMEL, M. W. 1960. *Plants that Poison Farm Animals.* Bull. 510A. U. of Florida, Agri. Exp. Sta., Gainesville, Florida.

THE PAIN-PRODUCING PROPERTIES OF THE STINGING TREE, *LAPORTEA*

W. V. MACFARLANE*

THE genus *Laportea* belongs to the Urticaceae. In New Guinea and Australia it grows as shrub or tree in rain forest. The New Guinea species is *L. condata*, while in the eastern rain forests of northern New South Wales and Queensland, *L. gigas* becomes a tree 30–40 m high and the Gympie bush, *L. moroides*, grows only 6–8 m. Webb (1948) has reviewed distributions of the species of the genus. The leaves and stems of all species are covered with fine stinging hairs (Fig. 1). On the leaf veins and stems larger stinging spines grow up to 2 mm long. Leaves reach 20 cm in diameter and they have a soft green colour (Fig. 2).

FIG. 1. Micrograph of the stinging hairs, illustrating the diversity of sizes. Small drops of clear fluid from the hairs appear at the tips of some hairs.

In Australia, as reported by Bancroft (1889), the effects of contact with the plants have been known since the 1840's, when expeditions first passed over the Queensland ranges. Horses, cattle and men were afflicted by the severe stings of *Laportea*, and deaths of horses were reported after extensive contact. Animals become violent and uncontrollable when stung. Men (cutting

*Australian National University, Canberra.

roads, railways, telegraph and telephone routes, or serving in the army) are incapacitated for several days and suffer an inexorable and enduring pain, after contact with the trees. Since the climate is hot and clothing is minimal, widespread stings on the body occur.

FIG. 2. Leaf and stem of *L. moroides*. The largest hairs are on the leaf veins, on the undersurface of the leaves, and on the green stems.

Subjective effects

The hairs do not easily penetrate the palmar or plantar skin, but all thinner types of skin are pierced by the hairs on gentle contact. A lateral movement of the hair relative to the skin is necessary to break the tip and release the stinging substance. About 20 sec after such contact there is a slight itch followed by a severe prickling sensation. There is always a latency of 20–40 sec, whether the sting is induced by penetrating hairs or from injection of a water extract of the hairs intradermally.

The initial bursts of sharp pain become intense radiating stabs, passing in all directions from the focal point. If the lesion is on the arm, pain is felt in the armpit, and referred pain on the face and opposite limb is commonly experienced. A sharp diffuse pain persists between the acute radiating bursts. The stabbing pain lasts for from 20 min to 3 hr but the diffuse pain remains for 2–3 days. The duller pain is increased by rubbing gently or by cold which causes it to become sharp again. The region that has been stung responds to touch and cold water for periods up to eight weeks, producing a sensation of prickling pain.

Probably some of the pain-producing material passes into the lymphatics, since a diffuse pain is felt along those channels towards the regional lymph nodes, which become tender.

Objective Reactions

The nettled area develops small red spots within a minute. These swell, fuse and become generally erythematous. Within 10 min axon reflex vasodilatations appear over a zone with a radius 2–3 cm greater than that of the erythema. The erythema lasts 12 to 36 hr.

Sweating, localized to the region of erythema, develops after 5 min and persists for 26 to 30 hr. It is most active after 6 hr. The transition from dry skin to wet, in the sweating zone, is easily detected by the increased resistance to moving a finger across the region. Piloerection occurs intermittently on the red oedematous zone during the first 10 hr.

Injection of 0.01 ml of saline extract of hairs produces the same pain and sequence of changes experienced after contact with the hairs. The latency for pain is 20 sec after intradermal injection; piloerection occurs within 1 min. The effects usually persist for a rather shorter time than after hair penetration. Most signs and symptoms are lost at the end of 3 weeks.

Dust from the dry leaves or volatile material from crushed hairs causes sneezing. This may be followed by watery discharge and after 4 hr an inflammatory response of nasal and sinus mucosa. The mucosa remains painful for a week and some sloughing and discharge persists for 2 weeks.

Mechanisms of Action

It has been claimed by Emmelin and Feldberg (1947) that *Urtica urens* produces its effects by a combined action of acetylcholine and histamine. These substances (or substances giving similar responses in bioassays on gut and uterus) together with 5-hydroxytryptamine (5-HT) as reported by Collier and Chester (1956) are present in hairs from *Laportea moroides*. The range of quantities per stinging hair in *Laportea* is: acetylcholine activity 0.01–0.02 μg/hair, histamine activity 0.02–0.05 μg/hair, 5-HT activity 0.001 μg/hair. Robertson and Macfarlane (1957) have discussed three lines of evidence indicating that these substances are not important in producing the stinging response.

1. Dialysis of a water extract of hairs does not detectably reduce the pain-producing activity. The effective substance appears to have a molecular weight greater than 1000. When the dialysed material is free of acetylcholine, histamine and 5-HT it produces the normal pattern of pain and skin reactions.

2. Antagonists (atropine, mepyramine, tryptamine) to these three substances injected with the extract produce analgesia for up to 30 min and prevent flare, but pain, redness and sweating appear after the effects of antagonists have passed. The usual sensations and reactions persist then for days.

3. The duration of the pain, sweating, redness and piloerection is of the order of days, while the effects of acetylcholine, histamine and 5-HT last

less than an hour. Acetylcholine, histamine and 5-HT injected together in quantities equivalent to those present in hairs do not produce any of the severe sharp pain experienced after *Laportea* stings, nor is the visible lesion similar to that induced by the plant.

Pain-producing Substance

There is thus evidence for the presence of a large active molecule in the hairs. Its chemical nature has not been determined, although, as reported by Robertson and Macfarlane (1957), some of its properties are known. It appears to cause the release of vasodilator, pilomotor and sudomotor substances in the skin, and to stimulate pain endings of several types.

The physicochemical properties so far determined are:

(a) The substance does not pass a cellophane membrane that allows molecules of 1000 MW to dialyse. It is stable and persists in the dry leaf for 40 years.

(b) Boiling for 10 min does not reduce the pain-producing activity. Boiling in 5 N hydrochloric acid for an hour or in 0.2 M sodium hydroxide cause almost complete loss of activity.

(c) Neither ether nor ethanol extracts a significant proportion of water-soluble pain-substance.

(d) There is no migration in an electrophoretic field at pH 8.4.

(e) Trypsin, pepsin, emulsin and papain fail to alter the pain-producing activity of dialysed extracts of *Laportea* hairs, though diastase, takadiastase and hyaluronidase have a small effect.

Pain-producing activity does not seem to be associated with a protein, polypeptide, glucoside, alkaloid or resin acid, and the evidence that a polysaccharide is involved is slender.

Activity on Nerves

The effects of the active material were examined on anesthetized cats, in which the spinal cord and lumbar roots were exposed. Extracts of *Laportea* hairs injected into the skin of a cat produced a slight increase in the frequency of discharge detected in dorsal root fibres. Since pain fibres are small in diameter it is unlikely that any great effect would be detected, unless single fibres were examined.

When 0.01 ml of extract was added to the slender dorsal root filaments there was a three or fourfold increase in the rate of firing. Discharge from the ventral root increased also. The monosynaptic reflex was not affected, but there was a fourfold increase in the amplitude and duration of the polysynaptic discharge. Some additional discharge occurred in the contralateral ventral root. When *Laportea* extract was injected into the cord, monosynaptic reflexes were blocked, but larger and longer polysynaptic potentials persisted (Fig. 3).

These findings suggest that nerve fibres and nerve cells are depolarised and discharged by *Laportea* extract. Activity of the interneurone pool is stimulated and this would account for the spread of pain, the intensity of pain and its reference to the other side of the body.

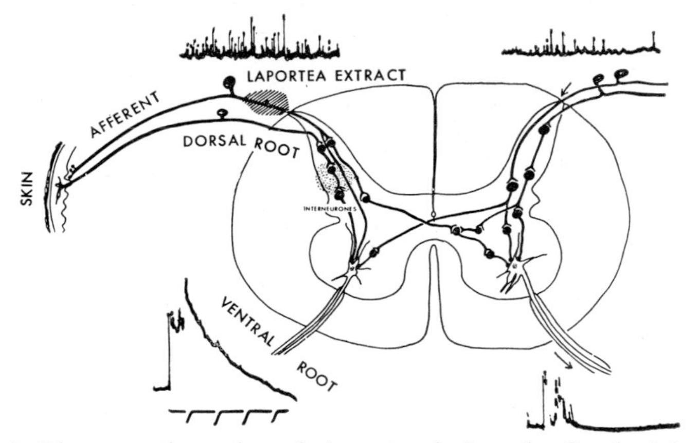

FIG. 3. Diagrammatic section of the cat spinal cord. On the left side, *Laportea* extract was applied to dorsal root fibres. These discharged vigorously compared with the untreated right side. The ventral root discharge increased in amplitude and duration as a result of the action of *Laportea* extract on either dorsal roots or interneurones of the dorsal horn of the cord. Most of the action was upon the late polysynaptic outflow through the ventral root. Time marks 10 msec.

Another approach was made to motor nerve endings by addition of the extract (0.01 ml in 10 ml Ringer solution) to rat phrenic nerve-diaphragm preparations. A slow increment took place in the rate of discharge of miniature end plate potentials from 2–4/sec to high rates (400–600/sec) at the nerve-muscle junction. These potentials were detected by a micro-electrode inserted in the motor end plate (Fig. 4). This effect persists on washing the original solution away with Ringer solution. It appears that the active substance may depolarize the bare nerve endings and cause them to discharge acetylcholine; this causes contracture of muscle.

Once fixed to the tissue there was a persistent action of the pain-producing substance. These observations suggest that action of *Laportea* extract on bare endings causes nerve fibre discharge and the unusually long duration of action is related to fixation of the substance on the nerve. The release of acetylcholine from sympathetic nerves (similarly to the release from somatic motor nerves) would also bring about the characteristic sweating, piloerection and vasodilatation found in the skin lesion induced by stinging hairs. The slow contraction of guinea-pig and rabbit ileum induced by dialyzed extract may originate in acetylcholine release from nerve endings. A similar explanation may account for the long contraction of rectus muscle noted by

Pilgrim (1959) using *Urtica ferox* extracts. He suggested that a guanidine-like substance produced the contracture. Guanidine injection, however, causes necrosis, but not pain in the skin.

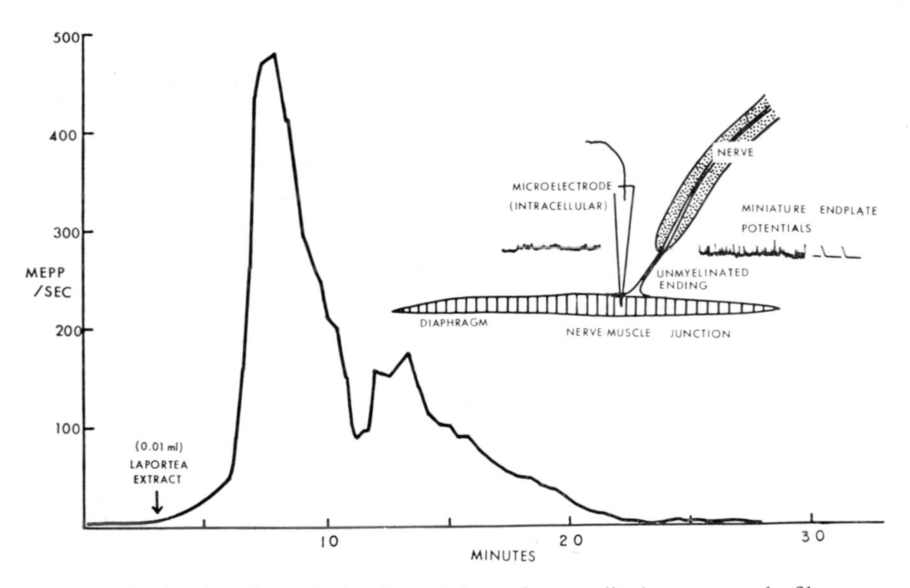

FIG. 4. A microelectrode in the endplate of a rat diaphragm muscle fibre, records slow miniature endplate potentials. Addition of 0·01 ml of *Laportea* hair extract to a 10 ml bath slowly increased the rate of miniature endplate potential firing. The graph shows the increase in frequency produced over 25 min by a single exposure to the extract.

Alleviation

Although there are many methods with popular reputations for relieving the pain of *Laportea* stinging, none of these was effective, when compared with a placebo. Firm rubbing produces a short-lived lessening of the pain. Inunction with local anaesthetics or antihistamines has some effect but it is short and incomplete.

Aspirin and similar compounds by mouth are ineffective in ordinary doses. Alcohol by mouth helps reduce the general level of misery.

Morphinones are useful, and relieve the more chronic element of the pain. Unfortunately this is not available to men working in the rain forest at the time of stinging, though later, under medical prescription it would be of value.

Until the substance causing the pain is identified no rational therapy is likely to be found. Some of the central amplification of the pain that may occur amongst interneurones might however be reduced by meprobamate or similar central blocking agents.

SUMMARY

The stinging hairs of *Laportea* contain a stable substance (or substances) which is (are) not dialysable through cellophane. It is many times more active in producing pain than the acetylcholine, histamine and 5-hydroxytryptamine that are also present in the hairs.

The active material appears not to be protein, polypeptide, glucoside or alkaloid in nature.

The dialysed extract causes a large and persistent increase in the discharge of miniature end plate potentials from motor nerves, while greater activity of dorsal roots is induced by direct action and this leads to greater reflex activity. Interneuronal discharge is increased by an injection of extract into the cord.

There is no satisfactory antidote, but morphinones at least are necessary to alleviate the pain.

REFERENCES

BANCROFT, T. L. 1889. On the materia medica and pharmacology of Queensland plants. *Trans. Intercolonial Med. Congress Austral.* **2**, 927.

COLLIER, H. O. J. and CHESHER, G. B. 1956. Identification of 5-hydroxytryptamine in the sting of the nettle (*Urtica dioica*). *Brit. J. Pharmacol.* **11**, 186.

EMMELIN, N. and FELDBERG, W. 1947. The mechanism of the sting of the common nettle (*Urtica urens*). *J. Physiol.* **106**, 440.

PILGRIM, R. L. C. 1959. Some properties of the sting of the New Zealand nettle (*Urtica ferox*). *Proc. Roy. Soc. B.* **151**, 48.

ROBERTSON, P. A. and MACFARLANE, W. V. 1957. Pain-producing substances from the stinging bush (*Laportea moroides*). *Aust. J. Exper. Biol.* **35**, 381.

WEBB, L. J. 1948. Guide to the medicinal and poisonous plants of Queensland *C.S.I.R.O. Bulletin* No. 232, p. 166.

Section II

COELENTERATES AND OTHER MARINE INVERTEBRATES

COELENTERATES OF MEDICAL IMPORTANCE

R. V. SOUTHCOTT*

INTRODUCTION

Until recent years jellyfish and other coelenterates have received little attention from medical writers. This has been due largely to the fact that in the past serious effects from their stings have occurred in remote places, e.g. in hunters and fishermen, often among primitive peoples. In addition there are difficulties in identifying the offending organism; the circumstances of major stingings usually do not lend themselves to the capture and preservation of these animals. Apart from one death recorded in North America by Parrish (1959) and F. E. Russell (1961) without any details, all of the 30 or so human fatalities so far recorded and reviewed by Cleland and Southcott (in press) have occurred in the seas between Northern Australia and the Asian mainland, as far north as Lingayen Gulf, Northern Philippines.

The Coelenterata or Cnidaria are characterized by the possession of minute stinging capsules or nematocysts, which may serve as weapons for offence or defence. These small organoids occur in many different forms, the ones of medical interest being those that inject venom—the " syringe type " or " injectors ". The functioning of one such nematocyst is illustrated in Fig. 1. On full discharge or eversion of the stinging thread (or possibly by rupture of the thread within the tissues, from trauma) the venom escapes into the tissues of the prey or victim. It may be calculated that a large medusa with many tentacles, e.g. one of the large box-jellies, can inject several cubic centimetres of venom into a victim at a single encounter. The nature of the venom is not fully known, as only limited studies have been made on it of recent years. The earlier work on this subject is summarized in Phisalix (1922); recent leading references are Phillips (1956), Phillips and Abbott (1957), Lane and Dodge (1958), Welsh (1956, 1960), Welsh and Brock (1958), Welsh and Moorhead (1960), and Yanagita (1959a, b). Phillips (1956) suggests that the venom of the sea-anemones he studied consists of a mucoprotein with either adsorbed or free hydroxyindoles. Welsh and his colleagues have stressed the importance of the tetramethylammonium compounds, at least as far as the paralytic effects upon invertebrates are concerned, and also place stress upon the indoles, considering that the pain-

*Honorary Zoologist, South Australian Museum.

producing factor in coelenterate tentacle extracts is probably 5-hydroxy-tryptamine.

While early workers, such as, Dujarric del a Rivière (1915) extracted various substances from coelenterate whole tentacle, in no case was tissue component certainly separated from the extracts injected into dogs, guinea pigs, pigeons,

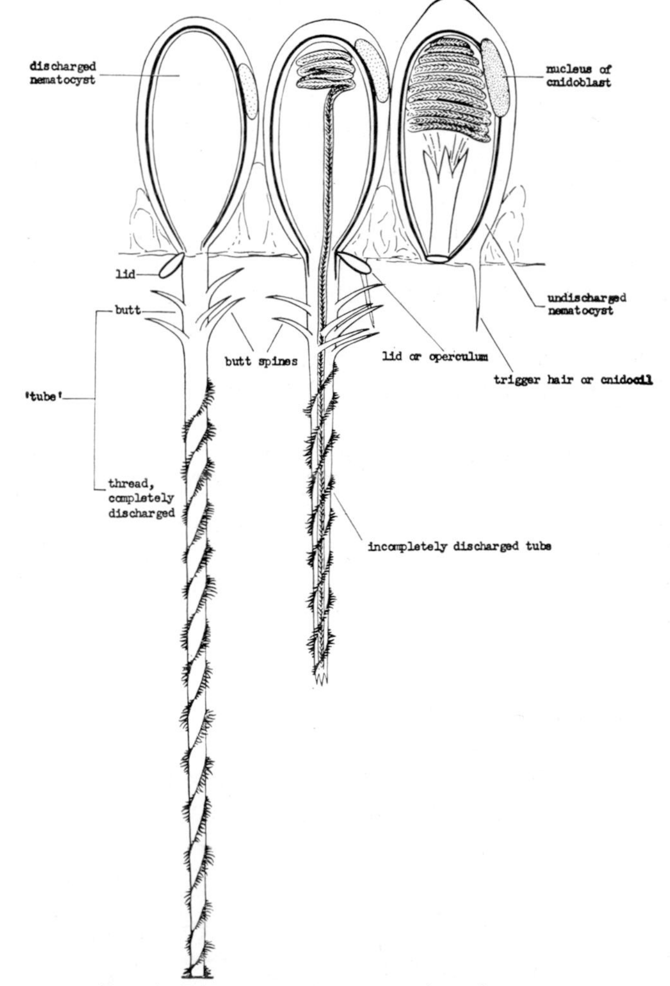

FIG. 1. Diagram to illustrate action of nematocyst.

and other animals. The results were well reviewed by Phisalix (1922). Only by the work of Phillips (1956) has a technique of obtaining pure nematocyst venom become available. Even so, it should be remembered many coelenterates have several types of nematocysts, whose venoms could differ qualitatively as well as in amount. For a further account of the physiology of nematocysts the works of Pantin (1942), Picken (1957) and Yanagita (1959a, b) will serve as guides to the literature. Classification of the different nematocyst types is dealt with by Weill (1934), or more summarily by Hyman (1940) or F. S. Russell (1953).

Potentially the majority of the coelenterates are stinging organisms, but the penetrating powers of the injectors are in many cases slight, and the threads may succeed, e.g. in penetrating only such thin membranes as those of the mouth and tongue, or the conjunctiva. Even with the more powerful stingers, e.g. the Cubomedusae (box-jellies,) penetration to living tissue may occur only with thinner skin, thus the palmar skin and the skin of the dorsum of the forearm may be unaffected, while the thinner skin of the front of the forearm and wrist may be penetrated. Lane and Dodge (1958) recorded tentacular nematocysts of large *Physalia physalis* (L.) as occasionally being able to penetrate heavy-gauge surgical gloves. Variations in skin thickness of individuals could thus in part explain the wide variation in clinical response to stings.

REMARKS ON CLASSIFICATION OF COELENTERATES

The coelenterates are classified into the classes Hydrozoa (hydroids, colonial or solitary forms, including stinging corals (*Millepora* spp.), Scyphozoa (" true " jellyfish), and Anthozoa (sea-anemones, most corals). For a further account the reader may consult Hyman (1940), whose classification will be followed here. All three classes contain medically important forms.

The best-known stinging jellyfish has been the colonial form *Physalia* (Fig. 2A, B, C, D) (Hydrozoa: Siphonophora), and until recent times it has been usual to blame most major stingings, including fatalities, upon it. Medically, however, the Cubomedusae (see Fig. 3) are of much more significance, and the semaeostomes and rhizostomes (Fig. 5) of the Scyphozoa are also important. *Physalia*, however, is a very obvious form.

The diagnosis of a sting in a bather is based largely upon the recognition of the jellyfish by the victim or his companions. However, in many instances the causative animal is not seen at all, and even if seen accurate identification is frequently not possible. Few swimmers can identify jellyfish, except in the case of a few obvious and very abundant forms, and even then the identification may be inaccurate. No reliance can be placed upon common names of jellyfish. Thus in Australia, for example, the term " man-o'-war " refers to *Physalia* in South Australia ; to *Catostylus mosaicus* in the vicinity of Sydney, New South Wales; and to large many-tentacled Cubomedusae in the vicinity of Townsville, Queensland; while " blue-bottle " refers to a small *Carybdea* in Perth, Western Australia, and *Physalia* in Sydney, New South Wales.

Identification of jellyfish is thus largely a task for a specialist in the group. Every effort should be made to preserve such jellyfish or any residual pieces or tentacles from them, which may remain upon the victim, as a research procedure. Jellyfish may be preserved by adding 2 to 10 per cent of liquor formaldehyde (40 per cent w/v formaldehyde) to the specimen in a non-rusting bucket or other container of sea-water, then moving it within the container several times a day for several days, to prevent distortion, until it is thoroughly fixed. A label written in soft pencil on good paper may be put in the fluid with the specimen, and will not deteriorate. The label should give the locality, date and name of the collector. Additional details may be added or sent separately, and in the latter case, an identifying number may need to be given to the specimen.

Further identification of the agent causing the skin weals may be aided by an examination of the lesion for residual nematocysts. The weal may be scraped with the edge of a microscopic slide or other sharp edge and the material obtained examined for nematocysts. They may also be obtained by pressing on the weal a slide prepared by drying upon it a film of clear gum-mucilage; the nematocysts will frequently adhere to this. The nematocysts may be examined in fluid, but permanent mounts may be made with glycerine jelly, or other water-based media. Staining is not necessary, but if desired methylene blue may be used. Such preparations are of the principal stinging nematocysts of the animal, usually from the tentacles. As noted by Kingston and Southcott (1960) and Barnes (1960), such studies may do little more than identify the stinging agent as a coelenterate, unless the nematocysts match accurately those that have been recorded from lesions, or unless concomitant studies are made upon the local jellyfish fauna. So far, in fact, such studies have been made only of *Carybdea*, *Chironex*, *Chiropsalmus* *Cyanea* and *Physalia*, whose nematocysts are illustrated in this article (Figs. 2–5). In the case of fatality, the characteristic pathology of the weals, and the presence of the nematocysts upon the surface will aid in diagnosis, and such a study may be of medicolegal importance.

CLASS I: HYDROZOA

Order Anthomedusae—The Athecate or " Naked " Hydroids

Sarsia tubulosa (Sars, 1835) has been recorded as causing injuries in Hawaii, by Chu and Cutress (1955), under the name used for the hydroid form, *Syncoryne mirabilis*. The lesions were scattered patches of dermatitis up to $\frac{1}{2}$ in. across over the legs and abdomen; these occurred in marine construction workers. In some cases the lesions became purulent. The hydroids were growing on the rocks nearby, and fragments of polyps and tentacles, as well as their medusae, had been scuffed away. Most of the lesions were under clothing, as the workers were fully clothed in the water. Initial contact produced a sensation of prickling; 6 to 12 hr later, an itching papular eruption appeared, subsiding after several days. Chu and Cutress were able to reproduce the lesions experimentally. Control was established by poisoning the water with copper sulphate. Large crystals were best for this purpose.

Pennaria tiarella (Ayers, 1852) has been recorded by Fish and Cobb (1954) as causing irritation to the skin of the abdomen of bathers clambering on to offshore swimming rafts in Hawaii; the specific identification of the hydroid requires confirmation, as this is normally considered an Atlantic species.

Order Leptomedusae—The Thecate or " Protected " Hydroids

Halecium beani Johnston, 1838 was recorded by De Oreo (1946) as causing dermatitis to swimmers in Hawaii, who had come in contact with a swimming raft moored offshore. Trial of several species of marine organisms found growing upon it incriminated this species. Two responses followed skin contact with this hydroid: (1) a rapidly developing urticarial reaction noticeable from within a few minutes up to 2 hr after contact, (2) a slower erythematopapular reaction, haemorrhagic and zosteriform, occurring 4 to 12 hr after contact. This was sometimes followed by a generalized morbilliform rash.

Other symptoms recorded were spasm of abdominal muscles, abdominal pain, chills, fever, malaise, apprehension, diarrhoea. In a few cases the skin lesions progressed to vesicles. In some patients leucocytosis and eosinophilia (4 to 16 per cent) occurred; there was also an increase of erythrocyte sedimentation rate. At biopsy of the skin lesions a nonspecific superficial dermatitis was present, with some eosinophilia of the superficial corium. No foreign body or foreign body reaction was observed. There were no respiratory symptoms. Recovery occurred in a few days. (These slow reactions to the hydroids *Sarsia* and *Halecium* are noteworthy; contrast the rapid reaction to jellyfish stings.)

Aglaophenia cupressina Lamouroux, 1816, " stinging seaweed ", occurs in the tropical Indian Ocean, East Indies, northwest and northeast coasts of Australia, occurring in large colonies in reef habitats. It causes nettle-like stinging on contact, with redness and vesiculation, lasting several days.

Lytocarpus philippinus (Kirchenpauer, 1872) occurs in the tropical Pacific and Indian Oceans, in similar habitats to the preceding species; its effects are also similar.

Order Milleporina—The Stinging Corals

Millepora alcicornis L. (and *M. complanata* Lamarck, 1816) are recorded as causing severe or moderate stings to the skin on contact, which may proceed to pustule formation and desquamation. This has been discussed by Halstead (1956) and Cleland and Southcott (in press). The millepores are found among true corals in all tropical seas, e.g. Caribbean and Red Seas, tropical Pacific and Indian Oceans.

Order Trachylina

Olindioides formosa Goto, 1903 (Fig. 2E). Strong (1942) (quoting Aoki (1922, 1923)) reported that in Japan this species has caused shock, acute cardiac distress, dyspnoea, muscle pain, and subsequent emaciation (the last appears rather doubtful).

Order Siphonophora

Genus Physalia Lamarck, 1801. *Physalia* (Fig. 2A–D) is the largest and best-known of the siphonophores, occurring in all tropical and subtropical seas, and occasionally in colder regions. The Atlantic form of this colonial hydroid is *Physalia physalis* (L.), which has several fishing or main tentacles (Fig. 2A); the Pacific form is *Physalia utriculus* La Martinière, 1787, which has only one main tentacle (Fig. 2B). The main tentacles may be many feet long, and are highly contractile. Along them are kidney-shaped " urticating buttons " (Fig. 2C), and packed over the surface of these are many spherical nematocysts. These occur in two main sizes (Fig. 2D), and on discharge they emit an unarmed butt-less tube; they are thus classified as " haplonemes " in Weill's (1934) classification.

The effects of a *Physalia* sting are local pain, pain along the lymphatic drainage, e.g. the axillary lymph nodes, joint and muscle pain, severe or moderately severe for some hours, then lessening. Although there has been a tendency for writers in Australia and elsewhere to blame deaths from jellyfish stings on *Physalia*, Cleland and Southcott (in press) have found no substantiated case of a death in man from *Physalia* stinging. In the earlier literature reviewed by Phisalix (1922), there are records of fatalities in animals from ingestion of fresh or prepared *Physalia* substance.

Barnes (1960) records that extended tentacle of *Physalia utriculus* causes a long thin linear injury, a discontinuous line of small papules, each with a small erythematous zone. A single extended tentacle may, however, cause multiple lines from rolling over the victim's skin.Contracted tentacle, with its more concentrated nematocysts, causes wider weals, often irregularly linear with sudden angles or replications. The wealing usually regresses in a few hours, while the pain lasts up to 24 hr. Pain is a marked feature from any but transient contact with *Physalia* tentacle.

Hercus (1944) has described a corneal injury which may be attributed to *Physalia*. The patient was stung while bathing, and at first she complained of severe pain; however, at examination, nothing was observed except slight ciliary injection. An intense ocular reaction developed, with oedema and crenation (at slit-lamp examination) of the corneal epithelium, with wide-spread degenerative changes in the corneal epithelium, with many minute spots staining with fluorescin. Fine crystalline bodies, which were possibly nematocysts were still adhering to the surface a week after the injury. Active degenerative changes were still present three weeks after the injury, and the

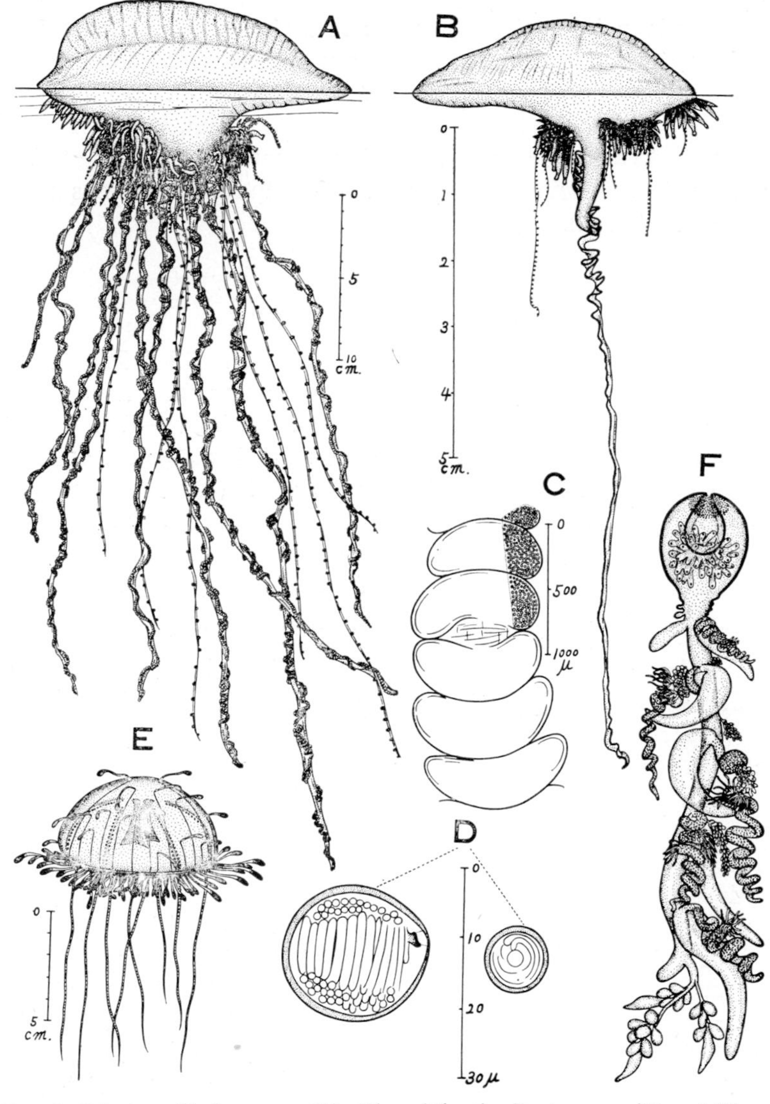

FIG. 2. Stinging Hydrozoa. (A) The Atlantic Portuguese Man-o'-War, *Physalia physalis* (L.). This has several main tentacles. (B) The Indo-Pacific Portuguese Man-o'-War or Bluebottle, *Physalia utriculus* La Martinière, 1787. This has only one main (" fishing ") tentacle. (C) Part of tentacle of preceding specimen to show the kidney-shaped " urticating buttons " along it; in contraction. (D) Nematocysts (" haplonemes ") from one of the urticating buttons, undischarged, to show their spherical form, the coiled spineless thread within the capsule, and the two sizes that occur. (E) *Olindioides formosa* Goto, 1903 (Order Trachylina) (after Goto 1903, per Mayer 1910). Note the tentacles arising over the bell surface as well as around the rim. (F) *Rhizophysa*, a stinging siphonophore (after Hyman, 1940, by permission of the publisher).

whole episode had a prolonged course of 5 weeks. The almost complete lack of vascularization was an unusual feature of such an eye lesion.

Genus *Rhizophysa* Péron and Lesueur, 1807, (Fig. 2F). *Rhizophysa áliformis* (Forskål, 1775), and *R. eysenhardti* Gegenbaui, 1860 are widespread in the tropical Pacific Ocean and have been recorded by Hirase *et al.* (1927) as causing stings to Japanese fishermen. The Japanese paper was quoted by Fish and Cobb (1954).

CLASS II: SCYPHOZOA

These animals are at times referred to as the " true " jellyfish. However, the term " jellyfish " itself has no exact meaning, nor have the terms " blubber " or " man-'o-war " (see earlier). Cleland and Southcott (in press) believe that use of the term " man-'o-war " for large Cubomedusae in northern Queensland misled Flecker into believing fatalities from jellyfish stings in that region were due to *Physalia*.

Of the Scyphozoa the orders Cubomedusae, Coronatae, Semaeostomeae and Rhizostomeae contain members of medical importance.

Order Cubomedusae—The Box-Jellies or " Sea Wasps "

This order contains translucent, lightly coloured or almost colourless jellyfish which are usually difficult to see in the water. The bell, although it has a well-rounded dome, tends to be cuboidal or box-shaped, and carries one or more (up to 16 in some forms) tentacles at each corner of the box, the interradius. These jellyfish are found in all the warmer seas, e.g. as far north as the Mediterranean and Japanese waters, and as far south as south-west Africa and South Australia. The large many-tentacled forms (family Chirodropidae) are exclusively tropical. While some Cubomedusae may be found in the open oceans, e.g. *Carybdea alata* Reynaud, 1830, in general, they tend to frequent sheltered bays or gulfs in tropical to temperate regions.

In recent years many workers including McNeill and Pope (1943a, b), Southcott (1952; 1956; 1958a, b, c; 1959), Flecker (1952a, 1957b), and Barnes (1960) have recognized that this coelenterate order is one of the greatest medical importance. The stinging powers of the Cubomedusae have been recognized for many years; thus Mayer (1910) refers to them and uses the term " sea wasp ". Light (1914a, b) originally suggested that *Chiropsalmus quadrigatus* Haeckel 1880 could be responsible for fatalities in the Philippines. The medical significance of these medusae was confirmed by the recognition of a medusa adhering to an 11–12-year-old boy in Darwin, Australia, in 1938 as a cubomedusa. The boy died a few minutes after the stinging. This case has been reviewed by McNeill and Pope (1943a, b; 1945) and McNeill (1945). It was identified by McNeill (in Flecker (1952a, c)) as *Chiropsalmus quadrigatus* Haeckel. Re-examination by the present author in 1961 showed that this badly mutilated specimen is probably one of *Chironex fleckeri* Southcott, 1956.

Family Chirodropidae—Many-Tentacled Cubomedusae. The systematics of this family are at present under revision; as is also our knowledge of its geographical distribution. Along the tropical west African coast the very large forms of *Chirodropus* Haeckel 1880 are found, at times in large numbers, e.g. at Accra, Ghana, but so far no reports are available of any stinging effects, nor are there any reports of fatalities from those regions which are ascribed to jellyfish stings.

Chiropsalmus quadrumanus (Müller, 1859) is recorded from North Carolina, Gulf of Mexico, Brazil, and other localities; it has a bell up to 14 cm (5½ in). across, according to Mayer (1910). So far there are no reports of stings.

In the tropical West Pacific and Eastern Indian Oceans two large forms occur, *Chiropsalmus quadrigatus* Haeckel, 1880 and *Chironex fleckeri* Southcott, 1956. Southcott (1956) outlined gonadal structures and other features which serve to distinguish between the two species. Of these the Coelenterates *Chironex fleckeri* (Fig. 3A, B) appears to be the more dangerous form. It is generally more massively built, with thicker and longer tentacles. Both species are found in north Queensland and the Philippines, where many of the recorded fatalities have occurred. While it is believed that *Chironex fleckeri* is potentially the more dangerous, no significant difference in nematocyst structure has been detected between them (see Fig. 3B, C), and in the subsequent discussion the terms *Chironex fleckeri* and *Chiropsalmus quadrigatus* may be used interchangeably until more is known of their effects. Another large chirodropid occurring in the same area is *Chiropsoides buitendijki* (Horst, 1907). This species has been found on only a few occasions; it may be distinguished by having a linear (as against a branching) arrangement of claws and tentacles arising along each pedalium (the tentacle-carrying fin or arm which arises at each corner or interradius of the " box "). So far no medical effects have been recorded for it.

Chironex fleckeri and *Chiropsalmus quadrigatus.* Skin lesions resulting from stings from these boxjellies vary in intensity, from purely local effects of severe pain, immediate wealing, oedema and vesiculation, proceeding to full thickness skin necrosis in the severe cases. These lesions finally heal by granulation and cicatrization over several weeks, the final result being scarring with pigmentation or depigmentation, or in some cases cheloid formation. The initial lesions are multiple linear weals, with transverse barring from the ringed structure of the tentacle. The purple or brown lines on the skin are often compared with the effects of a whiplash. Further effects from a sting are local or muscular pain with muscular spasm, respiratory difficulty, rapidity and weakness of pulse, prostration, pulmonary oedema, central vasomotor and respiratory failure and death. The pain is excru-

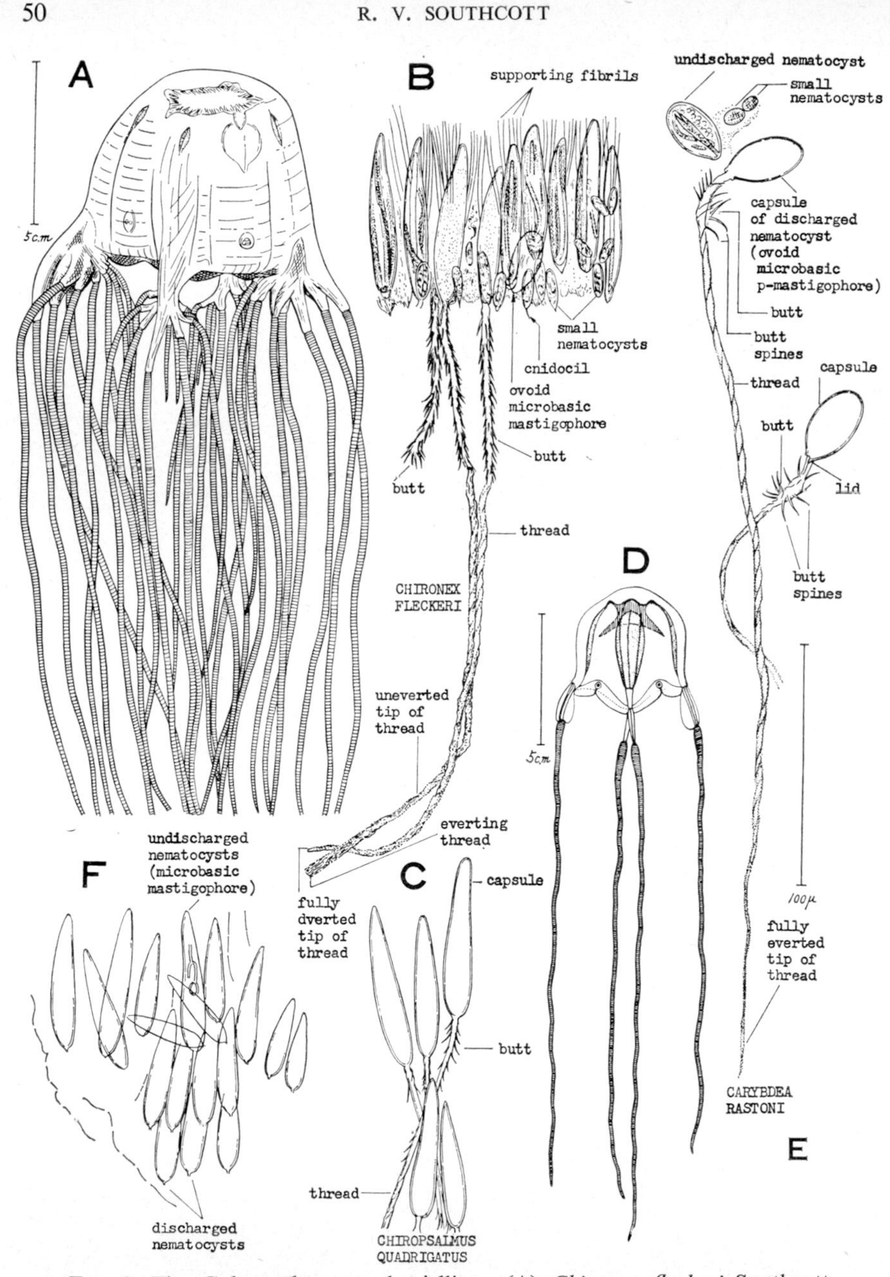

FIG. 3. The Cubomedusae or boxjellies. (A) *Chironex fleckeri* Southcott, 1956, a lethal species from the tropical Indo-West-Pacific region. Specimen from north Queensland. (B) Piece of tentacle of same species (from Holotype), showing nematocysts, some of which are discharged or discharging; in glycerine-jelly. (C) Discharged nematocysts of *Chiropsalmus quadrigatus* Haeckel, 1880, a similar species. Specimen from Malaya. (D) *Carybdea rastoni* Haacke, 1886, a widespread Indo-Pacific cubomedusa (figure by the late D. C. Swan from a South Australian specimen). (E) Principal tentacular nematocysts of same species. (F) Nematocysts from skin of a fatal case of jellyfish stinging in north Queensland, showing the correspondence to the principal tentacular nematocysts of *Chironex fleckeri* and *Chiropsalmus quadrigatus*. (All nematocysts figured to scale on right.)

ciating and the victim frequently screams and may become irrational. Death may ensue from under ½ min to up to 2 or 3 hr, but usually takes under 15 min, often in 3 to 4 min after contact. In many cases the victim dies before or soon after struggling the few yards to the shore. Cough and mucoid expectoration are not prominent features, and are usually absent. (The symptoms recorded are similar to those described for " medusocongestine ", obtained by Dujarric de la Rivière (1915) from *Rhizostoma cuvieri* Chamisso and Eysenhardt, 1821) (= *R. pulmo* (Macri, 1778) *teste* Mayer (1910, p. 609) see *Phisalix*, 1922).

Autopsy findings are pulmonary oedema, right cardiac dilatation, general venous congestion; renal and suprarenal congestion may be well marked. Detailed study has not been of the central nervous system (deaths usually occur in remote places, although some victims have been submitted to autopsy). The only detailed and careful autopsy study that has been published was by Wade (1928) for a Philippine case. Histopathological study of skin weals was made by Kingston and Southcott (1960), who reported nematocysts present in large numbers on the weals, matching those of the tentacles of *Chironex fleckeri* and *Chiropsalmus quadrigatus*; they were banana- or cigar-shaped microbasic mastigophores (compare Figs. 3B, C, F, 4C, D, E). The threads of the nematocysts penetrate through to the dermis. The stratum corneum is oedematous and its layers separated. The Malpighian layer is thinned, its cells degenerate, with pyknotic nuclei (see Fig. 4A–G). These findings may be of medicolegal importance.

Family Carybdeidae—The Simpler Boxjellies. This family is characterized by a lack of diverticula to the stomach-pockets; usually there is only a single tentacle to each interradial corner of the bell; however, *Tripedalia cystophora* Conant, 1897, from Jamaica is exceptional in tentacle and pedalium structure; and the oriental *Carybdea stiasnyi* Bigelow, 1938, has also an exceptional tentacle structure.

Carybdea rastoni Haacke, 1886 (Fig. 3D, E) is a widely distributed Indo-Pacific species, ranging from the coasts of South Australia, widely across the Pacific and north to Japanese waters; in the last area, according to Uchida (1929), it is known as *andon-kuragé* (lantern medusa). Its tentacles cause moderately painful weals on contact, with erythema and possibly vesiculation. Its nematocysts are shorter and plumper than those of *Chironex fleckeri*, etc.; they are illustrated in Fig. 3E.

Carybdea alata Reynaud, 1830 is a widely distributed large tropical species. Bigelow (1938) has recorded this organism from the Atlantic, Indian, and Pacific Oceans. In the Gilbert Islands it is known as " Te Baitari ", and used for food (Banner, 1952).

Tamoya sp. This form causes local weals, similar to those from the preceding species. (Much confusion has existed between this form and *Carybdea alata*, e.g. by Uchida (1929, 1947). The generic definitions are

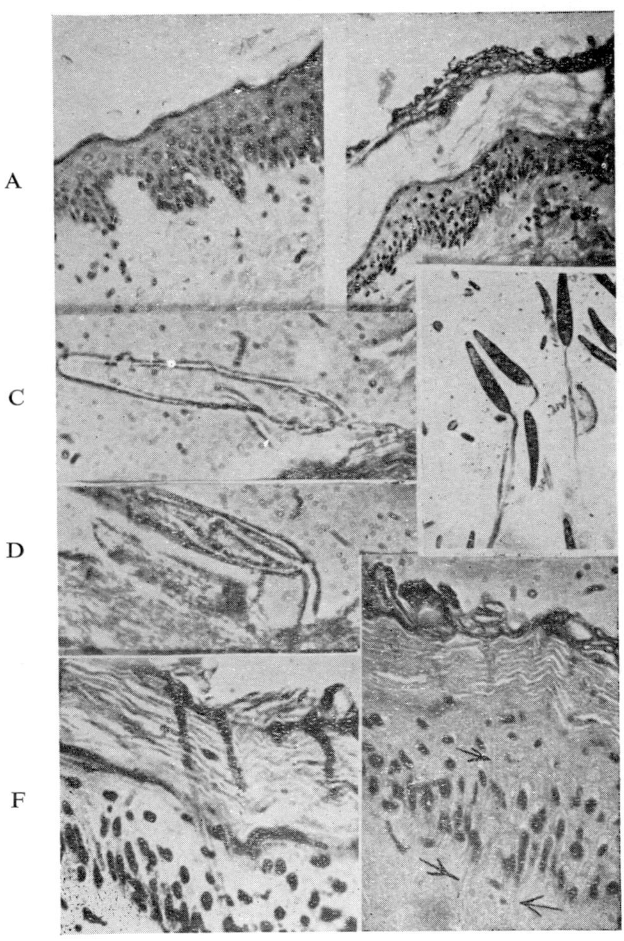

FIG. 4. Features of skin histopathology in a fatal case of jellyfish stinging in north Queensland (from Kingston and Southcott, 1960). (A) Normal skin near the weal (H. & E., × 150). (B) Section through centre of weal. On the surface of the skin are many capsules, seen in section. The stratum corneum is oedematous. The Malpighian layer is thin and degenerate, with pyknotic nuclei. (H. & E., × 150). The child died a few minutes after being stung. (C. D) Nematocysts upon the surface of the skin (frozen section, × 600). (E) Nematocysts of tentacle of *Chironex fleckeri* (Holotype specimen), stained by reticulum technique (× 150). (F, G) Sections through weal to show nematocyst tubes penetrating Malpighian layer and dermis (H. & E., × 375). The proximal part of the thread-track stains with haematoxylin. In G note the continuity of the thread with the capsule on the surface (upper arrow); the lower arrows indicate two cut threads in the dermis.

correctly set out by Mayer (1910) and Bigelow (1938). The last paper sets out clearly the present knowledge on the differentiation of these forms).

Order Coronatae

These are typically deep-water medusae; *Linuche*, however, occurs in superficial waters. There are only two species recorded as causing stings.

Linuche unguiculata (Swartz, 1788) (Fig. 5A), the " thimble jellyfish ".

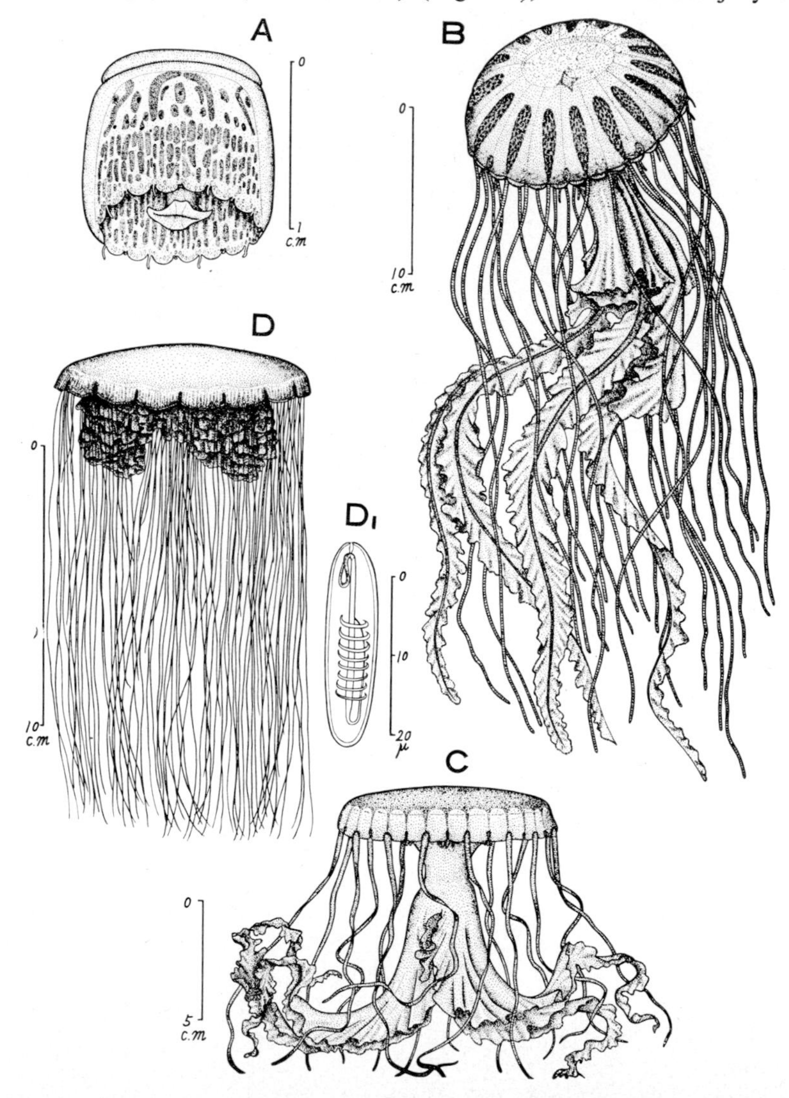

FIG. 5a. Stinging Scyphozoa. (A) Coronatae: *Linuche unguiculata* (Swartz, 1788). B–D Semaeostomeae: (B) *Dactylometra quinquecirrha* (Desor, 1848), mature specimen from Rhode Island, north Atlantic. (C) *Sanderia malayensis* Goette, 1886. (D) *Cyanea annaskala* Lendenfeld, 1882, specimen from Port Phillip, Victoria, Australia. (D_1) Principal tentacular nematocyst of *Cyanea*, north Queensland.

This species occurs in vast swarms in the superficial waters of the tropical Atlantic, and when abundant may cause severe stings (Strong, 1942). Mature specimens are recorded by Mayer (1910) as 13 mm high and 16 mm wide.

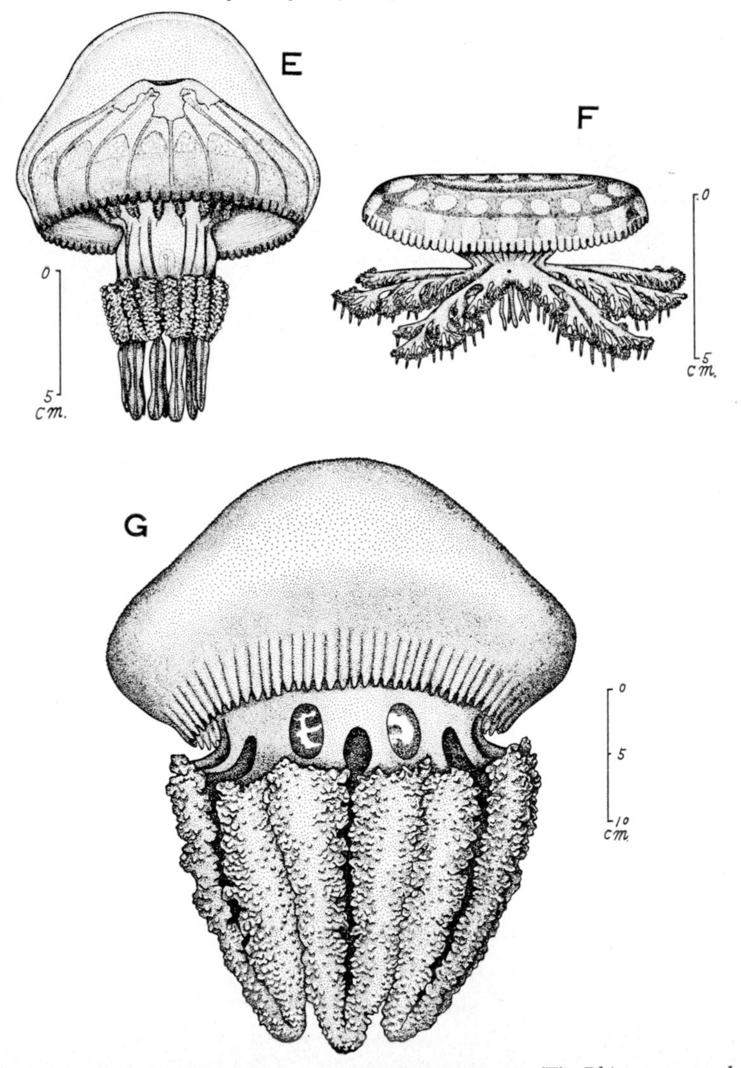

FIG. 5b (Stinging Scyphozoa *cont.*) Rhizostomeae: (E) *Rhizostoma pulmo* (Macri, 1778), Mediterranean specimen. (F) *Cassiopea xamachana* R. P. Bigelow, 1892, specimen from Tortugas, Florida. (G) *Catostylus mosaicus* (Quoy and Gaimard, 1824), east coast of Australia. (Figs. A–C, E, F after Mayer, 1910; D after Lendenfeld, 1882; D_1 after Barnes, 1960; G after Agassiz and Mayer, 1898.)

Linuche aquila Haeckel, 1880, from the Pacific, occurs similarly, and Bigelow (1938) declares it a synonym of *L. unguiculata*. In the water these small orange or brown " thimbles " spin around their long axis.

Stephanoscyphus racemosus Komai, 1935 is a colonial species; it forms colonies within sponges, and also attaches to other objects and animals. Komai (1935, 1936) recorded it as causing stings to fishermen, especially divers, in the Seto region of Honshu, Japan. The symptoms were pain and itching on contact, with a febrile illness lasting days or weeks.

Order Semaeostomeae (Fig 5B–D)

The semaeostomes are the best-known scyphozoans, the order containing *Aurelia* and *Cyanea*; they are abundant in all waters, including Arctic and tropical.

Dactylometra quinquecirrha Desor, 1848 (Fig. 5B) (= *D. ferruginaster* Kishinouye, 1892), occurs in the warmer Atlantic waters, including the Atlantic coast of North America as far as the southern New England coast (where it is known as " sea nettle "), also in Malaya, Philippines (there known as " fosforo ", " match " in Spanish, an allusion to the prominent head and the slender trailing mouth-arms), Japan, etc.

This species causes severe stings, which are followed by intense back pains and pain radiating from the site of the sting. Muscular cramps, mucoid expectoration and intense coughing are other symptoms, also at times depression (even suicidal desire may be experienced). Other symptoms are scrotal pain, restlessness, weakness, prostration, respiratory embarrassment, chest oppression, lacrymation, local linear weals, with erythema and vesiculation. Light (1914a, b) recorded the effects of this species, noting that at times it occurred in large numbers in Manila Bay, Philippines, particularly in October and November. Wade (1928) also contributed to our knowledge of the medical effects.

Sanderia malayensis Goette, 1886 (Fig. 5C), occurs in the Indian Ocean from the east coast of Africa to Singapore, and farther into the Pacific, including the Philippines and Japan. Hirase *et al.* (1927) have recorded it as causing severe effects in Japanese waters.

Genus *Cyanea* Péron and Lesueur, 1809 (Fig. 5D). This genus has a world-wide distribution, ranging from the polar seas to the tropics; it contains very large medusae in both these regions. Several forms have been recorded as causing severe stings. The Atlantic and Northern Pacific forms will be referred to as *Cyanea capillata* (L.), while the Australian forms are *C. annaskala* Lendenfeld, 1882 and *C. muellerianthe* Haacke 1887.

All species of *Cyanea* have a large number of fine tentacles originating in eight adradial crescentic groups, each of several rows, on the underside of the disc. Contact with the tentacles results in a multiple linear response of burning and prickling, proceeding to frank pain, with erythema and wealing. More extensive contact results in muscular pain, oppression of respiration, mucoid hypersecretion throughout the air passages; in more severe cases loss of consciousness may occur. These effects following contact with *Cyanea* are described by Wood (1874) and by Cleland and Southcott (in press). Wood's graphic account was used by Conan Doyle in his story *The Lion's Mane*, one of the *Adventures of Sherlock Holmes.* According to Hirase *et al.* (1927), as cited by Fish and Cobb (1954), immunity to the sting may develop in fishermen repeatedly exposed; however, such a development has not been confirmed by other students.

In Australia *Cyanea annaskala* (Fig. 5D) is recorded along the eastern and south-eastern coastline. Pope (1953a, b) has reported local lesions of the skin and conjunctivae from contact with tentacles, the effect being recorded as less than that of *Physalia utriculus.* Bloomfield (1959) also refers to the same medusa as the " giant blubber " (its disc being up to 2 ft across) under the name of *Cyanea muellerianthe*, and reported it as causing discomfort to bathers. He stated that this medusa frequently becomes fragmented in the seas off eastern Australia, with the individual fragments themselves causing stings. Southcott (1960) has recorded wealing in under-water swimmers from *Cyanea* in south Australian waters; on geographical grounds these medusae may with more confidence be referred to *C. muellerianthe.*

The large Cyaneas of north Queensland, Australia, have been studied by Barnes (1960). These medusae are called " snotties " locally on account of the large amount of mucus they exude. They may be referred to *Cyanea annaskala*, following Mayer (1910). Barnes describes them aptly as resembling a " mop hiding under a dinner plate ". The tentacles detach easily and foul fishing lines and nets, and fishermen suffer from stings from the small " worms ". The immediate sensation from contact with tentacles is one of stickiness, and if tentacles are removed at once, only a local burning sensation follows, with erythema and punctate wealing. Contact over 1 min results in a more severe burning pain and a fine stippled linear weal with a narrow red flare, the whole 2–3 mm wide. The weal and pain disappear rapidly but the erythema persists for days and is a useful diagnostic sign. Single linear weals are not uncommon, despite the multiplicity of tentacles of *Cyanea.* With more extensive lesions zigzag lines are common, and if the tentacles form a thick leash and sting *en masse* lesions of great severity occur, with vesiculation and tissue destruction, with slow healing. Systemic symptoms recorded from these stings are nausea, backache, and slight abdominal pain in moderate stings in children. More severe effects such as loss of consciousness have been mentioned above. Nematocysts are recoverable from the weals. As Barnes (1960) (Fig. 5D) has noted, these may be examined under the microscope in order to determine the identity of the jellyfish causing the accident. *Pelagia panopyra* Péron and Lesueur, 1807, is referred to by Bloomfield (1959) as the " mauve stinger " or the " mauve blubber ". The colour, however, ranges from pink to purple and violet.

This medusa is widely distributed across the Pacific Ocean. Bloomfield (1959) records it as causing mild stings, and states that when a swimmer comes in contact with 30 or more of the medusae severe pain and collapse may result.

Order Rhizostomeae (*Fig.* 5*E–G*)

Many of the rhizostomes look like a cauliflower hanging below an inverted basin. The cauliflower-like mass is the expanded group of mouth-arms. These jellyfish occur in temperate and tropical waters, their greatest development being in the Pacific region. Some of them are quite small forms, an inch or so across the bell, while some may be very large, a foot or more across.

Rhizostoma pulmo, Macri (1778) (Fig. 5E) and *R. cuvieri* Péron and Lesueur, (1809) have been recorded as causing symptoms. Dujarric de la Rivière (1915) and Evans (1943) record *R. cuvieri* (which Mayer (1910) accepts as conspecific with *R. pulmo*) as causing mild local effects—urticaria, pain, and itching; also constitutional effects which may be grave and alarming: dyspnoea, anxiety followed by depression, and muscular weakness lasting 24 to 36 hr. Mucoid expectoration is also a prominent feature. Lord and Wilks (1918) have recorded severe abdominal symptoms—pain and muscular spasms—with emotional disturbance in bathers in northern Wales, from stings from unidentified large jellyfish, probably *Rhizostoma* sp.

Lobonema smithi Mayer, 1910 (=*L. mayeri* Light, 1914) is recorded by Light (1914a) in the Philippines, where it is known by the local name of " lanterna ", as causing local papular weals, at first white, then red, similar to a nettle sting.

Cassiopea xamachana R. P. Bigelow, 1892 (Fig. 5F), a well-known medusa from the tropical Atlantic, has been recorded by Southcott (1959) as causing urticaria with weals, vomiting and arthralgia, following advice from Dr. P. C. Holzberger, Netherlands Antilles.

Catostylus purpurus Mayer 1910, has been recorded by Light (1921) as causing stings at Manila, Philippines. The effects noted were erythema and a pronounced stinging and burning sensation. The burning passed away in a few hours, but soreness was still present 12 hr later. In addition, 3 hr after the contact there was severe aching in the bones and joints, and severe backache, together with a dull headache.

Catostylus mosaicus, Quoy and Gaimard (1824) (Fig. 5G) is the commonest large jellyfish of the eastern Australian coastline, ranging from Queensland to Melbourne, Victoria. It is an estuarine form and at times is present in enormous numbers, the waters of, for example, Sydney Harbour and the Brisbane River appearing then as though carpeted with these medusae. It may be a foot or more across the bell. In Sydney it is known as " the blubber " or the " man-of-war ". Contact with the mouth-arm mass by bathers may cause local weals with severe stinging and pain. On one occasion more severe symptoms (severe wealing, cyanosis and muscular tremors) have been attributed to this medusa. Further details are given by Cleland and Southcott (in press).

STINGS FROM UNIDENTIFIED JELLYFISH

Irukandji sting, Type A sting, as described by Flecker (1945a, b; 1952c; 1957a, b), Southcott (1952, 1959), and Barnes (1960), is a well-defined syndrome for which the causative organism is as yet unidentified. Most cases have been described from the vicinity of Cairns, Queensland, Australia, where they have occurred from early December through to February, but Cleland and Southcott (in press) have reported others from New Guinea, Fiji, Gulf of Carpentaria, and Darwin.

The symptoms commence with a mild initial sting, causing a patch of local erythema up to the size of the palm of the hand, with transient wealing. After a delay varying from 5 to 60 min but averaging 25 to 35 min the pain increases in severity, firstly at the site of the sting, and then spreads, becoming excruciating, and followed by intense backache, pain in the back of the thighs and knees, arthralgia, and headache. Nausea is a constant symptom, and abdominal pain is frequent and may be severe, and is accompanied by vomiting. Sweating is profuse. Restlessness may be a marked feature, but is not invariable. Mild pyrexia, rapidity of pulse (which may be irregular) are other symptoms; sometimes mucoid expectoration and coughing are prominent, with haematemesis and haemoptysis, tightness of the chest and prostration. Recovery occurs in 1 to 2 days.

Treatment is symptomatic. Morphia is often required for relief of pain.

The name, " Irukandji sting ", bestowed by Flecker upon this syndrome, is not an indication of the causative organism, about which nothing was then known. " Irukandji " was the name of the local tribe of aboriginals, whose area was roughly the same as that of the stingings, as then known. There has been some evidence that the responsible organism is a small transparent jellyfish.*

CLASS ANTHOZOA

Subclass Zoantharia—sea-anemones and corals. A number of sea-anemones, particularly the larger ones, will sting on contact. Injuries are also recorded from the true or stony corals (Madreporia); the " stinging corals " (*Millepora*) are really colonial hydroids, and were considered above.

Order Actiniaria—Sea-Anemones

Sagartia elegans (Dalyell, 1848) (Fig. 6A_1, A_2). According to Halstead

**Note added in press:* Dr. J. H. Barnes of Cairns, Queensland has now demonstrated the causative organism is a small carybdeid medusa.

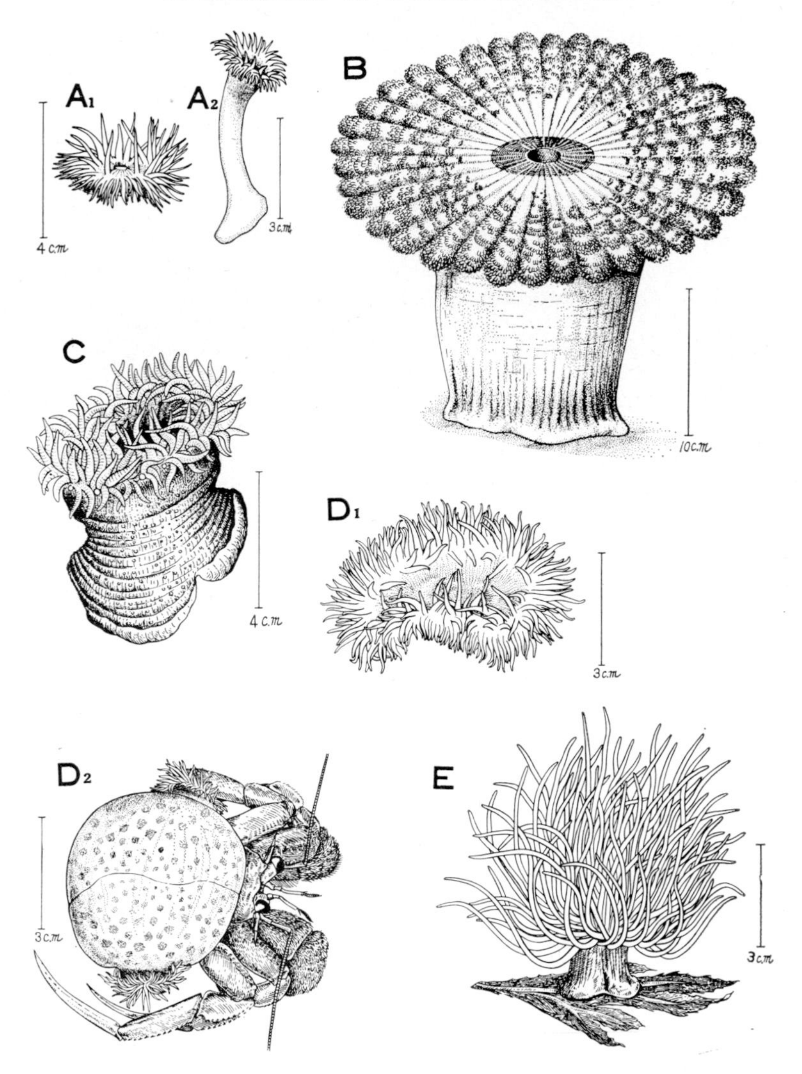

FIG. 6. Some stinging sea-anemones (Anthozoa: Actiniaria). (A) *Sagartia elegans* (Dalyell, 1848): (A_1) Posture adopted in a strong light; (A_2) Posture adopted in a dim light (after Stephenson, 1935). (B) *Actinodendron plumosum* Haddon, 1898, specimen from Mer, Torres Strait (after Haddon). (C) *Actinia equina* L., 1767, eastern Atlantic (after Johnston, 1847). (D) *Adamsia palliata* (Bohadsch, 1761), an eastern Atlantic and Mediterranean species (after Stephenson, 1935). (D_1) General form of disc and tentacles, (D_2) the anemone investing the body of the hermit crab *Eupagurus prideauxi* Leach. The disc of the anemone lies below the body of the crab and dorsally only the ends of the disc are visible. (E) *Anemonia sulcata* (Pennant, 1777), eastern Atlantic and Mediterranean (after Johnston, 1847). (Scales to A, B, D are approximate.)

(1959), the " rosy anemone " is found in the eastern Atlantic and Mediterranean region. To this species is attributed the " sponge divers' disease " or " maladie des plongeurs " of the eastern Mediterranean described by Zervos (1903), Phisalix (1922), and Evans (1943). The injuries inflicted on the divers are not due to the sponges but to the anemones growing upon them, which occur at depths between 25 and 45 m. Following contact the victim experiences itching, severe burning, erythema, which may proceed to local necrosis and ulceration, and if deep, there is sloughing of tissue and purulent discharge, with prolonged incapacity. Multiple abscesses have been recorded. The older sponge fisherman have scarred hands from many injuries.

Actinodendron plumosum Haddon 1898, (Fig. 6B) (=*A. alcyonoideum* Saville-Kent, 1893), *not* of Quoy and Gaimard, is recorded by Saville-Kent (1893) from the Great Barrier Reef, Queensland, as causing severe stings. Contact resulted in severe stings with a reaction similar to that from a nettle sting, the effects lasting about a week. This is a very large sea-anemone, with the crown of tentacles growing to over a foot across.

Actinodendron arboreum (Quoy and Gaimard, 1833) was recorded by its original authors as causing painful stings, with erythema and swelling of tissues. They commented that the effects of the sting are less upon the conjunctiva than upon the skin of the eyelids.

Actinia equina L., 1767 (Fig. 6C) (=*A. mesembryanthemum* Ellis and Solander, 1786 *teste* Stephenson 1935, p. 113) occurs in the eastern Atlantic, Mediterranean, Black Sea, Sea of Azov. It is recorded as venomous by Halstead (1959).

Adamsia palliata (Bohadsch, 1761) (Fig. 6D_1, D_2) is recorded by Halstead (1959) as venomous. This species usually occurs in association with the hermit crab *Eupagurus prideauxi* Leach (see figures). It occurs in the eastern Atlantic and Mediterranean.

Anemonia sulcata (Pennant, 1777) (Fig. 6E) is recorded by Allman (in Johnston (1847), Plate XLIV, legend) as causing erythema, urticaria with burning and tingling following contact with tentacles. The effect is of some severity and may last over an hour. Johnston (1847) quotes early comment by Rondelet (1554) on the stinging power of this species. It occurs in the eastern Atlantic and Mediterranean.

Order Madreporia—True or Stony Corals

Acropora palmata (Lamarck, 1816), " elk-horn coral ", is recorded by Halstead (1959) as causing stings. It is distributed in the Florida Keys, Bahamas, West Indies.

Unidentified corals, Indo-Pacific area, responsible for " *coral cut* ", " *coral ulcer* ", " *coral poisoning* ". Superficial lesions from coral in Australia, Melanesia, Indian Ocean and the Persian Gulf have been described by Cilento (1923), Cleland (1924), Byrne (1924), Paradice (1924), and Preston (1950) but so far no histopathological studies have been made. Byrne (1924) stated that such superficial lesions almost invariably become septic and then proceed to ulceration; if neglected chronic suppuration may ensue. Toxaemia is a marked feature of these injuries.

All students agree that prompt and vigorous treatment is necessary, e.g. cleansing by a vigorous scrubbing with a brush and soap and water or antiseptic solution, followed by some antiseptic and protective dressing.

The extreme reaction to these minor injuries suggests that the response is possibly a foreign-body reaction to the injection of coral polyp substance, possibly at the time of the injury or subsequently, e.g. from nematocyst action. Biopsy studies for histopathological purposes would appear well worth while to elucidate this problem. More attention should also be paid to the identification of the corals concerned, and their stinging abilities.

TREATMENT OF JELLYFISH STINGS

Initial measures should be the removal of the jellyfish and adherent tentacles. These must be wiped off or rubbed off with anything available, e.g. a rag, or wet or dry sand. The local application of alcohol, e.g. methylated spirits, or other lotions, may help to inhibit the action of nematocysts still remaining undischarged upon the surface of the victim's skin. Oily substances may also have an inhibitory action. If pain is severe, morphia or other agents to combat the pain may be necessary. The subsequent treatment of the local lesions is as for dermatitis, and numerous local treatments have been recommended by various observers, e.g. antihistaminic ointments and creams, topical cortisone or cortisone by mouth or parenterally, and late superficial X-ray therapy, to mention only a few. However, so far there is little or no real evidence as to which of the local remedies, at least, are effective. Among local remedies that have been advocated in various parts of the world are: sugar, soap, acids, such as vinegar or lemon juice, alkalies such as ammonia solution, sodium bicarbonate solution, powdered sodium bicarbonate, also pawpaw (papaya) juice, green pawpaw substance, salts, oils, various plant juices, boric acid solution, etc.

The treatment of " coral cut " has been mentioned above; this is equivalent to a debridement or wound excision, and such treatment is effective at least in the coral injuries.

In some cases of repeated exposure antiallergic therapy appears indicated. In general, however, evidence is lacking that allergy plays any significant part in the pathogenesis of lesions resulting from jellyfish stings.

For severer stings, with profound systemic effects, after the removal of the tentacles, adrenalin (epinephrin) may be required, and may be repeated. Painful muscle spasms may be treated by intravenous injection of 10 ml of

10 per cent calcium gluconate. Artificial respiration and oxygen are necessary for depression of respiration. A number of fatalities have followed stings on the lower legs, even in adults, and in a severe sting upon the limbs the immediate application of a tourniquet could conceivably be life-saving. It is doubtful if wound excision in such cases is ever likely to be a practical possibility, in view of the rapidity of many of the deaths, and the impossibility of knowing whether any particular sting has injected a lethal amount of venom into the dermis. Intense pain (with screaming in children) may be taken as some indication of the amount of venom that has been injected from the sting, and in areas where fatalities from jellyfish stings occur it may indicate a bad prognosis.

In general the fatal cases of stinging take place in a few minutes, and not many will be treated by a physician, who in any case will be able to do little when confronted by a rapidly failing patient. If the immediate period of envenomation is survived by the patient, then, the various measures mentioned above may be used. Cortisone or analogue therapy may also be useful. Other drugs that have been used or advocated are intravenous calcium chloride, intravenous calcium levulinate, noradrenalin, sodium amytal, sodium phenobarbital, diphenhydramine (benadryl), atropine, hypertonic glucose, codeine, morphine, etc. Use of these measures has been reviewed by Southcott (1959) and Keegan (1960).

In summary, in the treatment of severe and potentially fatal stings the victim should be removed from the water as soon as possible (there is no record of any helper or companion of a fatal case receiving a very severe sting), the tentacles removed, and the possibility of immediate application of tourniquets to the limbs considered; artificial respiration and oxygen therapy should next be considered.

Unfortunately there is no prophylactic available against these stings. Clearly, the most important preventive measure that can be adopted is to stay out of waters where lethal or other severe stings are known to occur: if such is not possible then the swimmer should wear protective clothing preferably 2 mm or more thick (such will effectively prevent most of the nematocysts penetrating the skin) covering as much of the individual as possible, including the limbs. Fatalities have occurred in adults stung below the the knees, and not elsewhere upon the limbs or body.

ACKNOWLEDGEMENTS

The author is indebted to Charles E. Cutress, Associate Curator, Division of Marine Invertebrates, United States National Museum, for advice upon the systematic position of *Actinodendron arboreum* (Q. & G.) and other comment (pers. comm., 1960).

Supported by a grant from National Health and Medical Research Council, Commonwealth of Australia.

REFERENCES

BANNER, A. H. 1952. Preliminary report on marine biology study of Onotoa Atoll, Gilbert Islands. Part I. *Atoll Res. Bull.* No. 13, 1 (mimeographed).

BARNES, J. H. 1960. Observations on jellyfish stingings in north Queensland. *Med. J. Aust.* **2**, 993.

BIGELOW, H. B. 1938. Plankton of the Bermuda oceanographic expeditions. VIII. Medusae taken during the years 1929 and 1930. *Zoologica, N.Y.* **23** (2), 99.

BLOOMFIELD, J. 1959. *Know-how in the Surf.* Sydney: Angus and Robertson.

BYRNE, K. 1924. Coral cut. *Med. J. Aust.* **2**, 649.

CHU, G. W. T. C. and CUTRESS, C. E. 1955. Dermatitis due to contact with the hydroid, *Syncoryne mirabilis* (Agassiz, 1862). *Hawaii Med. J.* **14** (5), 403.

CILENTO, R. W. 1923. Australia's special problems in tropical hygiene. *Health* (Cwlth. Health Dept., Melbourne), **1** (2), 37.

CLELAND, J. B. 1924. Injuries and diseases in Australia attributable to animals (except insects). *Med. J. Aust.* **2**, 339.

CLELAND, J. B. and SOUTHCOTT, R. V. (in press). Injuries and diseases in Australia attributable to animals. Series VI. Dept. of Health, Australia.

DE OREO, G. A. 1946. Dermatitis venenata resulting from contact with marine animals (hydroids), *Arch. Derm. Syph.* **54** (6), 637.

DUJARRIC DE LA RIVIÈRE, R. 1915. Sur l'existence d'une médusocongestine. *C.R. Soc. Biol.* **78**, 596.

EVANS, H. M. 1943. *Sting-Fish and Seafarer.* London: Faber and Faber.

FISH, C. J. and COBB, M. C. 1954. *Noxious marine animals of the western Pacific Ocean.* Research Report 36, Fish and Wildlife Service, U.S. Dept. of the Interior. U.S. Govt. Printing Office.

FLECKER, H. 1945a. Injuries by unknown agents to bathers in north Queensland. *Med. J. Aust.* **1**, 98.

FLECKER, H. 1945b. Injuries by unknown agents to bathers in north Queensland. *Med. J. Aust.* **1**, 417.

FLECKER, H. 1952a. Fatal stings to north Queensland bathers. *Med. J. Aust.* **1**, 35.

FLECKER, H. 1952b. Fatal stings to north Queensland bathers. *Med. J. Aust.* **1**, 458.

FLECKER, H. 1952c. Irukandji sting to north Queensland bathers without production of weals but with severe general symptoms. *Med. J. Aust.* **2**, 89.

FLECKER, H. 1957a. Further notes on Irukandji stings. *Med. J. Aust.* **1**, 9.

FLECKER, H. 1957b. Injuries produced by marine organisms in tropical Australia. *Med. J. Aust.* **2**, 556.

HALSTEAD, B. W. 1956. Animal phyla known to contain poisonous marine animals. In *Venoms*, Am. Assn. Adv. Sci., Wash., D.C., Symposium series Publn. No. 44.

HALSTEAD, B. W. 1957. Jellyfish stings and their medical management. *U.S. Armed Forces Med. J.* **8** (11), 1587.

HALSTEAD, B. W. 1959. *Dangerous Marine Animals.* Cambridge, Maryland. Cornell Maritime Press.

HERCUS, J. P. 1944. An unusual eye condition. *Med. J. Aust.* **1**, 98.

HIRASE, S. *et al.* 1927. *Illustrated Japanese Zoological Dictionary.* Tokyo: Hokuryu-kwan (teste Fish and Cobb, 1954, p. 40).

HYMAN, L. H. 1940. *The Invertebrates*: *Protozoa through Ctenophora*, New York: McGraw-Hill.

JOHNSTON, G. 1847. *A history of the British zoophytes.* Second Edition. Vols. I and II, London: John van Voorst (Vol. I = text; Vol. II = Plates I–LXXIV and legends.)

KEEGAN, H. L. 1960. *Some venomous and Noxious Animals of the Far East.* Medical General Laboratory (406), U.S. Army Medical Command, Japan.

KINGSTON, C. W. and SOUTHCOTT, R. V. 1960. Skin histopathology in fatal jellyfish stinging. *Trans. Roy. Soc. Trop. Med. and Hyg.* **54** (4), 373.

KOMAI, T. 1935. On *Stephanoscyphus* and *Nausithoe*. *Mem. Coll. Sci., Kyoto Imp. Univ.* **B10** (5), 289.

KOMAI, T. 1936. On another form of *Stephanoscyphus*, found in the waters of Japan. *Mem. Coll. Sci., Kyoto Imp. Univ.* **B11** (3), 175.

LANE, C. E. and DODGE, E. 1958. The toxicity of *Physalia* nematocysts. *Biol. Bull.* **115** (2), 219.

LIGHT, S. F. 1914a. Another dangerous jellyfish in Philippine waters. *Philipp. J. Sci.* **9B** (3), 291.

LIGHT, S. F. 1914b. Some Philippine Scyphomedusae, including two new genera, five new species, and one new variety. *Philipp. J. Sci.* **9D** (3), 195.

LIGHT, S. F. 1921. Further notes on Philippine scyphomedusan jellyfishes. *Philipp. J. Sci.* **18** (1), 25.

LORD, R. E. and WILKS, S. L. B. 1918. A case of jellyfish sting simulating an acute abdomen. *Lancet* **2**, 390.

MCNEILL, F. A. 1945. Injuries by unknown agents to bathers in north Queensland. *Med. J. Aust.* **2**, 29.

MCNEILL, F. A. and POPE, E. C. 1943a. A venomous medusa from Australian waters. *Aust. J. Sci.* **5** (6), 188.

MCNEILL, F. A. and POPE, E. C. 1943b. A deadly poisonous jellyfish. *Aust. Mus. Mag.* **8** (4), 127.

MCNEILL, F. A. and POPE, E. C. 1945. Injuries by unknown agents to bathers in north Queensland. *Med. J. Aust.* **1**, 334.

MAYER, A. G. 1910. *Medusae of the World.* Vols. 1–3. Wash., D.C. Carneg. Instn. Publn. No. 109.

PANTIN, C. F. A. 1942. The excitation of nematocysts. *J. Exp. Biol.* **19**, 294.

PARADICE, W. E. J. 1924. Injuries and lesions caused by the bites of animals and insects. *Med. J. Aust.* **2**, 650.

PARRISH, H. M. 1959. Deaths from bites and stings of venomous animals and insects in the United States. *Archiv. Int. Med.* **104**, 198.

PHILLIPS, J. H. 1956. Isolation of active nematocysts of *Metridium senile* and their chemical composition. *Nature* **178**, 932.

PHILLIPS, J. H. and ABBOTT, D. P. 1957. Isolation and assay of the nematocyst toxin of *Metridium senile fimbriatum*. *Biol. Bull.* **113** (2), 296.

PHISALIX, M. 1922. *Animaux Venimeux et Venins.* Vol. 1. Paris: Masson et Cie.

PICKEN, L. E. R. 1957. Stinging capsules and designing nature. *New Biol.* **22**, 56.

POPE, E. C. 1953a. Sea lice or jellyfish. *Aust. Mus. Mag.* **11** (1), 16.

POPE, E. C. 1953b. Marine stingers. *Aust. Mus. Mag.* **11** (4), 111.

PRESTON, F. S. 1950. Coral ulcer. *Brit. Med. J.* **1**, 642.

RUSSELL, F. E. 1961. Injuries by venomous animals in the United States. *J.A.M.A.* **177** (13), 903.

RUSSELL, F. S. 1953. *The Medusae of the British Isles.* Cambridge U.P.

SAVILLE-KENT, W. 1893. *The Great Barrier Reef of Australia: Its Products and Potentialities.* London: W. H. Allen and Co., Ltd.

SOUTHCOTT, R. V. 1952. Fatal stings to north Queensland bathers. *Med. J. Aust.* **1**, 272.

SOUTHCOTT, R. V. 1956. Studies on Australian Cubomedusae, including a new genus and species apparently harmful to man. *Aust. J. Marine Freshw. Res.* **7** (2), 254.

SOUTHCOTT, R. V. 1958a. Jellyfish stings. *Practitioner* **180** (1077), 377.

SOUTHCOTT, R. V. 1958b. South Australian jellyfish. *South Aust. Nat.* **32** (4), 53.

SOUTHCOTT, R. V. 1958c. The Cubomedusae-lethal jellyfish. *Discovery* **19** (7), 282.

SOUTHCOTT, R. V. 1959. Tropical jellyfish and other marine stingings. *Mil. Med.* **124** (8), 569.

SOUTHCOTT, R. V. 1960. Venomous jellyfish. *Good Health, South Aust.* No. **113**, 18.

STEPHENSON, T. A. 1935. *The British sea anemones.* Vol. II. London: The Ray Society, Vol. 121.

STRONG, R. P. 1942. *Stitt's Diagnosis Prevention and Treatment of Tropical Diseases,* 6th ed. Vols. 1 and 2. Philadelphia: Blakiston.

UCHIDA, T. 1929. Studies on the Stauromedusae and Cubomedusae, with special reference to their metamorphosis. *Jap. J. Zool.* **2** (2), 103.

UCHIDA, T. 1947. Some medusae from the central Pacific. *J. Fac. Sci. Hokkaido Univ.* Ser. VI, **9** (3), 297.

WADE, H. W. 1928. Post-mortem findings in acute jellyfish poisoning with sudden death in status lymphaticus. *Amer. J. Trop. Med.* **8** (3), 233.

WEILL, R. 1934. Contribution a l'étude des Cnidaires et de leurs nématocystes. *Trav. Sta. Zool. Wimereux.* **10**, 1; **11**, 348.

WELSH, J. H. 1956. On the nature and action of coelenterate toxins. *Deep Sea Res.* 3, Supp., pp. 287–297.

WELSH, J. H. 1960. Hydroxytryptamine in coelenterates. *Nature* **186** (4727), 811.

WELSH, J. H. and BROCK, P. B. 1958. Quaternary ammonium bases in the coelenterates. *Biol. Bull.* **115** (3), 551.

WELSH, J. H. and MOORHEAD, M. 1960. The quantitative distribution of 5-hydroxytryptamine in the invertebrates, especially in their nervous systems. *J. Neurochem.* **6**, 146.

WOOD, J. G. 1874. *Out of Doors.* A selection of original articles on practical natural history. London: Longmans, Green.

YANAGITA, T. M. 1959a. Physiological mechanism of nematocyst responses in sea-anemone. II. Effects of electrolyte ions upon the isolated cnidae. *J. Fac. Sci. Univ. Tokyo* Sect. IV, **8** (3), 381.

YANAGITA, T. M. 1959b. Physiological mechanism of nematocyst responses in sea-anemone. VII. Extrusion of resting cnidae—its nature and its possible bearing on the normal nettling response. *J. Exp. Biol.* **36** (3), 478.

ZERVOS, S. 1903. La maladie des pêcheurs d'éponges. Sem. méd: (24 June) (teste Phisalix 1922 : 76).

STUDIES ON THE TOXICITY OF *RHODACTIS HOWESII* (MATAMALU)

LIONEL FARBER and PETER LERKE*

THE nature and mode of action of coelenterate toxins has attracted the attention of numerous investigators. The subject has been approached from the point of view of general biology by Richet and Portier (1936), physiology by Cosmovici (1925), Cantacuzene (1926), Cantacuzene and Damboviceanu (1934), Welsh (1955), and Lane and Dodge (1958); pharmacology by Welsh and Prock (1958); and immunology by Phillips (1956) and Phillips and Abbott (1957). General conclusions from the above studies are difficult to make because of the variety of aims pursued, organisms studied and methods used. We became interested in coelenterate toxins as a result of information later published by Martin (1960) on fatal human cases following ingestion of a raw sea anemone, *Rhodactis howesii.* This coelenterate, locally known as " matamalu ", is commonly found on the reefs of American Samoa and, when cooked, is part of the native diet. Cases of poisoning occur after either accidental or intentional ingestion of the raw anemone. Frozen samples of the coelenterate were obtained and a project was started on the isolation of the toxic principle, its characterization and the elucidation of its mode of action. This paper describes some very preliminary findings which are intended to indicate the direction for more detailed investigations.

MATERIALS AND METHODS

Toxic material

The whole animal was used as starting material in all cases. As a rule, the frozen anemone was thawed and homogenized with three times its weight of a suitable diluent. The homogenate was then centrifuged at 6000 r.p.m. for periods up to 3 hr and the supernatant was used either for testing the effect of various manipulations on its toxic property or as a starting material for purification procedures.

In the following description the words " extract " and supernatant " are used interchangeably. The supernatant obtained after centrifugation of the aqueous homogenate was an extract insofar as it contained the toxic principle formerly present in the whole animal, even after 3 hr of centrifugation at 6000 r.p.m. However, the resulting liquid was opalescent and resembled a protein " solution ". Furthermore, both opalescence and toxicity could

*G. W. Hooper Foundation, University of California, San Francisco, U.S.A.

be removed by centrifugation at higher speeds. Thus, a more accurate term would be " toxic suspension ". The efficiency of extraction of the toxic principle was estimated by comparing the toxicity of a whole homogenate (1 : 4 w/w) with that of the supernatant obtained after 3 hr of centrifugation. No differences were found. Likewise, the toxicity remained the same whether the supernatant was obtained after 30 min or 3 hr of centrifugation at 6000 r.p.m.

In this communication, toxicity is expressed in mg of raw material yielding an extract causing the death of the experimental animal. For example, 100 ml of supernatant from a 1 : 4 homogenate would contain the equivalent of 25 g of anemone or 250 mg per ml. Therefore, if 0.1 ml of a 1 : 20 dilution of this supernatant is required to kill all mice in a group, we can calculate that the equivalent weight of anemone required to kill one mouse is 1.25 mg.

Homogenization of the frozen, whole coelenterate in various buffers ranging from pH 2.0 to pH 10.0, and in distilled water, showed that water was as good an extractant as any of the buffers used. Aqueous homogenates were therefore used throughout, unless otherwise indicated. An attempt was made to increase the efficiency of extraction by passing the homogenate through a press used for breaking up bacterial cells. This procedure, however, did not result in a greater concentration of toxin in the supernatant after centrifugation.

Test Animals

Mice were selected for assay purposes. Toxic extracts were at first fed to the animals in order to simulate as much as possible the conditions under which the anemone is toxic to man. But the technique was cumbersome and, although the mice showed a slightly greater susceptibility to toxin under these conditions, it was decided to use intraperitoneal injections because of the ease and precision with which they could be carried out. Four to six mice were injected with each dilution. Injection volume was 0.1 ml, and the mice used ranged in weight from 18 to 20 g. Death within 24 hr was taken as the end point.

The various methods used for characterization and fractionation will be described under separate subheadings along with the results obtained.

RESULTS

Gross Effects of the Toxin and Importance of Age and Species of Test Animal

The effect on man of the ingestion of the raw anemone has been described by Martin (1960). In mice which have received a lethal dose the onset of symptoms usually occurs within 30 min; there is a prominent bloody and mucous intestinal discharge and labored breathing. The animal sits motionless for long periods with its flanks drawn in; if disturbed it may snap out of this state and show some activity, but soon returns to its previous posture. When forced to move, the animal exhibits a peculiar staggering gait. Death results from apparent respiratory failure. Post mortem, the most prominent findings are intestinal, pulmonary and subcutaneous hemorrhages, a moist and sticky exudate on the intestines, an injected diaphragm and pale, soft

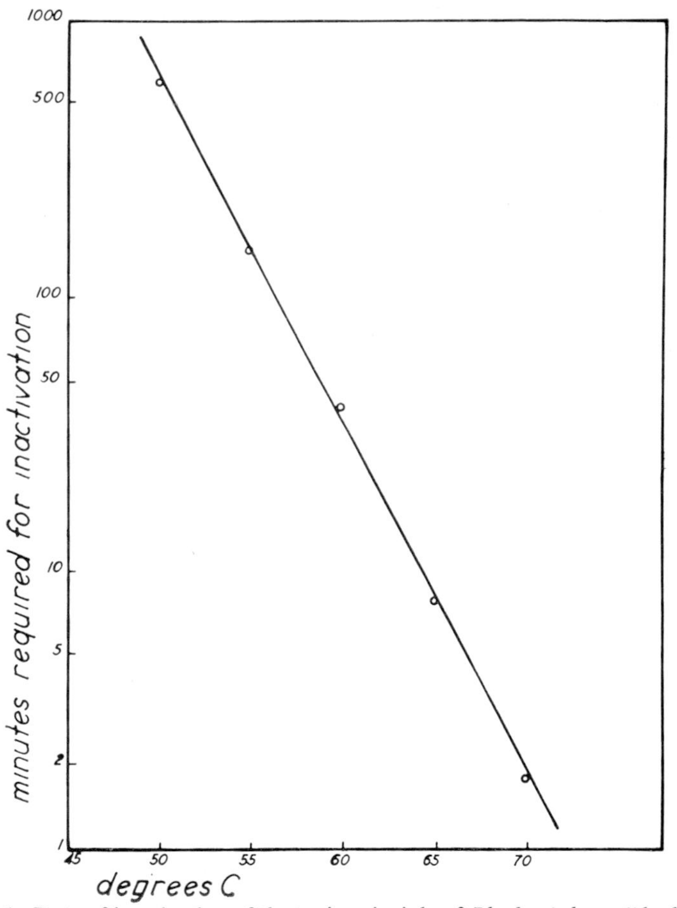

FIG. 1. Rate of inactivation of the toxic principle of *Rhodactis howesii* by heat.

kidneys. The age of the mouse appeared to affect only slightly its susceptibility to the toxin. Using an aqueous extract of *R. howesii*, mice of different weights were injected and the lethal dose was determined as described above. The lethal doses for mice weighing 15, 25 and 30 g were, respectively, 330, 250 and 270 mg of material per kg of body weight. Other species may be considerably more sensitive to the toxin: thus a partially purified preparation which had a mouse toxicity of 2.6 mg per kg body weight, was shown to have a toxicity of at least 0.21 mg per kg body weight when tested on two rabbits. The lethal dose for man is, of course, unknown.

Effect of Heat

Test tubes containing aqueous extracts of *R. howesii* were placed in a constant temperature water bath and removed at intervals. They were then frozen for subsequent assay. The data given in Figs. 1 and 2 show that the

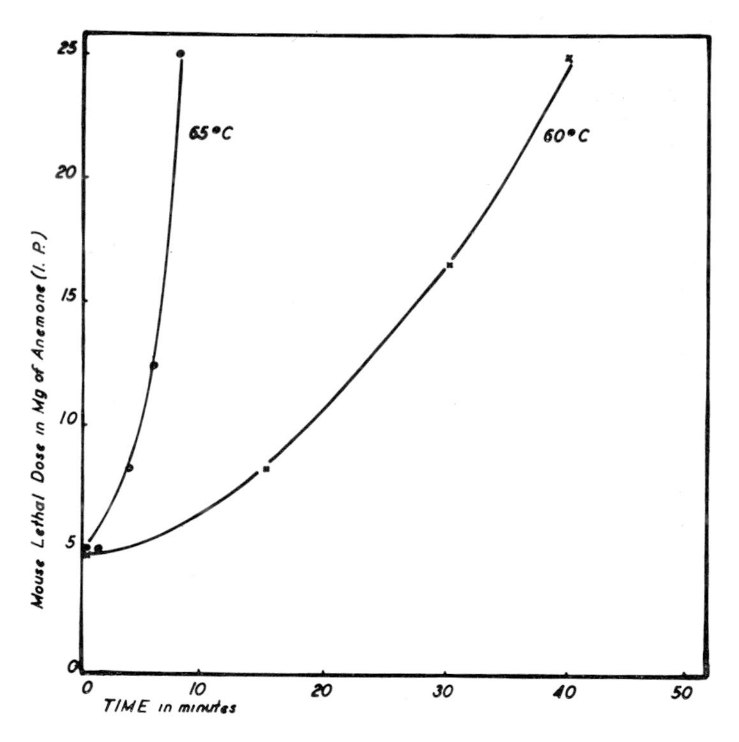

FIG. 2. Heat sensitivity of the toxic principle of *Rhodactis howesii*.

toxic principle is quite stable at room temperature, but is readily inactivated at temperatures above 65°C. We defined inactivation as the loss of the ability of 25 mg of the toxic material to kill an 18-g mouse in 24 hr when injected I.P. in a volume of 0.1 ml.

Effect of Proteolytic Enzymes

" Matamalu " toxin was subjected to the action of bromelin, papain and trypsin. Of these only trypsin proved to be active as shown in Fig. 3. Dolman (1957) has described the action of trypsin on *Clostridium botulinum* type E toxin and has shown that the breakdown of the toxin is preceded by an increased toxicity, which he attributed to a temporary unmasking of toxic groups within the toxin molecule. We looked for this type of effect with *R. howesii* toxin, but could find no evidence for such an occurrence.

Effect of Hydrogen Ion Concentration

An aqueous extract of *R. howesii* was prepared and aliquots were adjusted to pH 4.5, 7.0 and 10.0 electrometrically. The pH 7.0 extract was tested as such. The other two preparations were tested before and after adjustment to pH 7.0. No differences in toxicity were found among any of the preparations tested. It appears, therefore, that short exposures to pH's within the range of 4.5 to 10.0 do not affect the activity of the toxin.

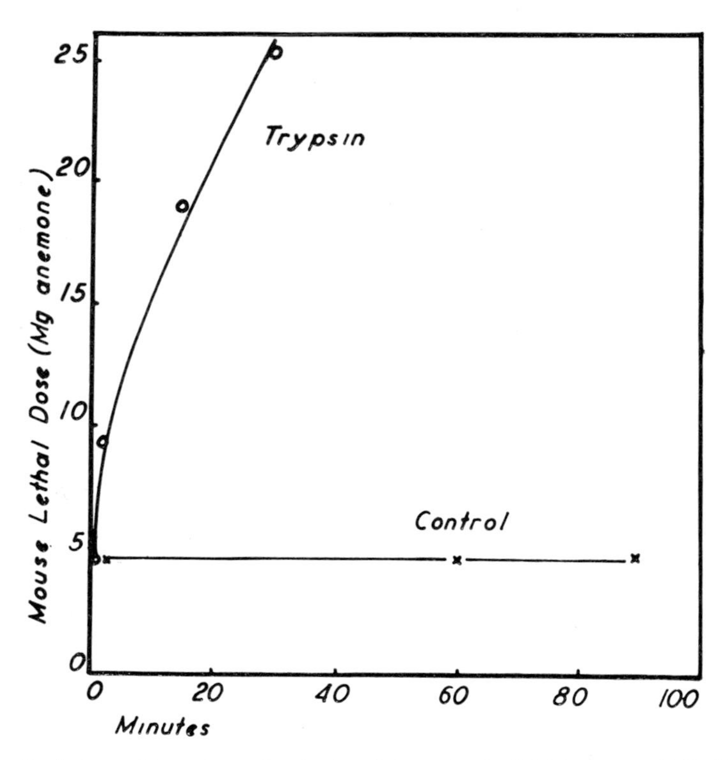

FIG. 3. Action of trypsin on the toxin of " matamalu " (0.1 per cent DIFCO 1 : 200 preparation; pH : 8.0; temperature: 39 °C).

Fractionation

The mouse toxicity of extracts from whole anemone was found to range between about 3 and 6 mg of whole anemone per mouse. In an attempt to increase this toxicity the raw anemone was homogenized in distilled water (1 : 3 ratio by weight) and the homogenate was then slowly poured into 10 volumes of acetone which had previously been cooled to —70 °C. The resulting precipitate, which contained all the activity, was removed on a Buchner funnel, washed 3 times with cold acetone and dried under vacuum. Here again, various buffers, ranging in pH from 4.5 to 10.0 were compared as to their ability to extract the toxin from the dry preparation. It was once more found that water gave the most potent extract, as shown in Table 1. The procedure involved the preparation of a 1 per cent suspension of the powder in the appropriate buffer (M/5), extraction with stirring for 24 hr at 0°C and centrifugation for 3 hr at 6000 r.p.m. The assays were carried out on the resulting supernatants. The most active supernatant was found to have a mouse toxicity equivalent to 0.12 mg of dry acetone powder per animal.

TABLE 1. EFFECT OF pH ON THE EFFICIENCY OF TOXIN EXTRACTION FROM AN ACETONE POWDER OF *Rhodactis howesii*

pH of the buffer	Dilution of extract sufficient to kill 50% of the mice
4.5	1 : 1
6.0	1 : 3
7.4	1 : 6
8.0	1 : 6
10.0	1 : 1.7
Water	1 : 7

Fractionation of Acetone Powder

Ammonium Sulfate. A 1 per cent aqueous suspension of the acetone powder was prepared and centrifuged at 6000 r.p.m. for 30 min. The supernatant was fractionated with solid $(NH_4)_2SO_4$ at 0°C. A precipitate formed when the solution reached 75 per cent saturation. It was collected, redissolved in water and dialyzed against distilled water in the cold. A precipitate also formed at 85 per cent saturation and it was treated similarly. No further precipitates were obtained at higher concentrations of the salt. After removal of the ammonium sulfate from the fractions, the latter were assayed. The 85 per cent fraction had a mouse toxicity of 0.48 mg per animal whereas the 75 per cent fraction had a toxicity of 0.048 mg per animal All of the first dialysis water (3 l) from the 75 per cent fraction was concentrated in the cold to a volume of 5 ml and assayed. It was found to be nontoxic, showing that the toxin is not dialyzable. The 75 per cent fraction itself gave a strong Millon's reaction, and positive xanthoproteic and biuret reactions. None of the tests for carbohydrates were positive.

Alcohol Fractionation. A 50 per cent concentration of 95 per cent ethyl alcohol in a 1 per cent solution of acetone powder was sufficient to precipitate all of the toxin. This procedure could not be used for purification, however, because a considerable decrease in activity occurred during precipitation.

Effect of Lyophilization

This procedure did not appear to destroy the activity of any of the relatively impure preparations tested.

Effect of High-Speed Centrifugation

A 1 per cent extract of the 75 per cent ammonium sulfate-precipitated fraction was prepared in distilled water and centrifuged for 2 hr at 6000 r.p.m. The supernatant was assayed, and then spun in an ultracentrifuge at 40,000 r.p.m. for 30 min. The supernatant was completely clear and all the toxicity was contained in the pellet.

Effect of Freezing

Freezing apparently does not affect the toxin. Although we obtained all our material in the frozen state, subsequent freezing–thawing cycles did not decrease the toxicity of any of the preparations tested.

Immunogenicity

The 75 per cent ammonium sulfate-precipitated fraction was tested for immunogenicity in laboratory animals. After an unsuccesful attempt at immunizing mice, it was decided to use rabbits for that purpose. The fraction was dissolved in physiological saline to a concentration of 4 mg per ml, 0.5 per cent of formaldehyde was added and the mixture was stored at 20°C until the mouse toxicity had decreased eightfold. This antigen was then emulsified in Freundt's adjuvant and 0.25 ml of the emulsion were injected I.M. into a rabbit; this was equivalent to 0.5 mg of detoxified antigen. Preliminary tests had shown that the rabbit lethal dose of the nondetoxified antigen was approximately 1 mg for an animal weighing 4800 g. The initial injection was followed by a series of four boosters of increasing toxicities, administered at intervals of 3 weeks. The last booster consisted of an intravenous injection of 3 mg of the nondetoxified material or three times the lethal dose. This was well withstood by the rabbit which was then bled and the serum tested for mouse-protective antibody. Optimal proportions of serum to toxin were determined *in vivo* using the precipitin reaction. Dilutions of serum on both sides of the optimal ratio were then tested *in vivo* by premixing with toxin prior to injection as well as by injection prior to challenge. So far, however, the unequivocal demonstration of mouse-protective antibodies has not been achieved.

CONCLUSION AND SUMMARY

From the results presented above it appears that the toxic principle of *Rhodactis howesii* is either a protein or a substance closely associated with a protein. This is indicated not only by the qualitative tests carried out, but also by the marked susceptibility of the toxic material to heat and to trypsin. The limited indications as to immunogenicity likewise point in the same direction. The toxic substance is, moreover, of fairly high molecular weight (nondialyzable), resistant to repeated freezing and thawing and relatively stable in the pH range of 4.5 to 10.0. The mouse toxicity of the impure preparations obtained to date is approximately one-fifth that of cobra venom and only one-seventeenth that of diphtheria toxin. The localization of the toxin within the anemone remains unknown. The preliminary nature of the work described should be emphasized, and it is felt that the results obtained should principally be used as guide lines for more detailed studies. It is our intention to concentrate our efforts first on the isolation and purification of the toxin and then to proceed on to pathological, pharmacological and immunological studies.

REFERENCES

CANTACUZÈNE, J. 1926. Activation des poisons de l'*Adamsia palliata* par la lécithine et pouvoir hémolytique. *C.R. Soc. Biol. Paris* **95**, 118.

CANTACUZÈNE, J. and DAMBOVICEANU. 1934. Caractères biologiques des acconities d'*Adamsia palliata* après déproteinisation. *C.R. Soc. Biol. Paris* **117**, 136.

COSMOVICI, N. L. 1925. Les poisons de l'extrait aqueux des tentacules et des nematocysted d'*Adamsia palliata.* Son-ils détruits par l'ébullition? Essais d'adsorption. *C.R. Soc. Biol. Paris* **92**, 1373.

LANE, C. E. and DODGE, E. 1958. The toxicity of *Physalia* nematocysts. *Biol. Bull.* **115**, 219.

MARTIN, E. J. 1960. Observations on the toxic sea anemone *Rhodactis howesii* (Coelenterata). *Pacific Science* **14** (4), 403.

PHILLIPS, J. H. 1956. Isolation of active nematocysts of *Metridium senile* and their chemical composition. *Nature* **178**, 2, 932.

PHILLIPS, J. H. and ABBOTT, D. P. 1957. Isolation and assay of the nematocyst toxin of *Metridium senile fimbriatum*. *Biol. Bull.* **113**, 296.

RICHET, C. and PORTIER, D. 1936. Recherches sur la toxine des Coelentérés et les phenomènes d'anaphylaxie. *Res. Camp. Sci. Monaco* **95**, 3.

WELSH, J. H. and PROCK, P. B. 1958. Quaternary ammonium bases in the Coelenterates. *Biol. Bull. Woods Hole* **115**, 557.

STUDIES ON THE PARALYTIC POISONS FOUND IN MUSSELS AND CLAMS ALONG THE NORTH AMERICAN PACIFIC COAST

EDWARD J. SCHANTZ*

ALONG certain areas of the North American Pacific coast, mussels and clams become very toxic and have caused death and temporary paralysis when consumed by humans. These areas include mainly southern and southeastern Alaska where the butter clam (*Saxidomas giganteus*) becomes toxic and

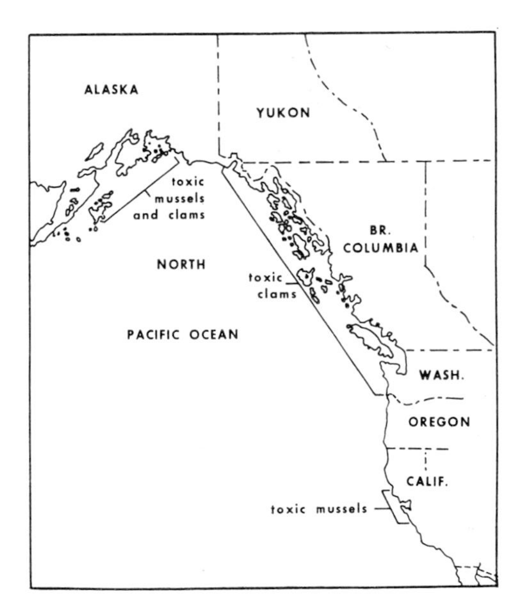

FIG. 1. Area of the Pacific coast of North America where toxic shellfish are most abundant.

along the California coast where the ocean mussel (*Mytilus californianus*) becomes toxic. The locations of these areas are shown in Fig. 1. The paralytic poisons found in the ocean mussels and butter clams in these areas have been isolated in pure form.

*U.S. Army Biological Laboratories, Fort Detrick, Frederick, Maryland.

The poison is not produced by the shellfish but is obtained from a toxic dinoflagellate *Gonyaulax catenella* which the shellfish consume as food. During a series of outbreaks of shellfish poisonings along the California Coast between 1920 and 1936 Meyer and Sommer (1937) and Sommer, Whedon, Kofoid, and Stohler (1937) found that the California ocean mussel became toxic only when *G. catenella* was present in the waters bathing the mussels, and that this organism produced a poison which was retained by the dark gland or hepatopancreas of the mussel. The poison causes no observable disturbance of the natural life processes of the mussel but is lethal to persons unfortunate enough to eat the mussels at the time that *G. catenella* is growing in the water bathing the mussels. A historical review of these developments was presented by Schantz (1960). " Mussel poisoning " in humans as described by Meyer and Sommer (1937) usually develops within ½ to 3 hr after consuming even a few toxic mussels. A numbness in the lips and finger tips is followed by an ascending paralysis and finally death from respiratory paralysis within 3 to 20 hr, depending upon the magnitude of the dose. If a person survives as long as 24 hr the prognosis is good, and as far as is known there are no lasting effects from the ordeal. Poisonings have occurred mainly along the Pacific Coast of the United States, Canada and Alaska, the estuaries of the St. Lawrence River, the Bay of Fundy region, areas around the North Sea and the English Channel, and in South Africa. In many of these areas mussel poisoning is a local public health problem and confined to local residents, picnickers, and campers. However, as reported by McFarren *et al.* (1960), in south-eastern Alaska the problem has additional significance because of the commercial shipment of shellfish to other areas.

The poison has never been isolated in pure form directly from *G. catenella*,* but recently has been isolated from California mussels (*Mytilus californianus*) and from Alaska butter clams (*Saxidomas giganteus*) through the combined efforts of workers at the Hooper Foundation of the University of California, Northwestern University, and the Chemical Corps Biological Laboratories. These results were published by Schantz *et al.* (1957). A comparison of the properties of these purified poisons with those of the poison from *G. catenella* indicate that the poison found in this organism is retained by the mussel unchanged. Chromatographic studies carried out by Burke *et al.* (1960) have shown that the poison from mussels and the organisms move together. Studies carried out in my laboratory indicate that the poisons from *G. catenella* and mussels are similar in gross physiological properties, stability to acid, alkali, and heat, and in the diffusion rates. Provasoli (personal

*After this paper was submitted, the poison was isolated in pure form from *G. catenella* and was found to be identical in all chemical and physical properties to the poisons isolated from mussels and clams. These data were presented at the 142nd National Meeting of the American Chemical Society (E. J. Schantz, J. M. Lynch and G. Vayvada, September 1962).

communication) has achieved the isolation of *G. catenella* free of bacteria, and has found that the poison is still produced by the organism. This fact would indicate that poison is a metabolic product of the organism, and not the result of a symbiotic effect of the bacteria usually associated with it. It appears that the mussel poison, and quite likely other poisons of this type found in shellfish, are the products of microorganisms of the sea.

The many attempts which have been made to purify the poison from mussels have been reviewed by Schantz (1960). In some of the early work, Sommer *et al.* (1948) and Muller (1939), working with Sommer and his associates at the Hooper Foundation, pointed out the basic character of the mussel poison, and employed Decalso as a cation exchange resin, along with chromatography on carbon for purification. These methods, however, brought about a partial purification only. The Decalso was not efficient in the removal of the poison from crude extracts, and a great portion of it was lost. Studies by Schantz *et al.* (1957) have shown that the most practical method for highest yields and purity is by chromatography on carboxylic acid exchange resins, followed by chromatography on acid-washed alumina. Although considerable success was achieved in purifying the poison from California mussels and Alaska butter clams by this procedure, it was not successful for purifying the poison occurring in toxic scallops. Needler (1949) presented evidence that poison found in scallops has its origin in *G. tamarensis*. This difference is believed to be due to a slightly different basicity of the scallop poison. The primary source of the poison occurring in butter clams is not known, but as indicated by Schantz (1960) some evidence exists that it may be produced by *G. catenella*.

For the purposes of this symposium, only the purified mussel and clam poisons will be discussed. These poisons were not obtained in crystalline form as simple salts from solution, although the dried preparations often appeared crystalline. Evidence for the purity of the poisons was obtained through countercurrent distribution studies. Mold, Bowden and co-workers, working in my laboratory found (1956) that distribution in a solvent system of n-butanol, ethanol, 0.1 M aqueous potassium carbonate, and α-ethyl caproic acid in a volume ratio of 146 : 49 : 200 : 5, with the aqueous layer adjusted to pH 8, resulted in the separation of the poisons into two components. The component present in the larger amount was somewhat more toxic than the smaller component. When either one of the two was isolated, allowed to equilibrate in acid solution, and re-run through the distribution, a similar distribution into two components occurred. It was assumed therefore that the poisons exist in two tautaumeric forms. Analyses of the components indicated that the poisons had a purity of at least 95 per cent.

Studies on the two poisons have shown that they must be similar if not identical in chemical structure. Both are basic substances forming salts with mineral acids. They are very stable in acid solution but labile in alkaline solution when exposed to the air. The dihydrochloride salts are white hygroscopic solids, very soluble in water, soluble to some extent in methanol and ethanol, and insoluble in all lipid solvents. They have a specific optical rotation of + 130°, show no absorption in the ultraviolet, and have the same infrared spectra with strong absorption at 3, 6, and 9μ. Two basic functions are present in equivalent amounts, pK_a 8.1 and about 11.5. The molecular formula was found to be $C_{10}H_{17}N_7O_4.2HCl$; the molecular weight is 372. The toxicity in terms of the average minimum lethal dose* is 5.5 $\times$ 10^6 MU per gram of poison. This amounts to 0.18 μg for a mouse or nine micrograms per kg of body weight. The intravenous dose for a rabbit is three to four micrograms per kg of body weight. The oral dose for humans has been estimated from accidental poisonings by Meyer and Sommer (1953) to be at least 20,000 MU, but Canadian works, Bond and Medcof (1958) and Tennant, Naubert and Corbeil (1955), believe that the dose may be as low as one third of this value. In terms of the purified poison, the minimum lethal oral dose for man would be between 1 and 4 mg.

Because of the strongly basic group one might expect the poison to be an amine or a quaternary ammonium compound. Methylation studies on the poison indicate that such structures are not present. Certain color tests have been helpful in yielding information about the molecule. The poisons react with certain aromatic nitro compounds to form colored complexes in much the same way as creatinine reacts with dinitrophenol in the Jaffe test and with dinitrobenzoic acid in the Benedict–Behre test. A comparison of the absorption spectrum of the color complex formed when the poisons and creatinine are reacted with the Jaffe or Benedict–Behre reagents suggests that at least some part of the structure of the poison must be similar to that of creatinine. Other compounds such as hydantoin and certain barbituric acid derivatives that give the test showed marked differences from the poisons and creatinine in absorption characteristics of the color complexes. The Irrevere-Sullivan test for creatinine-like compounds was found to be negative. The Weber nitroprusside test commonly used for substituted guanidines was positive for the poisons but the Sakaguchi test was negative, indicating that a free guanidinium group such as exists in arginine is not present in the poison. Negative tests were also obtained for the Weygland and Csendes test for enols of 1, 3 diketones, the Fearon and Mitchell test for primary and secondary alcohols, and the Benedict test for reducing sugars.

Howard, Mold and co-workers, in my laboratory (1960), found that the poisons were reduced with hydrogen gas at one atmosphere of pressure in the presence of a platinum catalyst to produce a completely nontoxic dihydro derivative ($C_{10}H_{19}N_7O_4.2HCl$). The loss in toxicity was directly propor-

*The mouse unit (MU) is defined as the minimum quantity of poison to kill a 20-gram white mouse (Webster Strain) in 15 minutes when one ml of poison solution is injected intraperitoneally.

tional to the uptake of hydrogen. This derivative no longer reacted with the dinitro compounds to yield a color complex. The presence of the unsaturated bond, therefore, appears to be a vital part of the toxic structure. This same bond is involved also in the reactions with the Jaffe and Benedict Behre tests. The Weber nitroprusside test, however, remained positive for the nontoxic reduced derivative.

Distribution studies on the dihydro derivative showed that the tautaumeric forms were no longer present, and that the substance moved as a single component. These data are additional evidence for the purity of the poisons.

Upon oxidation of the poison in mild alkaline solution (0.25 M $Ba(OH)_2$) exposed to the oxygen of the air, as carried out by Wintersteiner, Dutcher, and Walters (1960), the toxicity decreased in direct proportion to the oxygen uptake, and at the consumption of one mole of oxygen, all toxicity was gone. In this case, too, the Jaffe and Benedict–Behre tests were negative and the Weber test was positive. In addition, other breakdown products were formed that gave a positive Sakaguchi test. The mixture possessed a molecular extinction of 6000 to 7000 in the ultraviolet at 235 and 333 MU. None of these products was isolated in pure form, but the absorption and fluorescent properties were suggestive of pteridine-like compounds. The reduced derivative was not oxidized in alkaline solution under the above conditions. This fact, again, indicates that the unsaturated bond is at least one of the vital links in the toxic structure of the poison, and appears to be the point at which oxidation of the poison starts when exposed to air at pH values higher than seven. The good correlation of the Jaffe test with toxicity suggested its use as a chemical test for the poison, and methods worked out for its use in this respect have been described by Mold *et al.* (1954) and McFarren *et al.* (1958).

Stronger oxidation, such as with periodate and permanganate or strong acid hydrolysis, yielded Sakaguchi-positive compounds. Guanidoproprionic acid, urea, ammonia, carbon dioxide, and guanidine have been isolated and identified among the resulting oxidation products.

The relation of optical rotation to the toxicity of the molecule is not exactly clear, but all indications are that the structure responsible for toxicity is not involved in the optical center. Reduction of the poison to the non-toxic dihydro derivative did not change the optical rotation. When the poison was placed in alkaline solution the optical rotation dropped from $+130°$ to $+50°$. Under anaerobic conditions the toxicity did not change, and the optical rotation stayed in this region. However, under aerobic conditions at room temperature the toxicity dropped to zero in about 24 hr, and the optical rotation dropped to $-40°$ followed by a rise in rotation to zero as the ultraviolet absorption reached a maximum. These points appear important from the standpoint of probable synthesis of the poison. If the optical center is not involved in the toxic structure, the synthesis of the structure responsible for biological activity should be a greater possibility.

One of the difficulties encountered in work on the chemical structure of the poison was the isolation of a degradative product that could be easily identified and still represent a fair portion of the intact molecule. Past attempts met with only limited success. All products were too large and too close to the parent structure, or too small, to be of great value in postulating a structure. Rapoport (personal communication) at the University of California has recently reported the isolation of an eight-carbon fragment, probably a pyrrolo-[1.2-c]-pyrimidine, from a reduction with phosphorus and hydroiodic acid in glacial acetic acid. A structure of this size would be a great step toward elucidating the entire structure of the poison.

Certain properties of the poisons allow additional conclusions on the structure. The ultraviolet and infrared spectra indicate no aromatic structures, conjugate unsaturation, or isolated carbonyl groups. The elemental ratios, of course, require that ring structures be present. The high nitrogen content and the absence of nitro and nitrogen-to-nitrogen bonds, as indicated by kjeldahl analyses, strongly suggest that several of the nitrogen atoms must be involved in a heterocyclic structure. Titration suggests that one basic function (pK_a 11.5) may be a guanidinum group, and the other (pK_a 8.1), an amine.

Although the physiological action of the poisons has sometimes been described as curare-like, those substances that inhibit the action of curare have no inhibitory action on these poisons (20). The action, however, appears to be mainly at the myoneural junction. No antidote for the poisons is known. The administration of atropine to mice or rabbits challenged with shellfish poison did not change the symptoms or death time, and this fact would indicate that the poison is not a cholinesterase inhibitor. Bolton *et al.* (1959) have demonstrated from studies on end-plate potentials that the poison is not a cholinesterase inhibitor. No effect of the poisons has been found on the biochemical mechanisms of muscular contraction. O'Neill *et al.* (personal communication) have found that the mechanism converting ADP to ATP from creatinine phosphate is not inhibited by the poison.

The value of studies on toxins and poisons lies in the use of these substances for the elucidation of biochemical and physiological mechanisms. To date, no other known chemical structure has been shown to produce the same physiological action as that of the shellfish poisons. This would suggest that the unique structure of these poisons offers a novel tool for the elucidation of some biochemical and physiological mechanisms at the myoneural junctions.

ACKNOWLEDGEMENTS

The work reviewed in this paper extended to several laboratories. I wish to acknowledge the cooperation and assistance given to the U.S. Army

Biological Laboratories by Dr. Herman Sommer and Dr. K. F. Mayer and their associates of the Hooper Foundation, University of California, Dr. Byron Riegel and Dr. R. K. Summerbell and their associates of Northwestern University, Dr. Herbert E. Carter and his associates at the University of Illinois and Dr. Oskar Wintersteiner and his associates at the Squibb Institute for Medical Research.

REFERENCES

BOLTON, B. L., BERGNER, A. D., O'NEILL, J. J. and WAGLEY, P. F. 1959. Effect of a shellfish poison on end-plate potentials. *Bull. Johns Hopkins Hospital* **105**, 233.

BOND, R. M. and MEDCOF, J. C. 1958. Epidemic shellfish poisoning in New Brunswick, 1957. *Canad. Med. Assn. J.* **79**, 19.

BURKE, J., MARCHISOTTO, J., MCLAUGHLIN, J. J. A. and PROVASOLI, L. 1960. Analyses of the toxin produced by *Gonyaulax catenella* in axenic culture. *Ann. N.Y. Acad. Sci.* **90**, 837.

MCFARREN, E. J., SCHANTZ, E. J., CAMPBELL, J. E. and LEWIS, K. H. 1958. Chemical determination of paralytic shellfish poison in clams. *J. Assn. Official Agri. Chem.* **41**, 168.

MCFARREN, E. F., SCHAFER, M. L., CAMPBELL, J. E., LEWIS, K. H., JENSEN, E. T. and SCHANTZ, E. J. 1960. *Public Health Significance of Paralytic Shellfish Poison.* Advances in Food Research, Academic Press **10**, 135.

MEYER, K. F. 1953. Medical progress—food poisoning. *New England J. Med.* **249**, 848.

MOLD, J. D., HOWARD, W. L., BOWDEN, J. P. and SCHANTZ, E. J. 1956. Shellfish poisons: II. Studies on the chemical structure of clam and mussel poisons. *Ibid.* (Part II).

MOLD, J. D., BOWDEN, J. P., STANGER, D. W., MAURER, J. E., LYNCH, J. M., WYLER, R. S., SCHANTZ, E. J. and RIEGEL, B. 1957. Paralytic shellfish poison: VII. Evidence for the purity of the poison isolated from toxic clams and mussels. *J. Am. Chem. Soc.* **79**, 5235.

MULLER, H. 1939. The chemistry and toxicity of mussel poison. *J. Pharm. Expt. Ther.* **53**, 67.

MURTHA, E. F. 1960. Pharmacological study of poisons from shellfish and pufferfish. *Ann. N.Y. Acad. Sci.* **90**, 820.

NEEDLER, A. B. 1949. Paralytic shellfish poisoning and *Gonyaulax tamarensis*. *J. Fish. Bd. (Canada)* **7**, 490–504.

O'NEILL, J. Personal communication.

PROVASOLI, L. Personal communication.

RAPOPORT, H. Personal communication.

RIEGEL, B., STANGER, D. W., WIKHOLM, D. M., MOLD, J. D. and SOMMER, H. 1948. Paralytic shellfish poison. IV. Bases accompanying the poison. *J. Biol. Chem.* **177**, 1.

RIEGEL, B., STANGER, D. W., WIKHOLM, D. M., MOLD, J. D. and SOMMER, H. 1948. Paralytic shellfish poison. V. The primary source of the poison, the marine plankton organism *Gonyaulax catenella*. *Ibid.* **177**, 7.

SCHANTZ, E. J., MOLD, J. D., BOWDEN, J. P. and HOWARD, W. L. 1956. Shellfish poisons: I. The isolation and characterization of clam and mussel poisons. Chemical Corps Biological Laboratories Special Report 250 (Part I).

SCHANTZ, E. J., MOLD, J. D., STANGER, D. W., SHAVEL, J., RIEL, F. J., BOWDEN, J. P., LYNCH, J. M., WYLER, R. W., RIEGEL, B. and SOMMER, H. 1957. Paralytic shellfish poison: VI. A procedure for the isolation and purification of the poison from toxic clam and mussel tissues. *J. Am. Chem. Soc.* **79**, 5230.

SCHANTZ, E. J. 1960. Biochemical studies on paralytic shellfish poisons. *Ann. N.Y. Acad. Sci.* **90**, 843.

SCHANTZ, E. J., MOLD, J. D., HOWARD, W. H., BOWDEN, J. P., STANGER, D. W., LYNCH, J. M., WINTERSTEINER, O. P., DUTCHER, J. D., WALTERS, D. R. and RIEGEL, B. 1960. Paralytic shellfish poisons: VIII. Some chemical and physical properties of purified clam and mussel poisons. *Canad. J. Chem.* **39**, 2117.

SOMMER, H. and MEYER, K. F. 1937. Paralytic shellfish poisoning. *Arch. Path.* **24**, 560. 1948. Mussel poisoning—a summary. A manual for the control of communicable diseases of California. Calif. Sta. Dept. Public Health.

SOMMER, H., WHEDON, W. F., KOFOID, C. A. and STOHLER, R. 1937. Relation of paralytic shellfish poison to certain plankton organisms of the genus *Gonyaulax*. *Arch. Path.* **24**, 537.

SOMMER, H., MONNIER, R. P., RIEGEL, B., STANGER, D. W., MOLD, J. D., WIKHOLM, D. M. and KIRALIS, E. S. 1948. Paralytic shellfish poison. I. Occurrence and concentration by ion exchange. *J. Am. Chem. Soc.* **70**, 1015–1018.

SOMMER, H., RIEGEL, B., STANGER, D. W., MOLD, J. D., WIKHOLM, D. M. and MCCAUGHEY, M. B. 1948. Paralytic shellfish poison. II. Purification by chromatography. *J. Am. Chem. Soc.* **70**, 1019–1021.

SZENT-GYORGI, A. 1951. *Chemistry of Muscular Contraction.* 2nd ed. New York: Academic Press.

TENNANT, A. P., NAUBERT, J. and CORBEIL, H. E. 1955. An outbreak of paralytic shellfish poisoning. *Canad. Med. J.* **72**, 436.

VENOMOUS MARINE SNAILS OF THE GENUS *CONUS*

ALAN J. KOHN*

THE genus *Conus* includes a large group of marine gastropod molluscs, widely distributed and often abundant on coral reefs throughout the tropical Pacific and Indian Oceans. Rumphius (1705) was the first to report that these snails produce a virulent venom that may be lethal to humans upon injection by the animal. However, efforts to characterize the venom have only been made very recently. Few advances in knowledge of the venom have occurred since the publication of Kohn, Saunders, and Wiener (1960), but it has seemed appropriate in this volume to summarize the present status of knowledge and to report on cases of human injury and fatality known to have occurred in recent years. Reference may be made to the earlier paper for aspects briefly summarized here.

MORPHOLOGY

The shells of *Conus* stand out because of their shape, described by the name. Most are solid and conical or biconical, but others are more ovate and cylindrical. They have long apertures and many bear striking color patterns (Fig. 1).

The venom apparatus consists of several component structures that are prominent features in the anatomy of the animal (Figs. 2, 3). The venom is secreted in a long, irregularly coiled tubular venom gland, or venom duct (VD), leading from the prominent venom bulb (VB), of uncertain function, to the anterior part of the esophagus-stomach (E). Injection of the venom is by a highly modified, hollow, needle-like radula tooth (RT; Fig. 4). Many of these teeth are secreted in a large Y- or L-shaped radula sheath (RS), which enters the pharynx. Prior to injection, one tooth enters the pharynx and comes to lie within the lumen of the distal portion of the proboscis (P).

Despite accounts to the contrary, as that by Pelseneer (1935), the venom apparatus of *Conus* is not primarily a defense mechanism but is normally used in feeding. As described by Kohn (1956, 1959), the prey, typically annelids, other molluscs, or fishes, is impaled by the tooth, paralyzed by the

*Department of Zoology, University of Washington.

venom, and swallowed whole. The venom apparatus may be used in nature as a defense against predation by octopus, however. Cummings (1936) reported that *C. textile* stung the arm of an octopus that had begun to attack it after both molluscs were placed in a pail of sea water. The arm (*ca.* 22 cm long) was quickly withdrawn with a writhing motion and autotomized a few minutes later. The octopus was dead the following day.

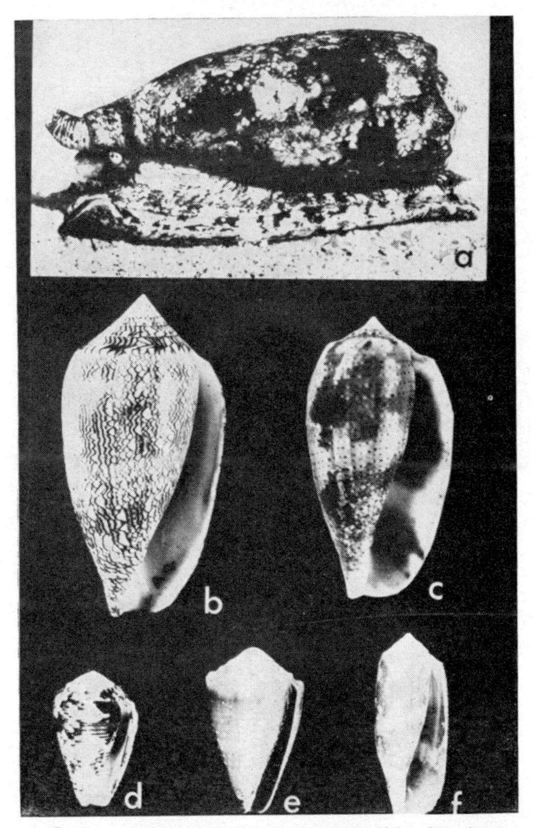

FIG. 1. Some of the species of *Conus* responsible for human injury and fatality. (a) *C. geographus* Linnaeus, living specimen from Seychelles; (b) *C. textile* Linnaeus, Hawaii; (c) *C. tulipa* Linnaeus, Maldive Islands; (d) *C. catus* Hwass in Bruguière, Hawaii; (e) *C. lividus* Hwass in Bruguière, Hawaii; (f) *C. obscurus* Sowerby, Hawaii. a, b, c approximately $\frac{1}{2}$ × natural size. d, e, f about $\frac{3}{4}$ × natural size.

The venom apparatus is probably homologous with the unpaired gland of Leiblein of other higher gastropods, the secretion of which was reported as being pharmacologically active by Marche Marchad *et al.* (1961). Amaudrut (1898) and Martoja (1960) were of the opinion that the venom apparatus is homologous with the esophageal pouches of more primitive gastropods. Erspamer (1954) and Erspamer and Anastasi (1962) reported that the salivary glands of cephalopod molluscs secrete a venom apparently similar in some respects to that of *Conus*. Paired salivary glands are present in *Conus* as in other gastropods; they appear to have no role in the production of venom. There is probably no morphological homology between the venom apparatus of *Conus* and paired salivary glands.

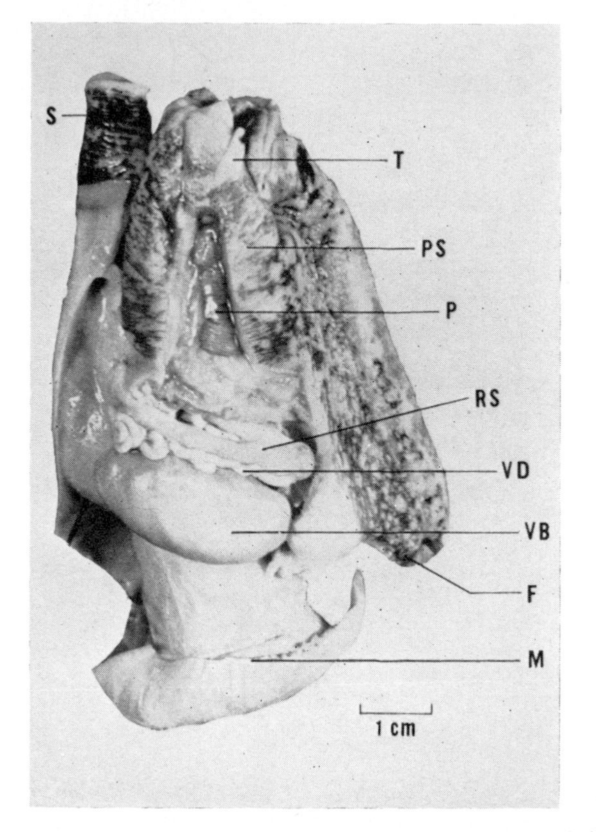

FIG. 2. Photograph of *Conus geographus* Linnaeus, from Seychelles, with shell, most of mantle, dorsal body wall, penis, and portions of columellar and proboscis retractor muscles removed. F, foot; M, cut posterior edge of mantle; P, proboscis; PS, proboscis sheath or rostrum, partly cut away to expose proboscis; RS, radula sheath; S, siphon; T, tentacle; VB, venom bulb; VD, venom duct.

TOXICOLOGY

Histological study and preliminary experimental injections by Kohn, Saunders, and Wiener (1960) of extracts of component structures of the venom apparatus, mainly from *Conus striatus* and *C. textile*, into other molluscs, fishes, and mice demonstrated localization of the venom in the venom duct. The minimum lethal dose of *C. textile* venom, tested on *Conus californicus*, is about 1/1000 of the total venom from one specimen, or

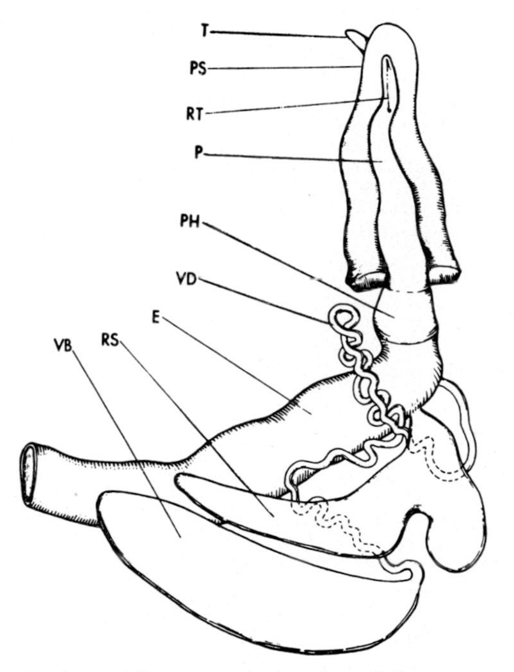

FIG. 3. Generalized, semidiagrammatic drawing of the organs of the venom apparatus and anterior portion of the digestive tract of *Conus*. E, esophagus-stomach; PH, pharynx; RT, radula tooth within lumen of proboscis. Other lettering as in Fig. 2. Reprinted from Kohn, Saunders and Wiener (1960), by permission of the New York Academy of Sciences.

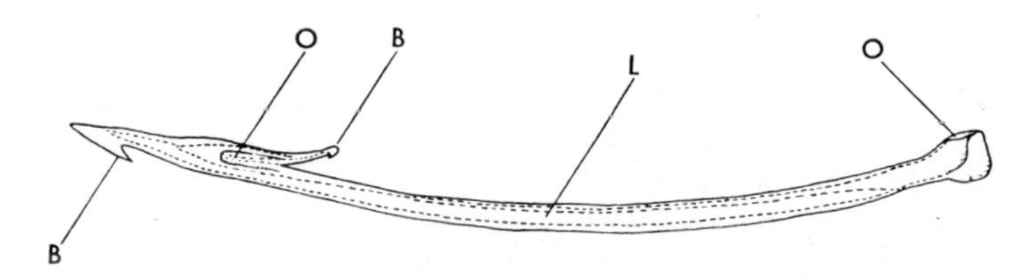

FIG. 4. Radula tooth of *Conus striatus* Linnaeus, length 10.9 mm. B, barbs; L, lumen; O, openings into lumen. Reprinted from Kohn, Saunders and Wiener (1960), by permission of the New York Academy of Sciences.

< 0.8 mm³ of whole venom duct extract. The MLD of *C. striatus* venom is <0.2 mm³ of venom duct contents injected into fishes 50–65 mm long. The LD_{50} of *C. striatus* venom injected into mice is $0.5–1.0 \times 10^{-4}$ mg tested intracerebrally, and 0.1–0.3 mg tested intravenously and intraperitoneally. The MLD of whole venom duct extracts of *C. textile*, injected intravenously, is <200 mm^3 in mice. Fishes usually died less than 10 min after injection; death in mice occurred within 4 hr of injection. Injections of extracts of *C. textile* venom bulbs and radula sheaths were not toxic to snails and mice. However, some venom is present in the venom bulb of *C. striatus*, as injection of its contents killed fishes and one mouse, although fishes died one to several hours later, in contrast to a few minutes after injection of duct contents.

Color change, ataxia, convulsions or quivering, and partial paralysis preceded death of fishes from injection of *C. striatus* venom. Mice developed ataxia, tonic spasms, dyspnea, hyperexcitability, violent scratching movements, and partial paralysis prior to death. *C. textile* venom induced flushing of tail and paws, sluggishness, dyspnea, paralysis and coma prior to death in mice. Failure of respiration followed by cardiac arrest caused death of mice in some experiments, but in others the exact cause of death is unknown.

Human Injury and Fatality.

Kohn (1958) reported 26 *Conus* stings known through February 1957. The case reported by Rumphius (1705) and included in the paper of Kohn, Saunders, and Wiener (1960) must be added to this list, making a total of 27; 7 were fatal. Of the latter, four were originally attributed to *C. textile* and three to *C. geographus*. Subsequent studies, however, suggest that *C. textile* was responsible for only one case, *C. geographus* for four and the other two are uncertain. This information is summarized in Table 1.

Table 2 summarizes ten recent and hitherto unreported cases of human injury, three of which were fatal, that have come to my attention. Only the first entry is not fully documented, being based on the following note on a Mr. Borden of Java, transcribed by Mr. R. C. Wood of Seychelles from oral remarks by Mr. C. M. Murdock of Johannesburg: " Borden went in search of them [*Conus gloriamaris*] in a small boat, only to drift into the harbour with his shells two days later a dying man. He had made the tragic mistake of collecting deadly ' cloth-o'-golds ' [*C. textile*] not worth 10s. for the six he sacrificed his life to gather."

The recent case from Samoa (Table 2) is well documented, thanks to a detailed account, including transcription of hospital medical report, kindly provided by the victim. No sharp pain accompanied the sting, observed by victim on the tip of his left middle finger, but the hand immediately became completely numb. The victim quickly fashioned a tourniquet from the rubber headstrap of his diving mask and was able to come ashore and obtain medical aid in 25 min. By this time the entire left arm had become numb and the victim complained of feeling constriction in the chest. The physician, unfamiliar with *Conus* stings, but noting symptoms similar to those of some types of snake bite, applied a treatment he had used successfully for the

TABLE 1. PREVIOUSLY REPORTED HUMAN FATALITIES FROM *Conus* STINGS

Original report	Date of sting	Location	Species originally reported responsible	Species now believed responsible	Reference to change	Reason for change
Rumphius (1705)	Unknown	Banda	*C. textile*	*C. textile*	—	—
MacGillivray (1860)	14 May 1859	Aneityum I., New Hebrides	*C. textile*	Unknown	Sting " believed " attributable to *C. textile*, but original report suggests specimen not seen by victim.	
Gill [1876]	Unknown (?)	Mare I., Loyalty Islands	*C. textile*	*C. geographus*	S. P. Dance (*in litt.*)	Specimen now in British Museum (Natural History), identified by S. P. Dance.
Cleland (1912)	Unknown	Kandavu I., Fiji	*C. geographus*	*C. geographus*?	Identification only by hearsay in original report	
Yasiro (1939)	28 June 1927	Okinawa	*C. geographus*	*C. geographus*	—	—
Iredale (1935)	25 June 1935	Hayman I., Queensland	*C. textile*	*C. geographus*	Flecker (1936)	Specimen now in Queensland Museum, identified by H. A. Longman.
Yasiro (1939)	29 June 1935	Okinawa	*C. geographus*	*C. geographus*	—	—

latter. This consisted of injection of one ampoule (2 ml) of Anthisan (mepyramine maleate 2.5 per cent) in the left arm and 0.5 ml adrenalin in the right arm. The feeling of chest constriction immediately vanished, and the medical report noted "in ward patient appears rather drowsy, pale and clammy. T. 98.8°, PR. 102, B.P. 140/50. No puncture wound seen . . . full movements [of] pupils, no ptosis. Rather excessive salivation. No paralysis but very weak movements (L) wrist and fingers with complete numbness of left hand and distal 1/2 left forearm." Four hours later the condition was unchanged. Two days later, movement returned to the left small and ring fingers, but the remaining fingers remained numb for 2 weeks. The numbness then gradually lessened and recovery was complete 3 months after the sting.

The symptoms evinced in this case and the others cited in Table 2 agree generally with those reported previously by Kohn (1958), which may be summarized as follows: The initial symptoms are either a sharp stinging or burning sensation, or localized numbness accompanied by ischemia and cyanosis in the region of the wound. Intensity of pain, if present, varies from the equivalent of a wasp sting to excruciating, probably depending on individual sensitivity, amount of venom injected and/or concentration of active principle(s) in the venom. Swelling of the affected part usually occurs. Numbness and paresthesia may spread rapidly from the wound site and involve the whole body and may be especially marked about the lips and mouth. Marked dysphagia and aphonia, blurring of vision and diplopia, excessive salivation, and generalized pruritus may occur. In severe cases the voluntary muscles may be paralyzed. Gastro-intestinal symptoms are usually absent. Coma may ensue, followed by death due to cardiac or respiratory failure.

Thirty-seven cases of stings, caused by at least 14 species of *Conus*, are known to me at present (Table 3). The severity of symptoms is correlated with the known size of the radula tooth and venom apparatus, as well as with the food habits of species of *Conus*. The severest stings have been from species with large radula teeth in absolute size as well as in proportion to shell length (tooth : shell length ratio about 1 : 10). Smaller species having a high tooth : shell length ratio, e.g. *C. catus*, *C. obscurus*, may not produce and/or inject as much venom with the sting. In other cases in which stings by rather large animals produced less severe symptoms, tooth size is relatively small, the ratio ranging from 1 : 25 to 1 : 62.

Nature and Mode of Action of the Venom

As described by Kohn, Saunders, and Wiener (1960) the crude venom of *Conus* is "yellow, viscous, and granular in appearance, and has a pH of 8. Protein and carbohydrate are present. No activity was lost on dialysis. Heating and incubation with trypsin altered but did not destroy the

TABLE 2. RECENT AND HITHERTO UNREPORTED CASES OF HUMAN INJURY FROM *Conus* STINGS

Date	Victim	Location	Species	Site of sting	Treatment	Symptoms and outcome	Reference
Unknown (prior to 1957)	Adult male	Java	*C. textile*	Unknown	Unknown	Death	R. C. Wood (unpublished notes)
22 March 1959	Adult female	Oahu, Hawaii	*C. quercinus*	Left arm	None	Sharp pain, reddening, slight swelling radius of 1cm around wound; white streaks along arm from site next day; complete recovery in 5 days.	HSN* **7** (6): 60 1959
Spring, 1959	Adult male	Oahu, Hawaii	*C. obscurus*	Left ring finger	Removal of radula tooth only	" Similar to a bee sting. Immediately the area blanched, began to throb then redden." Immediate area swollen, sore to touch for seven hours; slight soreness next day.	HSN **10** (11): 3, 1962
September, 1959	Adult male	Eniwetok	*C. litteratus*	Unknown	None	" Felt like a bee sting for about five minutes and then went away ".	R. C. Willis (*ni litt.*)

*HSN = *Hawaiian Shell* News, publication of the Hawaiian Malacological Society.

TABLE 2 (*continued*)

Date	Victim	Location	Species	Site of sting	Treatment	Symptoms and outcome	Reference
11 October 1960	Adult male	Koumac, New Caledonia	*C. geographus*	Palm	Unknown	Death within two hours of sting.	HSN **9** (2): 4, 1960; **9** (3): 1961
Unknown (probably 1960)	Adult female	Guam	*C. catus*	Hand	Unknown	Sharp immediate pain followed by local ache, " no worse than a wasp sting in a couple of hours ".	HSN **9** (2): 4, 1960
1961	Unknown	East Papua	Unknown	Unknown	Unknown	Death on day after sting.	C. H. Campbell (*in litt.*)
1 December 1961	Adult male	Samoa	*C. tulipa*	Tip of left middle finger	Tourniquet; injection of Anthisan and adrenalin	No pain; immediate numbness of hand; arm numb within 25 min; constriction in chest; weakness of left arm; gradual recovery, complete in 3 months.	R. E. Pahl (*in litt.*)
Unknown (prior to 1962)	Adult male	Oahu, Hawaii	*C. obscurus*	Leg; finger	None	" Stung . . . with the intensity of a wasp ".	C. S. Weaver (*in litt.*)

TABLE 3. SPECIES OF *Conus* KNOWN TO HAVE STUNG HUMANS, WITH EXTENT OF INJURY CAUSED, TYPICAL SIZES OF SHELLS AND RADULA TEETH, AND NORMAL FOOD

Species	Number of recorded stings	Fatalities	Near Fatalities and severe cases	Less severe cases	Outcome unknown	Typical Shell length (mm)	Radula tooth length (mm)	Tooth length : Shell length	Food in nature
C. geographus	9	5	3	0	1	100 77	11.9 10.0	1 : 8 1 : 8	Fishes†
C. textile	4	2	1	0	1	62 53	8.1 5.9	1 : 8 1 : 9	Gastropod molluscs
C. tulipa	5	0	3	2	0	41	3.1	1 : 13	Fishes†
C. omaria	1	0	1	0	0	*	*	*	*
C. obscurus	5	0	0	5	0	24 32	3.7 4.8	1 : 6 1 : 7	Fishes
C. catus	1	0	0	1	0	26 32.5	2.3 2.5	1 : 11 1 : 13	Fishes
C. imperialis	1	0	0	1	0	52 63	2.1 2.0	1 : 25 1 : 31	Polychaete annelids
C. lividus	1	0	0	1	0	51 37	1.9 1.5	1 : 27 1 : 29	Polychaete annelids and enteropneusts

C. quercinus	1	0	0	1	0	86 94	2.6 2.5	1 : 33 1 : 38	Enteropneusts and polychaete annelids
C. sponsalis	1	0	0	1	0	15 24	0.42 0.6	1 : 36 1 : 40	Polychaete annelids
C. marmoreus	1	0	0	0	1	56 86	1.4 2.1	1 : 40 1 : 41	Gastropod molluscs
C. pulicarius	1	0	0	1	0	55 53	0.95 0.85	1 : 58 1 : 62	Polychaete annelids and echiuroids
C. litteratus	1	0	0	1	0	*	*	*	*
C. aulicus	1	0	0	1	0	*	*	*	*
Unidentified species	4	3	1	0	0	*	*	*	*
Totals	37	10	9	15	3				

*No information available.Other data on food in nature from Kohn (1959)
†Kohn, unpublished data.

toxicity; death was usually delayed in fishes injected with venom so treated." These results suggest a partial role of protein or polypeptide.

Chromatograms of venom of several species of *Conus* prepared by Dr. J. H. Welsh showed the presence of the quaternary ammonium compounds N-methylpyridinium, homarine, and gammabutyrobetaine, and unidentified indole derivatives. The possibility of acetylcholine antagonism by the quaternary ammonium compounds was suggested, but there is no pertinent evidence. Collier (1958) had suggested that 5-hydroxytryptamine (5-HT) might occur in *Conus* venom. Application of the histochemical method of Glenner (1957) by Martoja (1960) has provided evidence for the presence in secretory granules of tryptophane and 5-HT basally, and abundant 5-HT distally, in the epithelial cells of the venom duct of *C. mediterraneus*.

Contractions of the smooth muscle caused by extracts of the gland of Leiblein of *Cymbium* (Family Volutidae) is attributed to 5-HT by Marche Marchad *et al.* (1961), although this activity apparently was not tested in the presence of 5-HT inhibitors.

Prevention of Conus *Stings*

All species of *Conus* are potentially dangerous and should be handled as little as possible. The safest procedure is first to disturb the animal so that it retracts within the shell, then pick it up by the broad, posterior part of the shell and quickly place it in a jar or other container which can be closed securely. The small anterior end should be observed constantly and the specimen dropped if the thin, tubular proboscis is seen to extend out of the mouth. Living specimens should never be allowed to rest on the hand with the aperture down. This is likely to lead to extension of the animal from the shell and possible eversion of the proboscis, and is probably the position from which most stings of humans have been inflicted.

Treatment of Conus *Stings*

The limited available information on the pharmacology of *Conus* venom does not permit recommendation of chemotherapy. Wiener (*in litt.*) found that the venom does not appear to be strongly antigenic, and hence does not offer promise of an effective antivenin.

Lancing of the wound and removal of as much venom as possible by suction and hemorrhage, and application of a tourniquet where feasible are recommended immediate procedures. Subcutaneous injection of adrenalin may be useful for vasoconstriction and augmentation of heart beat in severe cases.

SUMMARY AND CONCLUSIONS

The venom apparatus of *Conus* consists of (1) a long, tubular venom gland leading from (2) a muscular venom bulb of uncertain function, to the anterior extremity of the esophagus-stomach, (3) a very large radula sheath, in which are secreted (4) many highly modified, hollow, needle-like radula teeth which, with the aid of a muscular proboscis, inject the venom into prey. The venom apparatus functions primarily in predation on other molluscs, fishes, polychaete annelids and other marine worms.

Preliminary studies on toxicology by Kohn, Saunders, and Wiener (1960) are briefly reviewed.

Ten recent and hitherto unreported cases of human stings, of which three were fatal, are reported. Thirty-seven cases, 10 of which were fatal, are now known from at least 14 species of *Conus*. All the fatalities are probably attributable to *C. geographus* and *C. textile*. Severity of symptoms is correlated with absolute and relative size of the venom apparatus and with normal food of the species. Recommendations for the prevention and treatment of *Conus* stings are provided.

Present knowledge of the composition of *Conus* venom may be summarized within the framework suggested by Neumann and Habermann (1956) for describing complex venoms:

(a) *Small molecular-weight, chemically well-defined and pharmacologically active substances.* Several quaternary ammonium compounds are present, but their role in toxicity is unknown. It seems unlikely that histamine or acetylcholine are present in significant amounts. Histochemical evidence for the presence of 5-hydroxytryptamine has not yet been confirmed by pharmacological or chromatographic methods.

(b) *Enzymes.* The protein or protein-like components have not been tested for enzymatic activity. Kohn, Saunders, and Wiener (1960) have shown that *Conus* venom is not hemolytic.

(c) *High molecular-weight, pharmacologically active (toxic), but apparently not enzymatic, protein-like compounds.* Neumann and Habermann (1956) have reported that such fractions of bee venom induce a spectrum of symptoms, including neuromuscular block. A kinin (a peptide) similar to that described for wasp venom by Holdstock *et al.*, (1957) may be present and one or more compounds of this type may prove to be important active principles of *Conus* venom.

Analysis of the mode of action of *Conus* venom from available information is difficult if not impossible. The venom is quite certainly neurotoxic, and this action is probably peripheral, although effect on the central nervous system cannot be excluded. Several of the toxic manifestations, e.g. salivation, convulsions, and death due to respiratory failure, resemble those reported by Thienes (1945) for parasympathomimetic drugs, such as physostigmine (eserine). Other toxic responses resemble those induced by kinins, 5-hydroxytryptamine, and histamine. Research leading to further information on the presence of these substances in *Conus* venom should prove most fruitful.

ACKNOWLEDGMENTS

The author's studies on *Conus* are supported by a grant (G-23684) from the National Science Foundation. Gratitude is expressed to the respondents listed in Table 2 for permission to cite unpublished data; to Drs. E. Florey and A. W. Martin for critically reading the manuscript; to the New York Academy of Sciences for permitting the use of Figs. 2, 3 and 4; and to Mr. E. Ozaki for translating the paper by Yasiro (1939).

REFERENCES

AMAUDRUT, A. 1898. La partie antérieure du tube digestif et la torsion chex les mollusques gastéropodes. *Ann. Sci. Nat., Zool.* Sér. 8, **7**, 1.

CLELAND, G. B. 1912. Injuries and diseases of man in Australia attributable to animals (except insects). *Aust. Med. Gaz.* **32**, 269, 295.

COLLIER, H. O. J. 1958. The occurrence of 5-hydroxytryptamine (HT) in nature. *In*: Lewis, G. P., ed., *5-hydroxytryptamine*. Belfast: Pergamon Press.

CUMMINGS, B. 1936. Encounter between cone shell and octopus. *North Queensl. Nat.* **4**, 42.

ERSPAMER, V. 1954. Pharmacology of indolealkylamines. *Pharmacol. Rev.* **6**, 425.

ERSPAMER, V. and ANASTASI, A. 1962. Structure and pharmacological actions of eledosin, the active endecapeptide of the posterior salivary glands of *Eledone*. *Experientia.* **18**, 58.

FLECKER, H. 1936. Cone shell mollusc poisoning, with report of a fatal case. *Med. J. Aust.* **1**, 464.

GILL, W. W. 1876. Life in the southern isles; or, scenes and incidents in the South Pacific and New Guinea. London: *Religious Tract Society*, 360 pp.

GLENNER, G. G. 1957. The histochemical demonstration of indole derivatives by the rosindole reaction of E. Fischer. *J. Histochem. Cytochem.* **5**, 297.

HOLDSTOCK, D. J., MATHIAS, A. P. and SCHACHTER, M. 1957. A comparative study of kinin, kallidin, and bradykinin. *Brit. J. Pharmacol.* **12**, 149.

IREDALE, T. 1935. Fatal " sting " by a cone. *J. Conchol.* **20**, 166.

KOHN, A. J. 1956. Piscivorous gastropods of the genus *Conus*. *Proc. Nat. Acad. Sci.* **42**, 168.

KOHN, A. J. 1958. Recent cases of human injury due to venomous marine snails of the genus *Conus*. *Hawaii Med. J.* **17**, 528.

KOHN, A. J. 1959. The ecology of *Conus* in Hawaii. *Ecol. Monogr.* **29**, 42.

KOHN, A. J., SAUNDERS, P. R. and WIENER, S. 1960. Preliminary studies on the venom of the marine snail *Conus*. *Ann. New York Acad. Sci.* **90**, 706.

MACGILLIVRAY, J. 1860. Zoological notes from Aneiteum, New Hebrides. *The Zoologist* **18**, 7136.

MARCHE MARCHAD, I., GIONO, H., MAZER, A. and LEMAIRE, R. 1961. Effets pharmacodynamiques d'extraits de glande de Leiblen [sic] de *Cymbium patulum*. *C.R. Soc. Biol.* **155**, 873.

MARTOJA, M. 1960. Données histologiques sur l'appareil venimeux de *Conus mediterraneus* Brug. *Ann. Sci. Nat., Zool.*, Sér. 12, **2**, 513.

NEUMANN, W. and HABERMANN, E. 1956. Paper electrophoresis separation of pharmacologically and biochemically active components of bee and snake venoms. *In* Buckley, E. and Porges, N., eds., *Venoms*. Washington, D.C.: *Amer. Assn. Adv. Sci. Pub.* **44**, 171.

PELSENEER, P. 1935. Essai d'éthologie zoologique d'après l'étude des mollusques. *Acad. Roy. Belg.*, Cl. Sci. Publ. Fond. Agathon de Potter, No. 1.

RUMPHIUS, G. E. 1705. *Amboinische rariteitkammer*. Amsterdam.

THIENES, C. H. 1945. *Fundamentals of Pharmacology*. New York: Hoeber, 497 pp.

YASIRO, H. 1939. Fatal bite of *Conus geographus*. *Venus* **9**, 165.

Section III

LEECHES

LEECHES AS PESTS OF MAN IN THE PACIFIC REGION

HUGH L. KEEGAN*

IN several portions of the Pacific region, particularly southeast Asia and the islands of Malaysia and Melanesia, leeches are annoying pests of man. Although these annelids are not vectors of human disease, their bites may cause extensive blood loss and, as with any skin lesions in jungle areas, often become infected.

Exaggerated reports of the severity of leech attacks may produce apprehension in persons working in areas where they are prevalent and reduce efficiency of men working under strain in unfamiliar surroundings. This unjustified fear of leeches was noted by Archer (1957) as one of the problems of military personnel during jungle operations in Malaya.

Medically important leeches of the Pacific region are of four general types:

(a) *The common water leech or buffalo leech:* These are large, brightly colored leeches which may attain a length of 6 in. They are found in swamps, rice fields, and slow-moving streams.

(b) *Naso-pharyngeal leeches:* One of these, *Dinobdella ferox*, a small, dark, stream dwelling leech, is widely distributed in south and southeast Asia. It commonly invades the throat and nasal passages of man and various wild and domestic animals.

(c) *Common ground dwelling leeches:* Several species of genus *Haemadipsa* are found throughout southeast Asia. These rarely exceed 2 in. in length and show considerable variation in color.

(d) *Bush-climbing land leeches:* These are somewhat larger than the common land leeches and are more brightly colored. *Haemadipsa picta* is a common species on Borneo.

Field observations on the habits of ground-dwelling and bush-climbing leeches in North Borneo were made by Walton, Traub, and Newson (1956). Similar studies on aquatic and land leeches in Borneo and Malaya were published by Audy and Harrison (1954).

According to the latter of these workers, leeches quickly attach to the host and feed rapidly, becoming engorged in about 10 min. These authors

*Entomology Branch, Department of Preventive Medicine, Medical Field Service School, Brooke Army Medical Center, Fort Sam Houston, Texas.

estimated that a large aquatic leech would take from 5 to 10 ml of blood at one feeding, and that a terrestrial leech would take perhaps 1 ml. When feeding is completed, bleeding from the point of attachment may continue for some time. The wound may itch for days, and scratching is likely to reopen the wound and encourage secondary infection. Leeches may enter the urethra, causing acute discomfort. Although this rarely occurs, it is often the cause of acute apprehension among persons new to jungle areas.

Intensity of attack by either aquatic or land leeches is difficult to estimate in advance, as distribution of leeches in an infested area may be spotty. During their investigations on land leeches in North Borneo, Walton, Traub, and Newson (1956) found small, heavily infested foci, each several square meters in extent. The intervening territory had only sparse populations. Audy and Harrison (1954) cited an incident which took place in Malaya in 1951, when workers planting poles in a swamp were attacked by buffalo leeches. Each man was attacked by 12 or more leeches after only 3 to 4 min exposure. Progress on the job was slow, as workers would get out of the water every few minutes to pull off leeches. A Dusun chief from North Borneo stated that a man walking in an infested area during the wet season would pick up between 50 to 100 land leeches during a day.

Ground-dwelling land leeches usually attach themselves below the knee of the host. They may climb over boot tops, or crawl through eyelet holes and around the tongue of the boot. If trousers are worn tucked into close-woven socks or into jungle boots, the leech will usually succeed in finding its way downward between the sock or boot and the trouser. If this fails, it will move up the trouser and enter by the first available hole. It is not necessary for the leech to enter the sock in order to feed. It can insert only the anterior portion of its body through the mesh of sock and engorge. As the bite of the leech is quite often painless, the first indication of leech infestation may be the sight of blood welling over the boot tops.

Bush-climbing land leeches, *Haemadipsa picta*, may attack from the ground or may ascend vegetation, particularly in wet weather. They usually make contact with the human host from vegetation at knee to waist level but may make contact from vegetation at head level. Walton, Traub, and Newson (1956) did not see leeches drop on their hosts from above, but Audy and Harrison (1954) watched bush-climbing leeches drop from leaves and from a machete blade when the arm of the host was held 1 to 3 ft below the leech or when the leech appeared to reach an impasse. While waiting for hosts, the leech adopts a " searching " attitude. The caudal sucker is attached to the substrate and the anterior end of the leech elongates and sways back and forth upon the approach of an animal. At the slightest contact the leech releases the posterior sucker and attaches to the victim. This " searching " posture is shown in Fig. 1, which shows one feeding leech and another attached only by the caudal sucker.

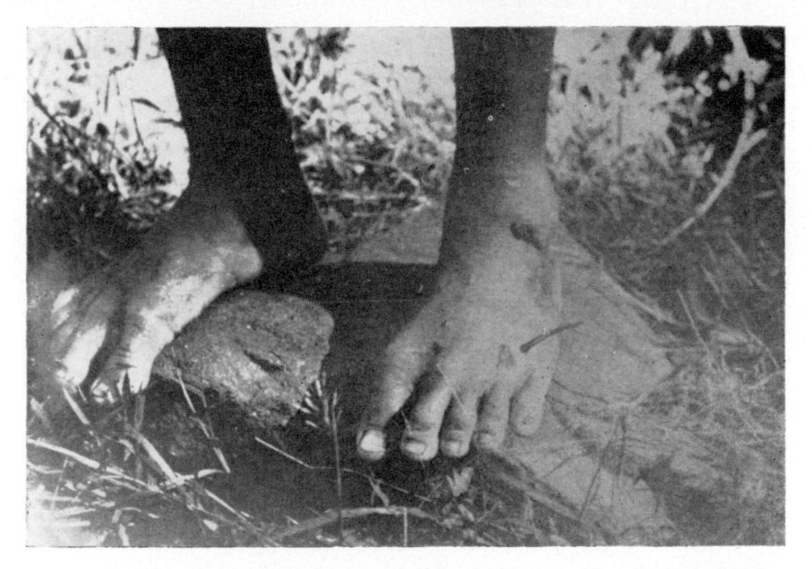

FIG. 1. Leeches on the leg of a man in North Borneo. One leech is feeding, the other is in a " searching " posture, and attached only by the caudal sucker.

Fig. 2 shows an engorged bush-climbing leech, *Haemadipsa picta*, on the leg of a Dusan in North Borneo.

Naso-pharyngeal leeches usually attach when the host is drinking from leech-infested streams. The most common species, *Dinobdella ferox*, occurs

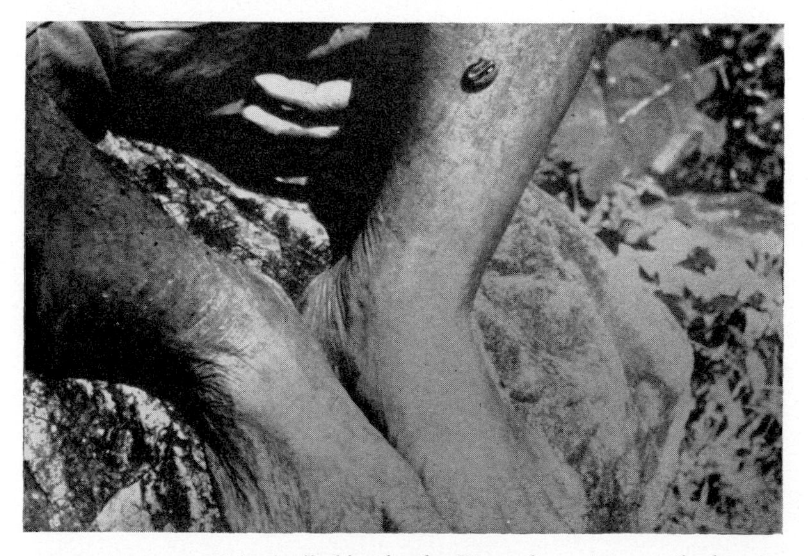

FIG. 2. An engorged bush-climbing leech, *Haemadipsa picta*, on the leg of a man in North Borneo.

in India, Burma, Formosa, and southeastern China. It attacks man, dogs, cattle, horses, deer, monkeys, and other wild animals. Walton (1955) took specimens from nasal passages of the large water rat, *Rattus mulleri*, at

FIG. 3. Young leech emerges from drinking water, ascends to highest point, and stretches out to a rigid, vibrating " searching " position on approach of rat.

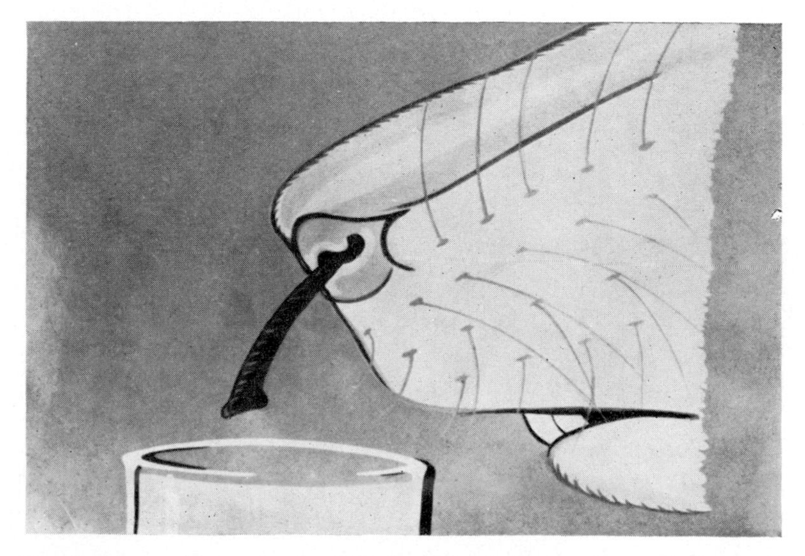

FIG. 4. On touching nose of rat, the leech immediately releases the hold with posterior sucker.

Ulu Langgat, Malaya, and from nasal passages of two dogs on Mt. Kinabalu, North Borneo. He found immature leeches in great numbers in streams far from human habitations or from domestic animals. Specimens were established in laboratory rats and showed rapid initial growth. Figures 3 to 6 are a series of drawings illustrating the method of attachment to a laboratory rat. Attachment to man, at least in North Borneo, is rare, as the native Dusans never drink directly from the stream surface, but always from a " straw " constructed from leaves, or from a hollow stem.

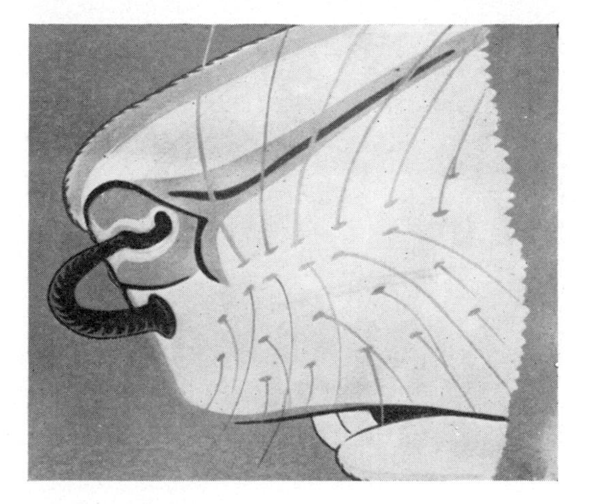

FIG. 5. The posterior sucker is drawn up close to the point of attachment of the anterior sucker and again attached. The anterior sucker is then released, and the head of the leech probes deep into the rat's nostril.

Audy and Harrison (1954) and Walton, Traub and Newson (1946) have found that clothing impregnated with some insect repellents affords protection against leech attack. Walton and his co-workers found that each of three repellent mixtures gave a high degree of protection against the ground-dwelling land leech, *Haemadipsa zeylanica*, and the bush climbing *H. picta*, in North Borneo. Two of these repellent mixtures were experimental and have never been adopted for general use. The third, known as M-1960, is the standard tick and mite repellent of the Armed Services of the United States. This material is composed of 30 per cent each of N-butylacetanilide; 2-butyl-2-ethyl-1, 3-propanedial; benzyl benzoate; and 10 per cent of an emulsifying agent. Even after an initial washing, a treated uniform gave complete protection against leech attack. After four additional washings the level of protection afforded was not adequate. The active components of M-1960 were not tested separately, but Stammers (1946) has found that benzyl benzoate was not effective in repelling land leeches of genus

Haemadipsa.

Archer (1957) reported that fairly effective protection against leeches in Malaya was afforded by the liberal application of mite or insect repellent (type unspecified) to the boots daily. Other measures used by British military personnel in Malaya included rubbing the boots with carbolic soap or smearing them with some acid fruit such as fresh limes. The degree of protection given by these means was not specified.

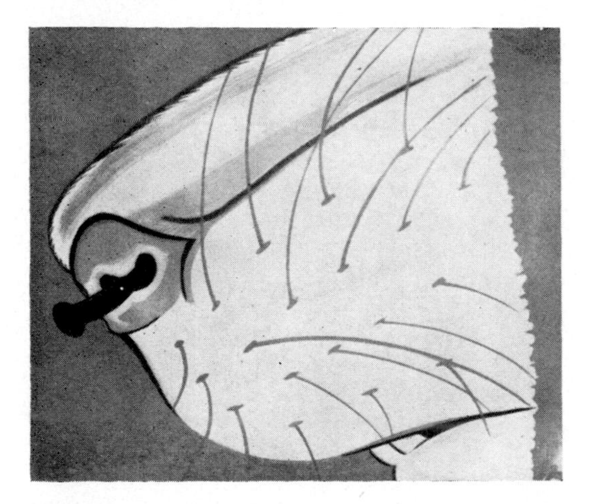

FIG. 6. Attachment of the anterior sucker to the nasal mucosa is made when the leech is extended as far as it can reach. The posterior sucker is then released, and the leech disappears into the nostril.

ACKNOWLEDGEMENT

Figures 1–6 were supplied through the courtesy of Major Bryce Walton, M.S.C., U.S.A., Third United States Army Medical General Laboratory, Fort McPherson, Georgia.

REFERENCES

ARCHER, T. C. R. 1957. Medical problems of the operational infantry soldier in Malaya. *J. Roy. Army Med. Corps.*

AUDY, J. R. and HARRISON, J. L. 1954. Field tests of repellent M-1960 against leeches. *Med. J. Malaya* **8**, 180.

STAMMERS, F. M. G. 1946. Observations on the behavior of land leeches (*Haemadipsa*). *Parasitology* **40**, 237.

WALTON, B. C. 1955. The " nasal-leech " *Dinobdella ferox* from Borneo and Malaya. *J. of Parasitology* **1** (6); Section 2, (supplement), p. 32.

WALTON, B. C., TRAUB, R. and NEWSON, H. D. 1956. Efficacy of the clothing impregnants M-2065 and M-2066 against terrestrial leeches in north Borneo. *Am. J. Trop. Med. and Hyg.* **5** (1), 190.

Section IV

ARTHROPODS

MEDICALLY IMPORTANT SCORPIONS IN THE PACIFIC AREA

F. W. WHITTEMORE and HUGH L. KEEGAN*

MEXICAN scorpions of genus *Centruroides* and a few of the South American species of *Tityus* are of considerable public health importance, but elsewhere in the Pacific area scorpions do not present a medical problem. While some of the Southeast Asian species, particularly members of genus *Heterometrus* (Fig. 1), may attain a length of 5 in. or more, size is not the sole criterion

FIG. 1. A large scorpion of genus *Heterometrus*. This specimen, from Malaya, was over 5 in. in length.

for determination of medical importance of a species. This was shown by Kopstein (1928) who described the relatively weak potency of venom of *Heterometrus cyaneus*, a large Javanese scorpion. Medical importance of a scorpion species is dependent upon a number of factors, including venom toxicity, amount of venom injected with one sting, geographic distribution,

*Entomology Branch, Department of Preventive Medicine, Medical Field Service School, Brooke Army Medical Center, Fort Sam Houston, Texas.

and habits. It is conceivable that many species of scorpions seldom encountered by man are dangerously venomous. Others, perhaps with less potent venom, may frequently enter houses and are important as causes of scorpion sting in man. In consideration of venom yield and venom toxicity as factors in medical importance of a species, it is essential to determine the number of LD_{50}s per average venom yield. This is here termed the *toxicity factor*. This factor varied markedly among species studied at the Medical Field Service School. Results of venom yield and toxicity studies of five species of medically important scorpions are shown in Table 1.

TABLE 1. VENOM YIELD AND TOXICITY DATA FOR FIVE SPECIES OF MEDICALLY IMPORTANT SCORPIONS

Species	No. venom collections[a]	Average yield (mg/scorpion)[b]	Mouse LD_{50} (mg)[c]	Toxicity factor (LD_{50}s/ average venom yield)
Centruroides limpidus tecomanus	1323	0.272	0.0068	40.0
Centruroides noxius	265	0.075	0.0030	25.0
Centruroides suffussus	355	0.155	0.0063	24.5
Centruroides undetermined species	2665	0.127	0.0069	18.4
Buthus quinquestriatus	192	0.483	0.260	18.6

[a] a collection = venom obtained from one scorpion on one occasion.
[b] dry venom.
[c] venom injected intraperitoneally into 14–18 g white mice.

Recent research on scorpions has been concerned with scorpion antivenin production and with tests of effectiveness of various insecticides in control of scorpions. In the field of antivenin research, Whittemore *et al.* (1961) conducted neutralization tests to determine effectiveness of scorpion antivenins in neutralizing homologous and heterologous scorpion venoms. Several instances of cross-protection were found, and in some tests heterologous antivenins were more effective than homologous products in protecting white mice against effects of venom injections. In another study of the same type, Tulga (1960) found that an antivenin prepared with venom of *Prionurus crassicauda* neutralized both the homologous venom and that of *Buthus qu nquestriatus*. The reverse was not true. Additional evidence of relationships of scorpion venoms was obtained by Glenn *et al.* (1962). In this study, which involved gel diffusion reactions, venoms of several species of scorpions from different geographic areas were found to have certain components in common. Shulov *et al.* (1959) reported that scorpion antivenin prepared by immunizing animals with a combination of injections of macerated telsons, and direct stings was of higher potency than that prepared with injections alone.

The chlorinated hydrocarbon insecticides have been used in scorpion control for several years. De Souza *et al.* (1954) reported effective use of BHC in controlling scorpions in Brazil. Bücherl (1955) obtained excellent results with DDT, also against Brazilian scorpions. More recently Deoras (1961) found that BHC in dust or sprays was effective in control of Indian species of *Buthus* and *Prionurus*. In studies at the Medical Field Service School, Ridgeway, McGregor and Flanigan (in press), and McGregor and Flanigan (in press) found that lindane, dieldrin and chlordane were far more toxic than DDT, malathion, and a commercially available sorptive dust for the Texas scorpion, *Centruroides vittatus* (Say).

ACKNOWLEDGEMENTS

Fig. 1 in this paper is a U.S. Army photograph taken in the Medical Illustration Section, 406th Medical General Laboratory, Camp Zama, Japan. The photograph has previously appeared in 1958 and 1960 versions of a U.S. Army publication, *Some Venomous and Noxious Animals of the Far East*.

REFERENCES

BÜCHERL, W. 1956. Scorpions and their effects in Brazil. IV. Observations on insecticides lethal to scorpions and other methods of control. *Mem. Inst. Butantan.* **27**, 107.

DEORAS, P. J. 1961. A study of scorpions: Their distribution, incidence and control in Maharashtra. *Probe* **1**, 45.

GLENN, W. G., KEEGAN, H. L. and WHITTEMORE, F. W. 1962. Intergeneric relationships among various scorpion venoms and antivenins. *Science* **135**, 434.

KOPSTEIN, F. 1927. Bijdragen tot de kennis der giftigheid van den Javanaanschen reuzenschorploen *Heterometrus cyaneus*. *Med. v.d. dienst d. volksgesondeid in Ne. Indie* **111**, 1.

MCGREGOR, T. and FLANIGAN, J. J. (*In press—J. Econ. Entomol.*). Effects of insecticides for the scorpion *Centruroides vittatus* (Say).

RIDGEWAY, R. L., MCGREGOR, T. and FLANIGAN, J. J. (*In press—Am. Entomol. Soc. Am.*). Toxicity of several insecticides for the scorpion *Centruroides vittatus* (Say).

SHULOV, A., FLESH, D., GERICHTER, CH., ESHKOL, Z. and SCHILLINGER, G. 1959. The anti-scorpion serum prepared by use of fresh venom and the assessment of its efficiency against scorpion stings. *Proc. Fifth Int. Mtg. Biol. Stand.* Jerusalem, Israel.

SOUZA, J. C., BUSTAMENTE, F. M. and BICALHO, J. C. 1954. Novos dados sobre o combate aos escorpioes em belo horizonte com o hexachorociclohexana. *Rev. Brazil de Malariol. e Doencas Tropicais.* **6**, 357.

TULGA, TURGUT. 1960. Cross-reactions between anti-scorpion (*Buthus quinquestriatus*) and anti-scorpion (*Prionurus crassicauda*) sera. *Turk. Bull. Hyg. Exp. Biol.* **191**.

WHITTEMORE, F. W., KEEGAN, H. L. and BOROWITZ, J. L. 1961. Studies of scorpion antivenins. I. Paraspecificity. *Bull. Wld. Hlth. Org.* **25**, 185.

SCORPIONS OF ARGENTINA

J. W. ABALOS*

FROM a medical and veterinary point of view, scorpions do not represent a problem in Argentina. Only one poisonous species, *Tityus bahiensis*, which in Brazil may cause accidents, is found in Argentina; its distribution is limited to the Province of Misiones in the extreme northeast of the country.

Scorpions occasionally sting persons, but medical literature of Argentina does not mention serious or mortal cases. *Tityus trivittatus* and *Tityus sectus* are apparently of domestic and aggressive habits, but the results of their stings are limited to a burning pain in the affected part that is felt deeply in the extremity of that region, producing affiiction, anxiety, and difficulties in swallowing. These symptoms disappear after two hours.

Thirty-seven species of scorpions have been recognized or described in our country. A check list of Argentina's scorpions and their distribution follows:

Family Buthidae Simon, 1879
Subfamily Buthinae Kraepelin, 1899
Genus *Isometrus* Hemprich and Ehrenberg, 1828

maculatus (De Geer, 1778)
Buenos Aires.

This domestic species which is widely distributed in tropical regions was listed as occurring in Argentina, but has certainly not been found there in recent years.

Subfamily Ananterinae Pocock, 1900
Genus *Ananteris* Thorell, 1891

balzani Thorell, 1891
Misiones, Salta.

Subfamily Centrurinae Kraepelin, 1899
Genus *Centruroides* Marx, 1889

argentinus Werner, 1939
Salta.

This species has been described by Werner from Campo Santo. Mello Leitao (1945) does not believe that this genus exists in Argentina.

*Instituto Nacional de Microbiologia, Santiago del Estero, Argentina.

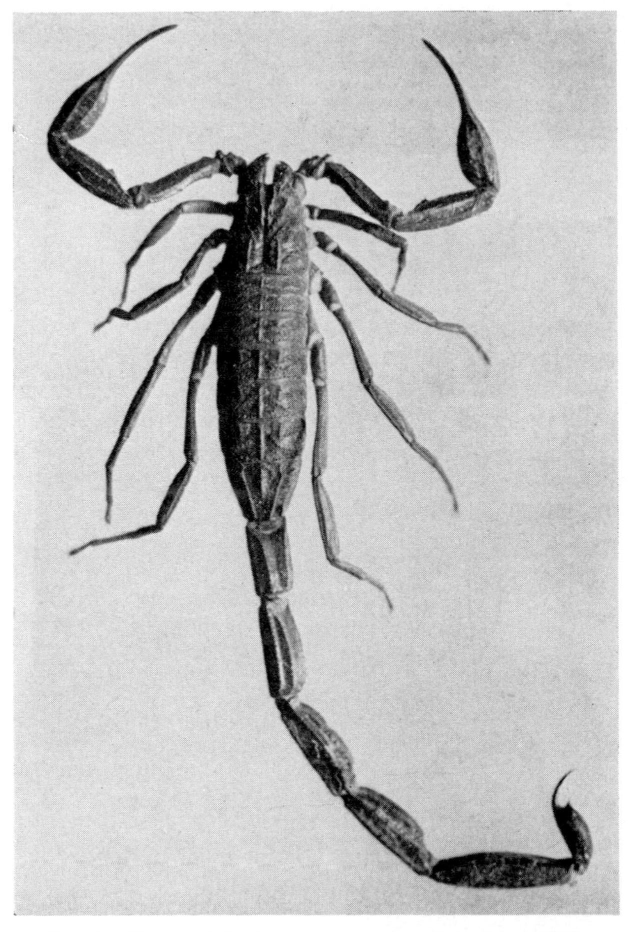

FIG. 1. *Tityus bolivianus argentinus* (Borelli, 1899).

Subfamily Titynae Kraepelin, 1905
Genus *Tityus*, C. L. Koch, 1836

bahiensis (Perty, 1934)
Misiones.

bolivianus argentinus (Borelli, 1899)
Misiones, Jujuy, Salta, Tucumán, Santiago del Estero, Córdoba.

carinatoides Mello Leitao, 1945
Santa Fe.

indecisus Mello Leitao, 1934
Jujuy.

mazzai Mello Leitao, 1934
Jujuy.

paraguayensis Kraepelin, 1895
Santa Fe, Buenos Aires.

sectus Mello Leitao, 1934
Salta, Santiago del Estero, Santa Fe.

trivittatus Kraepelin, 1898
Buenos Aires, Corrientes, Santa Fe, Chaco, Santiago del Estero, Tucumán.
This species is domiciliary, and people are frequently stung. The sting of this scorpion causes intense pains in the affected parts, and some transitory indisposition.

Genus *Zabius* Thorell, 1894

birabeni Mello Leitao, 1938
Buenos Aires, La Pampa, Río Negro.
Laboratory experiments with these species have shown that white mice are not affected by their sting.

fuscus (Thorell, 1877)
Buenos Aires, Córdoba, San Luís, Tucumán, Jujuy.

Family Bothriuridae Simon, 1880
Genus *Bothriurus* Peters, 1861

alticola Pocock, 1890
Mendoza, Buenos Aires, La Pampa.

bonariensis bonariensis
Jujuy, Misiones, Corrientes, Entre Ríos, Santa Fe, Córdoba, Buenos Aires, Río Negro.
This scorpion is uniformly coloured from dark brown to black. The male possesses an orange coloured characteristic cavity on the dorsal vesicle. Covelo de Zolessi (1956) described the copulation of this species and came to the decision that the paraxil apparatus is a true spermatophor carrier.

FIG. 2. *Bothriurus bertae* Abalos, 1955.

bonariensis asper (Pocock, 1893)
Buenos Aires, La Pampa.

bonariensis maculatus Kraepelin, 1910
"Argentina."

bertae Abalos, 1955
Misiones.
The smallest species of the genus (27.5 mm) reported by Abalos (1955).

burmeisteri Kraepelin, 1894
Distributed throughout the country, including Tierra del Fuego; a characteristic austral species.

chilensis (Molina, 1783)
Salta, Buenos Aires.

coriaceus Pocock, 1893
Córdoba, La Pampa, Neuquen.

dorbingyi (Guerin, 1843)
Distributed throughout the country, except in Santa Cruz and Tierra del Fuego; especially abundant in the North of Argentina. The largest species of the genus. Example may attain a length of 100 mm.

flavidus Kraepelin, 1910
Buenos Aires, Entre Ríos, San Luís.

Genus *Brachistosternus* Pocock, 1893

alienus Lonnberg, 1898
Buenos Aires, Mendoza, Río Negro, Chubut, Santa Cruz.

castroi Mello Leitao, 1941
Jujuy, Salta, San Juan.

intermedius (Lonnberg, 1902)
Salta.

holmbergi Carbonell, 1923
Santiago del Estero, Salta, Tucumán, San Luís, La Pampa, Jujuy.

reimoseri (Penter, 1913)
Mendoza.

weijemberghi (Thorell, 1877)
Córdoba, Jujuy, Salta, Santiago del Estero.

Genus *Iophoroxenus* Mello Leitao, 1933

exilimanus Mello Leitao, 1933
Santa Cruz.

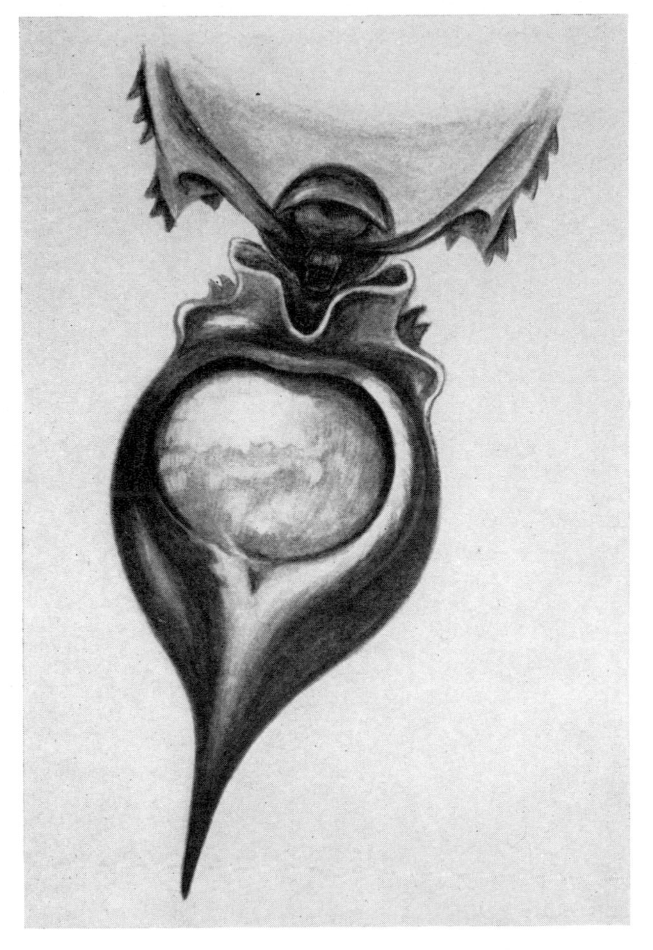

FIG. 3. *Bothriurus bonariensis bonariensis*. Vesicle of male specimen seen from above.

Genus *Iophorus* Penter, 1913

eugenicus Mello Leitao, 1931
Buenos Aires.
exochus Penther, 1913
Mendoza, Neuquen, Santa Cruz.

Genus *Urophonius* Pocock, 1893

brachicentrus (Thorell, 1877)
Buenos Aires, Córdoba, La Rioja, San Juan.
brachicentrus var. *bivittatus* (Thorell, 1877)
San Juan.
corderoi Mello Leitao, 1931
Mendoza, Buenos Aires.
granulatus Pocock, 1898
Chubut, San Juan.

Genus *Vachonia* Abalos, 1954

martinezi Abalos, 1954
Buenos Aires.

This scorpion is characterized by the numerous trichobothria on its palps (109 on each one); the femur possessing four trichobothria was reported by Abalos (1954) as being an exception to this group.

REFERENCES

Abalos, J. W. 1953. El género *Zabius* Thorell, 1894. *Ann. Inst. Medic. Regional, Tucumán* **3** (3), 349.

Abalos, J. W. 1954. *Vachonia*,, nuevo genero de escorpiones. *Ann. Inst. Medic. Regional, Tucumán* **4** (1), 119.

Abalos, J. W. 1955. *Bothriurus bertae* sp. n. *Ann. Inst. Medic. Regional, Tucumán* **4** (2), 231.

Abalos, J. W. 1959. Scorpionida. Ia. *Jornada Entomodpidemiologicas Arg. Bs. Aires* **2**, 591.

Covelo de Zolesi, L. 1956. Observaciones sobre el comportamiento sexual de *Bothriurus bonariensis*. *Fac. Agr. Montevideo, Bol.* **35**.

Mello Leitao, C. de. 1934. Estudo monografico dos escorpioes da Republica Argentina. *VII Reun, Soc. Arg. Pat. Reg. Nort., Bs. Aires* **1**.

Mello Leitao, C. de. 1945. Escorpioes Sul-Americanos. *Arq. Mus, Nac., R. de Janeiro* **40**, 9.

SCORPIONISM IN THE MEXICAN REPUBLIC

LUIS MAZZOTTI and M. A. BRAVO-BECHERELLE*

FOR the last three years we have been gathering information on the sting of scorpions in Mexico. This undertaking has been difficult since scorpion sting as a cause of death is not specifically given in the International Classification of Diseases.

Scorpions exist in all kinds of regions, with the exception of regions with continued frigid climates. Neither are they found on many islands, including some of such large size as New Caledonia. The species that can cause death in man occur for the most part in tropical or subtropical geographic areas, some of them more or less desert regions. In Mexico, scorpions have been well known since the pre-Colombian period, and, according to Herrera (1921), they were designated under the name of " Colotl ". Cardenas (1591), who practiced medicine in New Spain, in stating that the arthropods that sting men are more poisonous (toxic) in America than in Europe, said, " We note from experience that scorpions found in the Indies, especially, if in hot regions, possess a sting that is fatal to a child or even, at times, (*sic*) to adults, and that much pain and anxiety are caused by these incidents ".

Clavigero (1780), in his *Ancient History of Mexico*, observed the scorpion problem in Mexico in such an accurate manner that his assertions are still valid. He said: " The scorpions are common in all that country, but in the cold or temperate countries there are a few and these are not very harmful. In the hot and very dry regions, even if the heat is moderate, they are more abundant, and such is their venom that it kills a child and causes terrible pain to adults. It has been observed that the venom of the small and yellow scorpions is more active than that of the big gray ones."

Duges (1884) mentioned that " the sting of the scorpion in some places in Mexico (Guadalajara, Durango) is often deadly to children and to adults; it causes them a sort of trismus and epileptiform convulsions ".

Jackson reported in 1910 that deaths in the City of Durango due to scorpion sting totaled 51 in 1907, 53 in 1908 and 53 in 1909. He found that the approximate death coefficient was one per thousand.

This was also discussed by Baerg (1929), who made the first scientific study on scorpions in Mexico. He based his observations mainly on the City of

*Instituto de Salubridad y Enfermedades Tropicales (Institute of Health and Tropical Diseases) Mexico, D.F.

Durango and made a complete revue of the literature. This author found that from 1890 to 1926 there were 1608 deaths in said city, that is an average of 45 deaths per annum. He pointed out that the majority of deaths occurred during the summer months. He confirmed the observations of Clavigero with regard to the majority of deaths which occur in small children, and stated, also, that scorpions are found in various Western regions of the Mexican Republic, but nowhere are they as abundant as in the City of Durango.

Up to recent times, there has prevailed in international writings, the opinion that death due to scorpion sting in Mexico occurs mainly in the City of Durango. This erroneous concept comes as a result of the fact that this city had been an important town since colonial times, where medical services were available, and the sting and death caused by these arachnids was properly recorded.

In contrast with the above, and according to our tabulations, the State of Durango has, as a whole, a lower death rate, and in the city itself, scorpions cause a minimum mortality due to a large extent, to the activities of the health services of that city.

MORTALITY DATA IN MEXICO

Data compiled by the Direccion General de Estadistica (State Statistical Department) from 1940 to 1949, and those compiled by the Instituto de Salubridad y Enfermedades Tropicales (Institute of Health and Tropical Diseases) in the Civil Register from 1957 to 1958, showed that annual deaths by scorpion sting in the Mexican Republic during the period 1940 to 1949 varied, as shown on Table 1, between a minimum of 1588 deaths in the year 1943 up to a maximum of 1944 deaths in the year 1946. For the period 1957 to 1958 there was a decrease in the number of deaths, these being 1495 and 1107, respectively.

GEOGRAPHICAL DISTRIBUTION OF DEATHS

Mortality by scorpion sting in each of the states (entities) of the Republic for the years 1940 to 1949 and 1957 to 1958 is shown on Tables 2 and 3.

With computations obtained from the data shown in Tables 2 and 3, annual average rate for each of the states is given in Table 4 for the periods 1940 to 1949 and 1957 to 1958. It is noted that in 13 states there is a greater death rate due to scorpion sting than in the State of Durango, which falls in the 14th place.

However, the most accurate information on geographic distribution is obtained by studying records of deaths by scorpion sting in each municipality as reported by Bravo-Becherelle and Mazzotti (1961). This information is shown in the attached distribution map. Two zones are the most

TABLE 1. DEATHS BY SCORPION STING: MEXICAN REPUBLIC: 1940–1949 and 1957–1958

Year	Deaths	Rate per 100,000 Inhabitants
1940	1627	8.2
1941	1810	8.9
1942	1748	8.3
1943	1588	7.4
1944	1635	7.4
1945	1847	8.1
1946	1944	8.3
1947	1854	7.8
1948	1820	7.4
1949	1877	7.5
1957	1495	4.7
1958	1107	3.4

Note: Deaths entered in the Civil Register and tabulated by Direccion General de Estadistica (Statistical Department) and by the Instituto de Salubridad y Enfermedades Tropicales (Institute of Health and Tropical Diseases). Rates Tabulated by the Instituto de Salubridad y Enfermedades Tropicales (Institute of Health and Tropical Diseases).

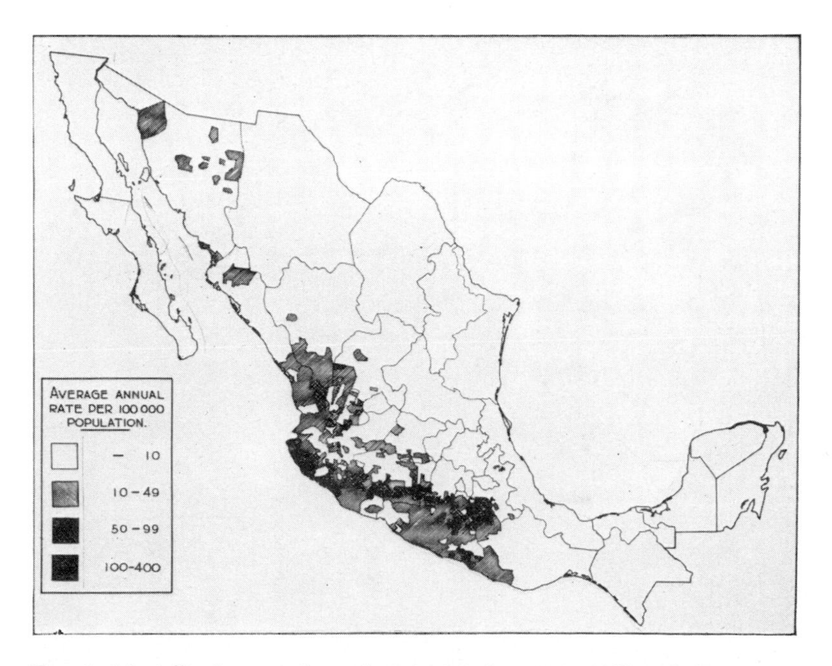

FIG. 1. Mortality by scorpion stings in Mexico, 1948–1949 and 1957–1958.

TABLE 2. DEATHS BY SCORPION STING ACCORDING TO STATES: Mexican Republic: 1940–1949 and 1957–1958

States	1940	1941	1942	1943	1944	1945	1946	1947	1948	1949	1957	1958
Aguascalientes	7	1	1	—	2	—	—	2	3	1	—	1
Baja California Norte	—	—	—	—	—	—	—	—	—	—	—	—
Baja California Sur	—	1	—	—	—	—	—	—	1	—	—	—
Campeche	—	—	—	—	—	—	—	—	—	—	—	—
Coahuila	—	1	—	—	—	—	—	1	1	—	—	—
Colima	60	90	82	83	69	80	94	96	103	111	68	48
Chiapas	—	—	—	—	4	1	1	—	3	—	1	1
Chihuahua	—	2	1	1	3	1	1	2	1	3	2	1
Distrito Federal	1	—	2	1	—	—	—	—	—	—	—	—
Durango	18	12	17	24	12	9	19	22	15	21	10	11
Guanajuato	104	82	88	84	79	130	136	88	65	74	87	77
Guerrero	328	399	367	317	333	385	385	396	354	386	334	232
Hidalgo	—	—	—	—	—	1	—	—	—	1	—	—
Jalisco	232	245	284	256	240	282	283	274	310	280	187	163
México	61	54	76	53	66	91	89	92	82	90	64	64
Michoacán	210	201	221	165	186	184	215	188	201	225	243	172
Morelos	59	103	83	88	103	116	91	113	83	87	68	29
Nayarit	85	110	94	110	86	74	109	91	82	88	83	64
Nuevo León	—	—	1	1	—	—	1	1	—	—	—	—
Oaxaca	92	123	86	89	135	121	147	95	126	116	89	61
Puebla	271	294	253	246	219	272	267	276	256	266	177	117
Querétaro	—	—	—	—	1	1	—	2	1	1	1	1
Quintana Roo	—	—	—	—	—	—	—	—	—	—	—	—
San Luis Potosí	1	—	2	—	—	—	—	1	—	—	—	—
Sinaloa	31	26	27	18	15	30	18	30	26	22	20	23
Sonora	28	21	25	19	26	23	21	21	18	18	8	7
Tabasco	—	1	—	—	—	—	—	—	—	—	—	—
Tamaulipas	—	—	—	—	—	—	—	—	—	—	—	—
Tlaxcala	—	—	—	—	—	1	—	—	—	—	—	—
Veracruz	—	2	—	1	—	2	2	1	1	2	1	1
Yucatán	—	—	—	—	—	—	1	—	—	—	—	—
Zacatecas	39	42	38	32	56	43	64	62	88	85	52	34
Total	1627	1810	1748	1588	1635	1847	1944	1854	1820	1877	1495	1107

Note: Deaths shown in the Civil Register and tabulated by the Direccion General de Estadistica (State Statistical Department) and by the

TABLE 3. MORTALITY BY SCORPION STING ACCORDING TO STATES: Mexican Republic: 1940–1949 and 1957–1958

States	1940	1941	1942	1943	1944	1945	1946	1947	1948	1949	1957	1958
Aguascalientes	4.3	0.6	0.6	—	1.2	—	—	1.1	1.6	0.5	—	0.4
Baja California, Norte	—	—	—	—	—	—	—	—	—	—	—	—
Baja California, Sur	—	1.9	—	—	—	—	—	—	1.7	—	—	—
Campeche	—	—	—	—	—	—	—	—	—	—	—	—
Coahuila	—	0.2	—	—	—	—	—	0.1	0.1	—	—	—
Colima	75.3	109.1	96.0	93.9	75.4	84.5	95.9	94.6	98.0	102.1	47.2	32.3
Chiapas	—	—	—	—	0.5	0.1	0.1	—	0.3	—	0.1	0.1
Chihuahua	—	0.3	0.1	0.1	0.4	0.1	0.1	0.3	0.1	0.4	0.2	0.1
Distrito Federal	0.1	—	0.0	0.0	—	—	—	—	—	—	—	—
Durango	3.7	2.4	3.3	4.6	2.2	1.6	3.3	3.8	2.5	3.4	1.4	1.5
Guanajuato	9.9	7.6	8.0	7.4	6.8	11.0	11.2	7.1	5.1	5.7	5.4	4.7
Guerrero	44.4	52.9	47.6	40.2	41.3	46.7	45.7	46.0	40.2	42.9	30.1	20.4
Hidalgo	—	—	—	—	—	0.1	—	—	—	0.1	—	—
Jalisco	16.3	16.8	19.1	16.9	15.5	17.8	17.5	16.7	18.5	16.3	8.5	7.2
México	5.3	4.6	6.3	4.3	5.3	7.2	6.9	7.0	6.1	6.6	3.7	3.6
Michoacán	17.7	16.6	17.9	13.1	14.6	14.1	16.2	13.9	14.6	16.1	14.0	9.7
Morelos	31.9	53.5	41.5	42.3	47.6	51.6	38.9	46.5	32.8	33.1	19.5	8.1
Nayarit	38.9	48.9	40.6	46.2	35.1	29.4	42.0	34.1	29.9	31.1	23.0	17.2
Nuevo León	—	—	0.2	0.2	—	—	0.2	0.1	—	—	—	—
Oaxaca	7.7	10.1	6.9	7.1	10.5	9.3	11.1	7.0	9.2	8.3	5.6	3.8
Puebla	20.8	22.1	18.6	17.7	15.4	18.7	17.9	18.1	16.4	16.7	9.5	6.2
Querétaro	—	—	—	—	0.4	0.4	—	0.7	0.4	0.4	0.3	0.3
Quintana Roo	—	—	—	—	—	—	—	—	—	—	—	—
San Luis Potsí	0.1	—	0.3	—	—	—	—	0.1	—	—	—	—
Sinaloa	6.2	5.1	5.2	3.4	2.7	5.3	3.1	5.1	4.3	3.5	2.7	3.0
Sonora	7.6	5.5	6.4	4.7	6.2	5.3	4.7	4.5	3.8	3.6	1.2	1.0
Tabasco	—	0.3	—	—	—	—	—	—	—	—	—	—
Tamaulipas	—	—	—	—	—	—	—	—	—	—	—	—
Tlaxcala	—	—	—	—	—	0.4	—	—	—	—	—	—
Veracruz	—	0.1	—	0.1	—	0.1	0.1	0.1	0.1	0.1	0.0	0.0
Yucatán	—	—	—	—	—	—	0.2	—	—	—	—	—
Zacatecas	6.9	7.3	6.5	5.4	9.2	7.0	10.2	9.8	13.6	13.0	6.9	4.4
Total	8.2	8.9	8.3	7.4	7.4	8.1	8.3	7.8	7.4	7.5	4.7	3.4

Note: Rates per 100,000 inhabitants tabulated by the Instituto de Salubridad y Enfermedades Tropicales (Institute of Health and Tropical Diseases).

affected: (a) That part of the Pacific coast which includes the State of Colima and the neighboring parts of the States of Jalisco and Michoacan, and (b) the Valley of Rio Balsas, beginning in the southern part of the State of Puebla and including parts of the States of Morelos, Mexico, Guerrero, and Michoacan.

TABLE 4. MORTALITY BY SCORPION STING ACCORDING TO STATES: Mexican Republic: Average annual rate 1940–1949 and 1957–1958

Order	State	Average annual rate per 100,000 Inhabitants
1st	Colima	83.7
2nd	Nayarit	41.6
3rd	Guerrero	41.5
4th	Morelos	37.3
5th	Puebla	16.5
6th	Jalisco	15.6
7th	Michoacán	14.9
8th	Zacatecas	8.4
9th	Oaxaca	8.0
10th	Guanajuato	7.5
11th	México	5.6
12th	Sonora	4.5
13th	Sinaloa	4.1
14th	Durango	2.8
15th	Aguascalientes	0.9
16th	Baja California, Sur	0.3
17th	Chihuahua	0.2
18th	Querétaro	0.2
19th	Chiapas	0.1
20th	Nuevo León	0.1
21st	Veracruz	0.1
22nd	Coahuila	0.0
23rd	Distrito Federal	0.0
24th	Hidalgo	0.0
25th	San Luis Potosí	0.0
26th	Tlaxcala	0.0
27th	Yucatán	0.0
28th	Tabasco	0.0
29th	Baja California, Norte	—
30th	Campeche	—
31st	Quintana Roo	—
32nd	Tamaulipas	

Note: Average annual rate tabulated by the Laboratorio de Epidemiologia y Bioestadistica del Instituto de Salubridad y Enfermedades Tropicales (Laboratory of Epidemiology and Biostatistics of the Institute of Health and Tropical Diseases).

During 1948–1949 and 1957–1958, the average annual death rate due to scorpion sting in 31 municipalities was higher than 100 for each 100,000 inhabitants.

MORTALITY BY AGES

In Table 5 are consolidated numbers of deaths during the decade 1940 to 1949 by sex and by the age groups used by the Direccion General de Estadistica (State Statistical Department) at that time. In analyzing these data we find that the majority of deaths occurred in the first three groups given, that is, between the ages of 0 to 9 years. 94.3 per cent of deaths occurred in children of this age group. In that same decade, 29.6 per cent of the deaths occurred in minors under one year of age.

TABLE 5. DEATHS BY SCORPION STING, ACCORDING TO AGE AND SEX: Mexican Republic: 1940–1949

Age groups	Deaths			Percentage	
	Male	Female	Total	Simple	Cumulative
Under one year	2709	2552	5261	29.6	29.6
From 1 to 4	4776	4471	9247	52.1	81.7
From 5 to 9	1204	1036	2240	12.6	94.3
From 10 to 14	204	164	368	2.1	96.4
From 15 to 19	60	41	101	0.6	97.0
From 20 to 39	136	90	226	1.3	98.3
From 40 to 59	68	61	129	0.7	99.0
From 60 and over	87	78	165	0.9	99.9
Unknown	3	10	13	0.1	100.0
Total	9247	8503	17,750	100.0	—

Note: Deaths registered in the Civil Register and tabulated by the Direccion General de Estadistica (State Department of Statistics).

To determine the number of deaths in each year of age in the one to four-year age group, deaths were separated by year of age during the years 1957 and 1958. From these data, shown in Table 6, it may be observed that 31 per cent of the total deaths by scorpion sting occurred in infants under one year of age. The accumulated death percentage for the same cause in the two- and three-year age group was 63.7 and 74.9 per cent, respectively, and reached up to 95.7 per cent in the nine-year age group. This shows that the death-by-scorpion-sting problem is fundamentally one of infants and small children.

It should be noted, however, that deaths have occurred among members of all age groups, and that scorpions constitute a danger to all the inhabitants of the endemic areas. The problem seems to be mainly introdomiciliary.

DEATH RATES OF MALES AND FEMALES

With regard to sex, the number of deaths are slightly higher in men than in women, especially in the school age. This perhaps may be due to the greater activity in the male child in comparison to the girls. The differences are not significant.

TABLE 6. DEATHS BY SCORPION STING, ACCORDING TO AGE AND SEX: Mexican Republic: 1957–1958

Age groups	Deaths			Percentage	
	Male	Female	Total	Simple	Cumulative
Under 1 year	412	395	807	31.0	31.0
1 Year	251	234	485	18.6	49.6
2 Years	191	175	366	14.1	63.7
3 Years	149	143	292	11.2	74.9
4 Years	115	74	189	7.3	82.2
From 5 to 9	195	155	350	13.5	95.7
From 10 to 14	33	18	51	2.0	97.7
From 15 to 24	9	4	13	0.5	98.2
From 25 to 44	12	7	19	0.7	98.9
From 45 to 64	8	6	14	0.5	99.4
From 65 and over	11	5	15	0.6	100.0
Total	1386	1216	2602	100.0	—

Note: Deaths registered in the Civil Registry and tabulated by the Instituto de Salubridad y Enfermedades Tropicales (Institute of Health and Tropical Diseases).

CASUISTIC

It is only possible to ascertain the approximate number of cases of persons stung by scorpions in the Republic, because the majority of these incidents take place in the rural areas. The production and demand for antiscorpion serum could give an approximate idea of that number but it must be considered that a great number of the people will not have access to this product, but will suffer the more or less severe effects caused by the venom. However, considering that approximately 15,000 doses of antiscorpion venom are produced by the Instituto de Higiene (Health Institute) annually, and at least 20,000 are produced by commercial laboratories, we can suppose that the number of stings occurring each year, and to which said venom is applied, is at least half of the total of these figures.

SEASONAL VARIATIONS

Baerg (1929) pointed out the seasonal variation of death by scorpion sting in the City of Durango and showed that this is greater in the summer.

When we analyze the monthly deaths in the whole Republic during the period 1957 to 1958 we find that there is an increase in death during the months of April, May, June, and July. This is shown on the attached graph.

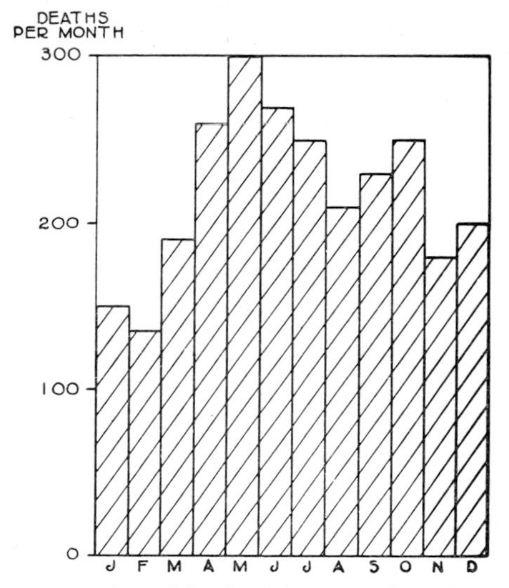

FIG. 2. Variation in number of deaths due to scorpion stings recorded monthly in the whole Republic of Mexico, 1957–1958.

The variation in mortality is well known in almost all the places explored, especially in rural areas, where at the beginning of the rainy season scorpions take refuge in the high parts of the ground, in trees and in homes.

POSSIBILITIES OF MAKING A CAMPAIGN AGAINST THE SCORPION

The scorpion creates an unusual problem, different than that posed by other arthropods that we have had to fight in the field of public hygiene (public health), and which, for the most part, act as disease vectors. Most of the latter have a need to be in contact with men or other vertebrate animals, either to suck their blood, or to feed on the food or organic products which are found in the homes of humans or vicinity thereof. The bionomics of other arthropods is generally well known, and their control, although difficult, is possible to a greater or lesser degree.

In the case of scorpions, we find that the scorpion does not need man or any other vertebrate animal for its existence, as its food consists of live arthropods which it obtains in nature. The scorpion invades the homes of humans in order to find shelter, and people are stung when they accidentally touch it or when it falls from the ceiling on people. In extensive regions of the Western Cascade of Mexico, ecological conditions are such that the numbers of these arachnids can reach figures of great magnitude. Suffice it to point out, for example, that in the region of Iguala, Guerrero, a person charged with the collecting of these arachnids to prepare the antiscorpion serum, collected a total of 500,000 scorpions in a few days with the help of his aids, at the proper time of the year, that is, at the beginning of the rainy season. On the other hand, according to Antunez (1956), in the City of Durango, when there were no insecticides to control scorpions, and authorities bought these arthropods, 100,000 specimens were collected in the year 1865.

Scorpions can well live away from human lodgings, but may take refuge in isolated houses or in badly constructed old houses with numerous cracks on the walls and roofs as well as in neglected, debris-littered, surrounding yards.

In order to plan a campaign against these arachnids, it is necessary to obtain more information on their biology and to experiment both in the laboratory and in the field with different control techniques.

A year ago we established a laboratory colony of 500 scorpions, *Centruroides limpidus*, which had been collected in the region of Iguala, Geurrero. These specimens were fed with roaches (*Blatella germanica*), as well as flies (*Anastrepha lutens*). The arachnids gradually died off and all specimens were dead twelve months after the colony had been established. No young were produced. Lately, we initiated in the same manner, a new colony of the same species and we found in it, a month later, a female specimen with its newly-born brood of 24 scorpions lodged on its dorsum. We will attempt to follow development of these.

The study of the biology of these arthropods may yield information which can have practical application in the campaigns that may be made against them. For example, it is interesting to note scorpions make an annual migration at the beginning of the rainy season. At this time, they have been observed to move from the surface of the ground towards high places, such as trees and houses which are isolated, or which are found in the outskirts of towns.

In attempting to control this problem, two things have to be considered: Medical care to the victims (persons stung) and actual control of scorpions.

The wide use of antiscorpion serum has undoubtedly influenced the decline in mortality which has been noted in the years 1957 and 1958. Without having yet obtained an accurate evaluation on the effectiveness of the application of insecticides, it is very commendable that the Health Services of the States of Colima and Durango have organized campaigns using gamexane and dieldrin, respectively. Results of these experiments will be evaluated in the future for possible use in other endemic areas. The experience acquired in Colima, where cost per house and per inhabitant has been computed, will be especially useful in carrying out other campaigns later.

In considering scorpion control, it is impossible to accurately measure the effects of use of insecticides which have been applied throughout the Republic for malaria control, individual insect control measures by house-holders, and urban improvement in many areas.

It seems evident that well-constructed homes will do much to prevent scorpion infestation. Specific recommendations for construction of homes to prevent scorpion infestation should include:

1. Wire screens on doors and windows.
2. High flooring on the homes and covering of steps with tile or other sleek material on which it is difficult for scorpions to climb.
3. Walls should have continuous horizontal strips of glazed tile, or rust-proof metallic sheets, or other material with a sleek surface upon which arachnids cannot climb.
4. Sleek roofs of concrete tile or with soffit or canvas ceiling.
5. Walls free from cracks in which scorpions may hide.

In addition to the above, areas around homes should be cleared of brush and debris, fences should be close-knit, and attempts should be made to prevent entrance of scorpions into outbuildings.

REMARKS

From a public health viewpoint, scorpions are the most important of the venomous animals of Mexico. During the periods 1940–1949 and 1957–1958, a total of 20,352 persons were killed by scorpion sting. During the same periods, 2068 persons died from snake bite, 274 by spider bite, and 1933 from bites or stings caused by venomous animals which had not been identified specifically (Table 7). It is likely that many deaths in the latter group were actually caused by scorpion sting, since these deaths were particularly numerous in states where scorpions had been given as a definite cause of death in the majority of cases. Also, the number of persons killed by scorpion sting is relatively low in relation to the total population of Mexico. In many areas, scorpion sting is one of the main causes of death, and in some places, during certain months of the year, scorpion sting has been listed as the most important cause of death.

Although the advantages of scorpion antivenin in treatment of scorpion sting are incontestible, we should also take into consideration the danger of serum sensitivity in some individuals. Administration of antivenin undoubtedly causes serious illness and even death on occasion. At least one death due to this cause was reported by Valdez (1945) in the State of Durango.

SUMMARY

Data were given on death by scorpion sting in the Mexican Republic during the periods of 1940–1949 and 1957–1958. The rates have consistently shown a downward trend, although the absolute number of deaths due to this cause has averaged more than 1000 per year. The states with the greatest scorpion problem were Colima, Nayarit, Guerreo, and Morelos, with annual average rates of 83.7, 41.6, 41.5 and 37.3, respectively, per 100,000 inhabitants. Three-fourths of the deaths occurred in children from 0 to 3 years of age. Mortality predominated during the summer. Possibilities for scorpion control were discussed.

TABLE 7. DEATHS BY ATTACK OF VENOMOUS ANIMALS: Mexican Republic: 1940–1949 and 1957–1958

States	Scorpion	Snake	Spider	Unspecified	Total
Aguascalientes	18	15	8	8	49
Baja California, N.	—	8	—	5	13
Baja California, S.	2	4	1	1	8
Campeche	—	19	—	—	19
Coahuila	3	25	9	19	56
Colima	984	2	3	67	1056
Chiapas	11	148	—	13	172
Chihuahua	18	41	1	47	107
Distrito Federal	4	1	—	8	13
Durango	190	32	9	44	275
Guanajuato	1094	22	21	121	1258
Guerrero	4216	26	11	124	4377
Hidalgo	2	191	4	15	212
Jalisco	3036	36	81	516	3669
México	882	15	13	58	968
Michoacán	2411	22	27	251	2711
Morelos	1023	3	3	13	1042
Nayarit	1076	5	11	55	1147
Nuevo León	4	40	—	14	58
Ozxaca	1280	269	4	40	1593
Puebla	2914	185	7	28	3134
Querétaro	8	10	4	10	32
Quintana Roo	—	21	—	1	22
San Luis Potosí	4	177	5	21	207
Sinaloa	286	14	8	162	470
Sonora	235	19	7	133	394
Tabasco	1	146	—	7	154
Tamaulipas	—	19	2	8	29
Tlaxcala	1	6	1	7	15
Veracruz	13	439	7	32	491
Yucatán	1	58	—	8	67
Zacatecas	635	50	27	97	809
Total	20,352	2068	274	1933	24,627

Note: Deaths registered in the Civil Registry and tabulated by Direccion General de Estadistica (State Statistical Department) and by the Instituto de Salubridad y Enfermedades Tropicales (Institute of Health and Tropical Diseases).

REFERENCES

ANTUNEZ, FRANCISCO. 1956. *Los alacranes en el folklore de Durango* (Scorpions in the Folklore of Durango). Aguascalientes, Ags. Imprenta Antunez.

BAERG, W. J. 1929. Some poisonous arthropods of North and Central America. *Trans. 4th Intern. Congress of Entomology* **2**, 418

BRAVO-BECHERELLE, M. A. and MAZZOTTI, L. 1961. Distribucion geografica de la mortalidad por picadura de alacran en la Republica Mexicana (Geographic Distribution of Mortality by Scorpion Sting in the Mexican Republic). *Rev. Inst. Salubr. Enferm. Trop.* **21**, No. 4.

CARDENAS, JUAN DE J. 1591. *Primera Parte de Problemas y Secretos Maravillosos de las Indias.* (First Part of the Problems and Wonderful Secrets of the Indies). Mexico: Pedro Ocharte Ed. Segunda Edicion. Museo Nacional de Arqueologia. 1913.

CLAVIGERO, F. J. 1780. *Historia antigua de Mexico y de su Conquista.* (Ancient History of Mexico and Its Conquest). Translation from the Italian. Mexico: Dublan y Cia., 1883 Edition.

DUGES, ALFREDO. 1884. *Elementos de Zoologia* (Elements of Zoology). Mexico Secretaria de Fomento.

ESCOBEDO VALDEZ, E. 1945. Personal communication.

HERRERA, MOISES. 1921. Los escorpiones de Mexico (The Scorpions of Mexico). *Mem. Soc. Cientif. Antonio Alzate.* **39**, 137.

JACKSON, H. V. 1910. A Preliminary Study of the Poisonous Scorpion. *Interstate Med. J.* **17**, No. 7 (cited by Antunez, 1956).

VENOMOUS SPIDERS OF THE PACIFIC AREA

HUGH L. KEEGAN*

ALTHOUGH it is possible that many of the spiders in the Pacific region may be dangerously venomous to man, reports of spider-bite in this area have, with few exceptions, incriminated the black widow spider, *Latrodectus mactans*;

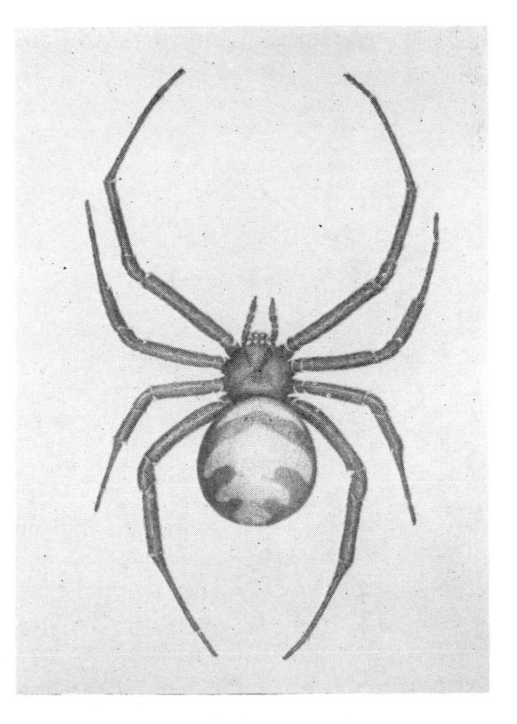

FIG. 1. Dorsal view of a specimen of *Latrodectus hasselti* from Ishigaki Island, Southern Ryukyus.

the redback spider, *L. hasselti*; the Australian funnel-web spider, *Atrax robustus*; *Glyptocranium gastracanthoides* and species of *Loxosceles* in western South America. *Chiracanthium diversum* and the gray widow spider, *L. geometricus*, both found in the Pacific area, possess potent venom, but, apparently, rarely bite man.

*Entomology Branch, Department of Preventive Medicine, Medical Field Service School, Brooke Army Medical Center, Fort Sam Houston, Texas.

In addition to his contribution to this volume, Wiener (1956, 1957, 1959, 1961a, b, c) has described preparation of an antivenin against venom of *L. hasselti*, has reviewed the problem of spider-bite in Australia, and has made extensive studies of the venom of *Atrax robustus*. Other developments of interest in this field during the past few years included a monograph on genus *Latrodectus* by Levi (1959); a study by Russell (1962) on muscle relaxants in treatment of black widow spider poisoning; and the demonstration by Keegan *et al.* (1960) of seasonal variation in toxicity of venom of *L. mactans* in Texas.

FIG. 2. Ventral view of the specimen of *L. hasselti* shown in Fig. 1.

In his monograph on genus *Latrodectus*, Levi (1959) stated that *L. hasselti*, found from India to New Zealand, was actually *L. mactans*, but that for the sake of reference with the older literature, the species in this area of the world should be recognized as *Latrodectus mactans hasselti*. Levi recognized *L. geometricus* as a species, but noted that the new world spider *L. curacaviensis* had been frequently confused with *L. mactans*.

Russell (1962) found that methocarbamol (Robaxin) given intravenously gave greatest relief from muscle pain and spasms of patients suffering from black widow spiderbite in California. Methocarbamol was superior to calcium gluconate for this purpose.

Keegan, Hedeen, and Whittemore (1960) found marked seasonal variation in toxicity for white mice of venom of black widow spiders, *L. mactans*, collected near San Antonio, Texas. In late fall the venom was roughly ten times as toxic as in May. The cause of this variation is not known.

Figures 1 and 2 are dorsal and ventral views of a specimen of *Latrodectus hasselti* from Ishigaki Island, Southern Ryukyus.

Figure 3 is a dorsal view of a specimen of *L. geometricus* from Luzon Island, Philippines. Figure 4 is of a specimen of *Atrax* from Australia.

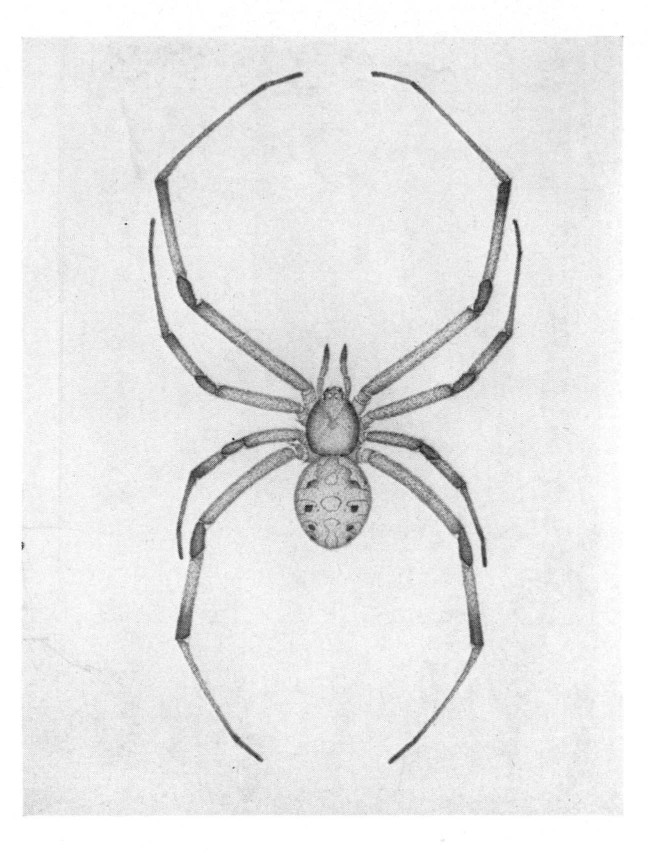

FIG. 3. Dorsal view of a specimen of *Latrodectus geometricus* from Luzon Island, Philippines.

ACKNOWLEDGEMENT

Figures 1–3 were prepared by artists of the Taxonomic Section, Department of Entomology, 406th Medical General Laboratory, U.S. Army Medical Command, Camp Zama, Japan. Figure 4 is a U.S. Army photograph taken at the 406th Medical General Laboratory. These figures have previously appeared in 1958 and 1960 versions of a U.S. Army publication, *Some Venomous and Noxious Animals of the Far East*.

FIG. 4. A specimen of *Atrax* from Australia.

REFERENCES

LEVI, H. W. 1959. The spider genus *Latrodectus* (Araneae, Theridiidae). *Trans. Am. Microscop. Soc.* **77**, 7.

KEEGAN, H. L., WHITTEMORE, F. W. and HEDEEN, R. A. 1960. Seasonal variation in venom of black widow spiders. *Am. J. Trop. Med. and Hyg.* **10**, 477.

RUSSELL, F. E. 1962. Muscle relaxants in black widow spider (*Lactrodectus mactans*) poisoning. *Amer. J. Med. Sci.* **243** (2) 1, 81–83.

WIENER, S. 1956. The Australian redback spider (*Latrodectus hasseltii*). I. Preparation of antiserum by the use of venom adsorbed on aluminum phosphate. *Med. J. Aust.* **1**, 739.

WIENER, S. 1957. The Sydney funnel-web spider (*A. robustus*). I. Collection of venom and its toxicity in animals. *Med. J. Aust.* **2**, 377.

WIENER, S. 1959. The Sydney funnel-web spider (*A. robustus*). II. Venom yield and other characteristics of spiders in captivity. *Med. J. Aust.*

WIENER, S. 1961a. Redback spiderbite in Australia: an analysis of 167 cases. *Med. J. Aust.* **2**, 44.

WIENER, S. 1961b. Observations on the venom of the Sydney funnel-web spider (*A. robustus*). *Med. J. Aust.* **2**, 693.

WIENER, S. 1961c. The Sydney funnel-web spider (*A. robustus*). III. The neutralization of venom by haemolymph. *Med. J. Aust.* **2**, 449.

SPIDERS OF THE GENUS *LATRODECTUS* IN ARGENTINA
LATRODECTISM AND *LATRODECTUS* ANTIVENIN

I. PIROSKY* and J. W. ABALOS†

THE Argentina spider fauna comprises about 400 species. Some of these have been erroneously considered to be venomous. *Lysoca raptoria* is found in various provinces, but it does not seem to produce the dermal necrosis caused by this species so frequently in Brazil where a specific antivenin is produced against its venom. In Argentina there is also *Mastophora gasterocanthoides*, the " cat's head spider ", which causes serious incidents in Peru. There are no records of bites by this species in Argentina. *Loxosceles laeta* is very common and undoubtedly because of its domestic habits frequently bites man, but from available information it apparently does not cause serious incidents such as are described in Chile and other countries where this species is numerous and where *Loxosceles* antivenin is produced.

Latrodectus mactans and *curacaviensis* are the two species which definitely figure as causing serious and deadly incidents in man in Argentina. A third species of genus *Latrodectus*, which is a cosmopolitan city dweller, is *L. geometricus*. It is well known that the venom from this spider is not dangerous to man.

L. curacaviensis and *L. mactans* have been mistaken for one another by different writers in our country. This makes it almost impossible to determine which spider is being described in various papers on distribution and habits of *Latrodectus* species and which of these two is responsible for cases of spider bite in man. Most papers have described the species involved as *Latrodectus mactans*.

At the present time, one of us (Abalos) is working under a subsidy by the National Council for Scientific and Technical Investigations on a study to determine means for proper identification of these species. This study involves morphology, systematics, habits, behavior in captivity, and the differences in each of the stages of the life cycle.

The information given here on these two species refers to the *mactans*–

*Director of the Instituto Nacional de Microbiologia (National Institute of Microbiology), Buenos Aires, Argentina.

†Technician in venomous animals at the Institute, Nacional de Microbiologia Santiago del Estero, Argentina.

curacaviensis complex. Spiders of this complex are found throughout the entire continental American territory of Argentina, from the northern tip to Tierra del Fuego on the extreme south.

FIG. 1. *Latrodectus* sp. in a web which it made in the laboratory.

In the province of Santiago del Estero, in the northern part of the country, are many excellent natural breeding places of *Latrodectus*. The spiders are numerous in the palms of a cactus, *Opuntia quimili*, where they spin their strong irregular trapping webs. These fields of cacti often extend over hundreds of hectares of unpopulated areas, and spiders multiply by tens of thousands. They are also found on the surface of the ground, lodged in abandoned armadillo (*Disipodidae*) burroughs. Frequently they are found in domestic areas lodged in brick or rubble piles and in such places as latrines, out-buildings, and among garden plants.

They are known locally under such names as " stubblers ", " flax spiders ", " little red-cup spiders ", and " coral spiders ".

These spiders generally occur in domestic surroundings. Frequently laborers are victims when they are harvesting wheat and flax.

There are no statistics on latrodectism in Argentina, but undoubtedly there are hundreds of cases annually. There are no accurate data concerning fatalities, although newspaper obituaries occasionally cite spider bite as a cause of death.

Because of the inadequate system of reporting spider bites, it was formerly believed that these did not occur in Santiago del Estero. However, after the establishment of the Institute for Venomous Animals, it was discovered that spider bites are actually quite frequent in this area.

In the majority of cases the bite occurs when a person is dressing. The spiders have taken refuge in the clothing or shoes, and bite upon being crushed. Generally the victim feels a prick and thus discovers the spider.

Sometimes, however, the attack is unnoticed. Only a small pinkish spot may be noticed. In this small area the punctures caused by the chelicerae of the spider may sometimes be found. Frequently, however, the location of the bite cannot be discovered.

The time that lapses from the moment of the bite to the beginning of the symptoms usually varies between a few minutes to an hour. The sequence of events, in which the symptomatology evidences the neurotoxic action of the venom, is similar to that described for latrodectism in various countries of the world. Its foremost characteristic is violent pain and muscular contractures.

Argentina produces an antilatrodectus serum in sufficient quantity to supply the needs of the country. This antivenin is produced at the National Institute of Microbiology of Buenos Aires with venom obtained in Santiago del Estero. In 1960, 25,000 specimens of *Latrodectus* were captured for this purpose.

Houssay and Negrete (1919) were the first to attempt immunization of laboratory animals in Argentina. Troise (1928) produced a *Latrodectus mactans* antivenin using rabbits as a test animal. Recently, Pirosky (1942) and his associates produced a concentrated and purified serum for public use.

The antilatrodectus serum that is produced by this Institute is obtained by immunization of equines through subcutaneous administration of a suspension of *Latrodectus* glands. In the first immunization the initial dose is one gland, and the last is 500 glands. During the course of immunization, 3000 glands are injected into a horse within a 14-week period.

The serum is concentrated and purified by enzymatic digestion with a purification index of six. A milliliter of serum protects 50 per cent of the white mice against effects of 3000 MLD of venom. Treatment with this antivenin gives spectacular results in spider bite patients. The recovery of victim begins half an hour after injection of the antivenin and recovery is complete not later than three hours.

Finlayson and Hollow (1945) and Mason (1961) have reported that this antivenin neutralizes the venom of *L. indistinctus* and *L. tredecinguttattus*. Dempster (1961) has reported that it neutralizes the venom of *L. hasseltii*.

This year it is planned to collect 100,000 specimens of *Latrodectus* in Santiago del Estero. Venom obtained from these spiders will be used to carry out studies on purification of venom and on various immunochemical problems.

Insecticides may be used in homes infested by *Latrodectus*. Romana and Abalos (1948) found that spiders placed in contact with surfaces sprayed with water-wettable DDT at a rate of 2 g per m^2 for 30 sec died within 24 hr. Direct dusting on the spiders produces death in 15 min. BHC seems to be the preferred insecticide for the control of *Latrodectus*. If spiders walk for 5 sec on surfaces treated with the product at the rate of 0.5 g of gamma isomer per m^2, they die in 30 to 90 min. The residual action of the product lasts several months. In closed areas, the fumigation with BHC at the rate of 4 g of the product per 100 m^3 is effective. It is recommended that fumigation be repeated 30 days following the initial fumigation to destroy spider broods which emerged in the meantime.

SUMMARY

In Argentina, the only spiders which have been proven to cause serious or deadly bites to man are *Latrodectus mactan* and *L. curacaviensis*. A report is given on a region in the northern part of Argentina where these spiders are very numerous. Information is given concerning the habits of the spiders and of the circumstances in which bites occur. A description is given of the antivenin production program of the National Institute of Microbiology.

REFERENCES

Dempster, F. J. 1961. Personal communication.

Finlayson, M. H. and Hollow, K. 1945. Treatment of spider-bite in South Africa by specific antisera. *S. African Med. J.* **19**, 431.

Houssay, B. A. and Negrete, P. 1919. New experimental studies on the physiological action of the venom of spiders. *Rev. Inst. of Microbiology, Buenos Aires* **2**, 189.

Mason, J. H. 1961. Personal communication.

Pirosky, I., Sampayo, R. and Franceschi, C. 1942. Production and purification of anti *Latrodectus* serum. *Rev. Soc. Arg. Biol., Buenos Aires* **18** (3), 169.

Romana, C. and Abalos, J. W. 1948. *Latrodectus mactans*: Its control. *An. Inst. Med. Reg., Tucuman* **2** (2), 153.

Sampayo, R. 1942. *Latrodectus mactans* and latrodectism. Thesis. Univ. Nac., Buenos Aires.

Troise, E. 1928. Preparation of immunization serum against *Latrodectus mactans*. *Argentine Biological Review, Buenos Aires* **4** (6), 467.

ANTIGENIC AND ELECTROPHORETIC PROPERTIES OF FUNNEL WEB SPIDER (*ATRAX ROBUSTUS*) VENOM

SAUL WIENER*

IN Australia fatalities from bites inflicted by spiders have been caused by the red back spider, *Latrodectus hasseltii*, and by the Sydney funnel-web spider, *Artax robustus*. This problem has been reviewed by Ingram and Musgrave (1933).

The last recorded fatality following a bite by *L. hasseltii* occurred in 1955 in New South Wales. This was reported by Wiener (1961a) in a discussion of the problem of red back spider bite in Australia.

Preparation and assay of this antivenene was discussed by Wiener (1956) and Wiener and Fraser (1956). Wiener (1961a) reported on therapeutic value of the antivenene as determined by its effectiveness in treatment of cases of spider bite.

Wiener (1961b) discussed the continuing occurrence of fatalities from the bite of *A. robustus*. After Wiener (1957, and 1959) had developed methods for collecting venom from this spider, and for assaying its toxicity for laboratory animals, attempts were made to produce a specific antivenene against the venom of *A. robustus*. Since the toxic fractions of venom were found to be non-antigenic, studies were also carried out on the various components of venom which could be separated electrophoretically.

EXPERIMENTAL

Venom was obtained by " milking " spiders and from the dissected venom glands as described previously by Wiener (1957).

The venom used for injection into animals was either in an aqueous solution or it was mixed with Freund's adjuvant. Because relatively large amounts of venom were required, female spider venom, which was more plentiful, was mainly used. However, in the case of rabbits, male spider venom was also used during the course of injections.

Tests for neutralizing antibodies were carried out in mice and Drosophila as described previously by Wiener (1956), and Wiener and Drummond (1956). In the case of mice, the subcutaneous, intravenous and intracerebral routes

*Columbia University, College of Physicians and Surgeons, New York 32, New York.

were used. In each case, one certainly lethal dose of venom was mixed with varying dilutions of serum. The mixtures were incubated at 37 °C for 1 hr, before being injected into the test animals.

Precipitin tests were performed by layering an aqueous solution of venom over serum diluted with normal saline solution.

ANTIGENICITY OF VENOM IN VARIOUS SPECIES OF ANIMALS

Horse

The primary course of injections with increasing doses of venom extended over a period of eight months. During this time a total of 170 mg of venom was injected by the subcutaneous route. The first and last doses contained 0.5 mg and 30 mg of venom, respectively. An interval of one to three weeks was allowed to elapse between injections. Neither local nor general reactions occurred during this time.

Samples of blood were collected during the course of injections and two weeks after the final dose had been given. Precipitating antibodies were detectable one week after the fourth injection of venom and continued to be present from then on. However, at no time could neutralizing antibodies be detected.

Six months after the last dose of venom had been administered, three further doses of venom were injected into the same horse, at weekly intervals. The first dose consisted of 30 mg of venom. A few hours after this amount of venom had been injected, the horse frothed at the mouth and appeared sick for 24 hr. One week later, 69 mg of venom were injected. The animal lost its appetite and appeared to be sick again, but not to the same extent as after the previous injection. A final dose of 110 mg was given 1 week after the second dose. Some twitching of the skin occurred at the site of injection but otherwise the animal remained well. Eight days later, the animal was bled on two consecutive occasions, and 11.1 of blood were collected. The serum was refined and concentrated to yield a final volume of 250 ml containing 16.2 gr of protein per ml.

The concentrated serum produced a heavy precipitate when mixed with the venom of *A. robustus*. A dilution of serum of 1 : 64,000 produced a positive ring test with venom. Two lines of precipitation were obtained, when serum and venom were allowed to diffuse in agar.

Repeated tests under varying conditions failed to detect the presence of neutralizing antibodies in the concentrated serum.

Sheep

Increasing doses of venom were injected into a sheep over a period of 3 months. The first and last doses contained 0.5 mg and 60 mg of venom, respectively. A total of 147 mg of venom was injected.

Precipitating antibodies were present a few weeks from the commencement of immunization. No neutralizing antibodies could be detected in the serum of the animal.

Rabbit

One rabbit received 118 mg of venom, by the subcutaneous route, over a period of 6 months. The maximum single dose of venom was 24 mg. Another rabbit received 80 mg of venom by the intramuscular route, over a similar period of time. The maximum single dose of venom in this animal was 30 mg. In neither animal were any toxic effects observed.

The precipitate, which resulted when congo-red is added to venom, as reported by Wiener (1961b), was also used. In this form a total of 60 mg of venom was injected into a third rabbit over a period of 3 months, without causing any ill effects.

Two other rabbits were exposed to weekly bites by a male spider. Only a "short" bite was permitted at first, but both animals died after the third and fourth bites, respectively.

In the sera of these animals no neutralizing antibodies were detectable at any stage. In every case precipitating antibodies were present relatively early during the course of injections. They were also present in the sera of the two animals, which had been exposed to repeated bites by a spider.

The serum of an animal injected with male spider venom produced a precipitate when mixed with the venom of the female spider and vice versa. The sera of all animals also precipitated with venom from which coagulable material had been removed by heating, and also with the haemolymph of the spider (Wiener, 1961c).

When venom and serum were allowed to diffuse in agar, three distinct zones of precipitation were produced.

Guinea Pig

Increasing doses of an aqueous solution of venom were injected into a guinea pig by the subcutaneous route. The initial dose was one milligram of venom. Once or twice weekly the amount of venom was increased by 0.5 mg. Whenever an injection of venom was made, the animal showed temporary signs of pain afterwards. Towards the middle of the course, when 6 mg or more of venom were being injected, necrosis of skin occurred at the site of injections, unless these were placed deeply under the skin. Otherwise the animal remained well and continued to gain weight.

No general reactions occurred except towards the end of the course when 10 mg and 10.5 mg, respectively, had been injected with an interval of 1 week between injections. On both occasions temporary weakness of the hind limbs developed, and the animal was lying on its side for short periods of time during the next 3 to 4 hr. On both occasions the animal completely recovered within 24 hr afterwards.

At the time when 10.5 mg of venom was being injected, the animal weighed 400 gr. Into three " non-immunized " guinea pigs, each weighing 400 gr, the following respective amounts of venom were injected, 4.5 mg, 5 mg, and 7.5 mg. The animal which had received 4.5 mg of venom developed signs of intoxication from which it recovered within 24 hr. The guinea pigs which had received 6 mg and 7.5 mg of venom, died in 4 hr and 1½ hr after the injection of venom, respectively. Before death both animals showed signs typical of envenomation. These included, a profuse watery discharge from the nose and mouth, dyspnoea, spasms followed by paralysis of the hind limbs, lack of reaction to painful stimuli and moist sounds in the chest.

Blood was collected from the " immunized " animal 5 days after a dose of 10.5 mg of venom had been injected. The serum strongly precipitated with venom, but no neutralizing antibodies could be detected. Two days later, i.e. 7 days after a previous injection of 10.5 mg of venom, the animal received 11 mg of venom by the subcutaneous route. Within half an hour afterwards, the animal developed weakness of the hind limbs which then progressed to complete paralysis. The animal became comatose and died from failure of respiration, 2 hr after the injection of venom. The absence of muscular spasms and the minimal amount of secretion were the only features which differed from those observed when a " non-immunized " animal died following the injection of a lethal amount of venom.

Thus, by administering increasing amounts of venom to a guinea pig, up to 10.5 mg could be tolerated in an animal weighing 400 g. In a non-immunized animal of the same weight an injection of 6 mg of venom caused death to occur in 4 hr. However, no neutralizing antibodies were detectable in the serum of the " immunized " animal.

ELECTROPHORETIC FRACTIONATION OF VENOM

Preliminary studies indicated that electrophoretic separation of the components in venom was maximal, if the venom was dissolved in 33 per cent acetic acid. This gave a pH of 1.7. At pH 7.5 a smaller number of components separated. It was also found that ninhydrin stained several components, presumably consisting of amino acids, which were not stained by bromphenol blue.

The electrophoretogram and the scanning pattern of the venom of *A. robustus* are shown in Fig. 1. At least eight separate components with different mobilities could be identified. Fractions 1 to 5, constituting 33.8 per cent of all fractions which stained with ninhydrin, moved towards the anode, whilst fractions 6 to 8 which constituted 66.2 per cent, moved towards the cathode. Analysis of the scanning pattern showed that fraction 4 and 7 each consisted of four components with overlapping mobilities, and that each of fractions 5 and 8 consisted of two components. Thus, at least 16 different components were present which stained with ninhydrin.

The areas which corresponded to the position of the eight major fractions were eluted with normal saline solution, and each solution was injected into a mouse by the intravenous route. It was found that fraction 8 was toxic, the animal dying with signs typical of venom intoxication. The injection of fraction 1 produced slight toxic effects from which the animal recovered. No toxic effects were produced by any of the other fractions.

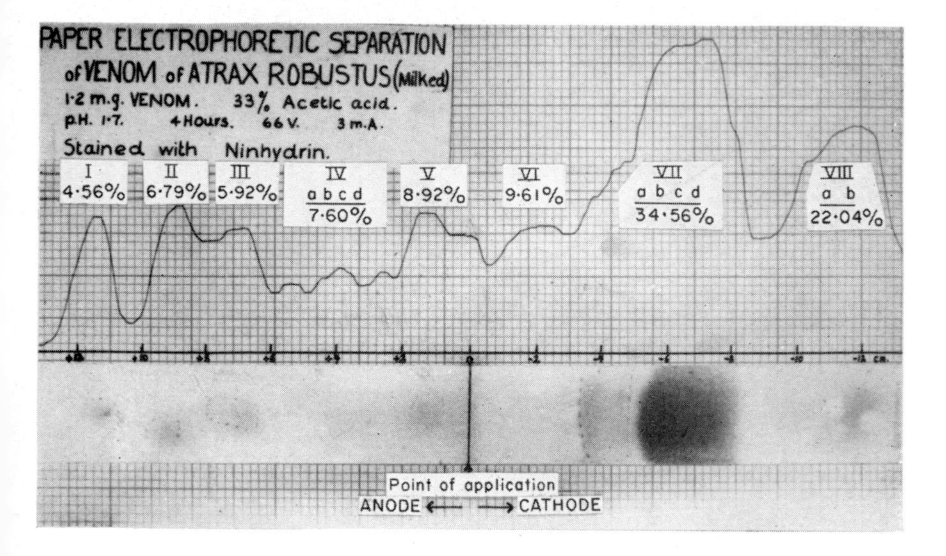

FIG. 1. Paper electrophoretic separation of venom of *Atrax robustus*.

Continuous Electrophoresis of Venom

In order to obtain the separate fractions of venom in amounts which would permit weighing and a more accurate estimation of the toxic properties of each fraction to be made, the components of venom were separated by means of a continuous electrophoresis apparatus.

A solution of venom was prepared by dissolving 310 mg of venom in 12 ml of 33 per cent acetic acid. It was applied to the top of the sheet of filter paper at the rate of 0.5 ml per hr, for 20 hr at 5°C. A current of 7.1 mA at 180 V was used. The separated components of venom were collected as 32 fractions, fraction 1 and 32 being nearest to the anode and cathode, respectively. The electrophoretogram produced on the filter paper after staining with ninhydrin is shown in Fig. 2.

Each of the 32 fractions was freeze-dried in the container in which it was collected and tested for toxicity in mice by the intravenous route. About 1 ml of the original venom solution which had remained unused was freeze-dried to remove acetic acid. Its LD_{50} dose had remained unchanged and was 0.3 mg.

FIG. 2. Continuous electrophoretic separation of the venom of *Atrax robustus*.

In six fractions sufficient dried material was obtained to permit weighing and an estimation of the LD_{50} dose to be made (Table 1). In each of the other 26 fractions, there was only a thin film of material on the inside wall of the container in which they had been freeze-dried. In order to determine the toxicity of these fractions, 2 ml of normal saline solution was used to dissolve any material adhering to the wall of the container. Of each solution 0.1 ml, 0.2 ml, 0.5 ml and 1 ml, respectively were then injected into mice by the intravenous route. On the basis of their toxic properties and appearance after freeze-drying, the 32 fractions could be grouped in the following manner:

Fractions 1 *to* 16

A dry deposit was adhering to the wall of the container in which each of these fractions had been freeze-dried. When dissolved in normal saline solution, a clear solution, neutral to litmus paper, was obtained in each case. Unlike native venom, none of the solutions precipitated a solution of congo red. A blue color was obtained when they were heated with ninhydrin.

TABLE 1. TOXICITY OF FRACTIONS OF ATRAX ROBUSTUS VENOM

No. of fraction	Weight (in mg)	Toxicity in mice	LD_{50} dose (in mg)
1–16	Not determinable	Not toxic	—
17–20	Not determinable	Toxic	—
21	5.9	Toxic	1.0
22	Not determinable	Toxic	—
23	9.0	Toxic	0.7
24	8.6	Toxic	0.4
25	3.3	Not toxic	($>$1.5)
26	7.4	Toxic	0.8
27	Not determinable	Not toxic	—
28	2.6	Not toxic	($>$ 1.6)
29–32	Not determinable	Toxic	—

No toxicity was detectable in any of these fractions.

Fractions 17 *to* 20

A moist granular deposit was obtained after freeze-drying. When dissolved in normal saline solution, a pale yellow solution was obtained, which was neutral in reaction, precipitated congo red and gave a blue color with ninhydrin.

Each of these four fractions was toxic to mice. Death resulted when one quarter and more of the total of each fraction was injected by the intravenous route. The signs preceding death were similar to those which followed the injection of whole venom, except for the absence of the watery discharge from the nose and mouth.

Fractions 21 *to* 26

A white flaky residue was obtained after freeze-drying. In five of these fractions, the amount of material obtained was sufficient to permit weighing. When dissolved in normal saline solution, fractions 21 and 22 were pale yellow in color, whilst the solutions of the other fractions were colorless. The pH of all these solutions ranged from 6.5 to 7.0, and they precipitated a solution of congo red. All of these fractions were toxic to mice, except fraction 25 which produced no observable toxic effects when up to 1.5 mg was injected. The LD_{50} doses of the other fractions ranged from 0.4 to 0.8 mg (Table 1). The signs preceding death were indistinguishable from those which follow the injection of whole venom.

Fractions 27 *and* 28

Both fractions appeared as a white, flaky material after freeze-drying. There was too little material in fraction 27 to permit weighing, whilst fraction 28 weighed 2.6 mg. A clear, colorless and neutral solution resulted when these fractions were dissolved in normal saline solution. When heated with ninhydrin, no blue color was produced.

Neither fraction was toxic to mice. With fraction 28, an amount of 1.6 mg was tolerated without producing any ill effects.

Fractions 29 *to* 32

There was hardly any visible residue in the containers in which these fractions had been freeze-dried. A clear solution resulted when normal saline solution was added. The pH of each of these solutions was about 4, and they changed the color of congo red to blue. When heated with ninhydrin, no blue color was produced by any of these fractions.

Each of these fractions was toxic to mice. Death occurred when 10 per cent to 25 per cent of the total of each fraction was injected. The signs preceding death were similar to those produced by whole venom.

DISCUSSION

Since no neutralizing antibodies could be produced when the venom of *A. robustus* was injected into four species of animals, it must be assumed that one or more toxic fractions in venom were not antigenic. This is supported by observations of Wiener (1961b), concerning the dialyzability of venom, the resistance of its toxic components to the action of heat and trypsin, and by the demonstration that one group of toxic substances, obtained by means of electrophoresis, did not contain amino acids.

Results obtained in the horse and guinea pig indicate that some resistance to the toxic effects of venom had been induced, although no neutralizing antibodies were detectable in the serum. In the case of the guinea pig, this resistance broke down when less than two lethal doses of venom had been injected. In the case of the horse insufficient venom was available to enable the dose to be increased beyond 110 mg of venom. On the evidence available it is unlikely that this resistance was due to an immunological response of the same type as occurs with other venoms. No evidence of cellular immunity could be obtained in animals immunized against snake venom as described by Kellaway and Williams (1932).

In the case of the venom of the bee, it is well-known that people exposed to repeated bee stings eventually develop some resistance to the local effects of bee venom, despite the absence of neutralizing antibodies in their serum. This phenomenon has been reported by Derevici and Derevici (1939), Anton (1943), Haberman and El Karemi (1956). Similarly, a guinea pig exposed to an increasing number of bee stings eventually tolerated the stings of 50 bees, which was twice the lethal dose. According to Derevici and Derevici (1939), no neutralizing antibodies were detectable in the serum of the animal. A similar lack of antigenicity was recorded by Anton (1943) when large amounts of bee venom had been injected into rabbits repeatedly. More recently, Haberman and El Karemi (1956) have reported that in rabbits, which had been immunized with bee venom, antibodies were produced against hyaluronidase and phospholipase-A, which are two of the enzymes present in venom. However, the toxic effects of bee venom in mice and on isolated tissues were not diminished by the sera of immunized rabbits to a greater degree than they were by normal rabbit serum.

There can be little doubt that some of the toxic fractions in bee venom, like those of the venom of *A. robustus*, are not antigenic. Kaiser and Michl (1958) have discussed the acquired resistance of apiarists to the effects of venom. This has been ascribed to the development of tolerance (Tachyphylaxis) by susceptible cells. According to Seevers (1958), the mechanism by which tolerance, in the absence of circulating antibodies, is developed against pharmacologically active substances remains a matter for speculation. It is possible that the injection of repeated doses of venom block receptor sites of susceptible cells, or that specific enzymes are elaborated which destroy or detoxify a limited amount of venom.

It is evident from the results obtained by electrophoresis and of chemical studies by Wiener (1961b), that the venom of *A. robustus* is a mixture of a great variety of different substances. These included proteins, polypeptides and amino acids. Not all of them possessed toxic properties, and there were also toxic substances which did not contain amino acids. The presence of non-toxic proteins were presumably responsible for the production of preciptating antibodies when venom was injected into animals.

By the use of chromatographic and electrophoretic methods of separation, Neuman, Haberman and Amend (1952) identified at least six fractions in the venom of *Aranea diadematus* which stained with ninhydrin but not with protein stains. Muic, Stannic and Meniga (1956) working with venom of *L. tredecimguttatus* identified six protein constituents and two additional components which stained with ninhydrin. In the venoms of *S. raptoria*, and *C. ferus*, Fisher and Bohn (1957) found four protein components, free glutamic acid and lysine. In none of these investigations was any attempt made to study the pharmacological activity of the individual fractions. However, Barrio (1955) reported that one protein fraction of the venom of *S. raptoria* had a pharmacological action on striated muscle which was similar to that of whole venom.

In none of the toxic fractions of the venom of *A. robustus* was the toxicity greater than that of whole venom. It would thus appear that the toxic effects of venom are the result of the combined and possibly synergic action of a number of toxic components. Such a synergic effect has been demonstrated in the case of snake venom by Micheel and Jung (1936) and postulated for the venom of coelenterates by Welsh and Prock (1958).

The series of toxic components, with slightly different mobilities, which extended from fraction 17 to 24, and those from fraction 29 to 32, may have been derived from a common precursor, respectively. A slight difference in the chemical structure of these compounds could account for their different mobilities and the observed difference in the LD_{50} dose, whilst their pharmacological effects remained similar. This phenomenon occurs in the case of other pharmacologically active substances such as those derived from *Rauwolfia serpentina*. These alkaloids possess similar pharmacological actions, but as reported by Ing 1956, and Garattini *et al.* (1959), the effective dose varies amongst the different compounds, which vary slightly in chemical structure.

Since the venom of *A. robustus* was dissolved in acetic acid before being separated electrophoretically, further work is required to determine if new compounds have been produced thereby. The LD_{50} dose and the toxic effects of venom were not altered by treating venom with acetic acid.

SUMMARY

The injection of the venom of *A. robustus* into the horse, sheep, rabbit and guinea pig, failed to induce the formation of antibodies which could neutralize the toxic and lethal effects of venom.

Antibodies which precipitated with venom were produced against the non-toxic protein components of venom.

Electrophoretic separation of the components of venom yielded several distinct toxic fractions. Their toxic effects were similar to those produced by native venom. One group of toxic components did not contain amino acids.

It is postulated that the toxic and lethal effects of the venom of *A. robustus* are due to the combined action of a number of non-antigenic substances.

ACKNOWLEDGEMENT

This work was done at the Commonwealth Serum Laboratories, Melbourne, Australia.

REFERENCES

ANTON, H. 1944. Bienengift und immunitat. *Ztschr. Immunitatsforsch.* **105**, 241.

BARRIO, A. 1955. Spastic action of the venom of the spider *Phoneutria fera*. *Acta. Physiol. Latinoamerica.* **5**, 132.

DEREVICI, A. and DEREVICI, M. 1939. Les modifications humorales provoquées par la venin d'abeile. *C.R. Soc. Biol.* **130**, 1150.

FISCHER, F. G. and BOHN, H. 1957. Die giftsecrete der brasilianischen tarantel, *Lycosa erythrognatha* und der wanderspinne, *Phoneutria fera.* *Ztschr. Physiol. Chemie.* **306**, 265.

GARRATINI, S., MORTARI, A., VALSECCHI, A. and VALZELLI, L. 1959. Reserpine derivatives with specific hypotensive sedative activity. *Nature* **183**, 1273.

HABERMAN, E. and EL KAREMI, M. M. A. 1956. Antibody formation by protein components to bee venom. *Nature* **178**, 1349.

ING, H. R. 1956. Structure-action relationships of hypotensive drugs; in *Hypotensive Drugs.* London: Pergamon Press.

INGRAM, W. W. and MUSGRAVE, A. 1933. Spider bite (arachnidism): A survey of its occurrence in Australia, with case histories. *Med. J. Austr.* **2**, 10.

KAISER, E. and MICHL, H. 1958. *Die Biochemie der Tierischen Gifte.* Wien: F. Deuticke.

KELLAWAY, C. H. and WILLIAMS, F. E. 1932. Some observations on cellular immunity to snake venom. *J. Path. & Bact.* **35**, 193.

MICHEEL, F. and JUNG, F. 1936. Zur kenntniss der schlangengifte. *Ztschr. Physiol. Chemie.* **239**, 217.

MUIC, N., STANNIC, M. and MENIGA, A. 1956. Beitrag zur kenntnis der spinnengifts von *Latrodectus tredecimguttatus.* Rossi. *Ztschr. Physiol. Chemie.* **305**, 70.

NEUMAN, W., HABERMAN, E. and AMEND, G. 1952. Quoted by Kaiser and Michl (1958).

SEEVERS, M. H. 1958. Termination of drug action by tolerance development. *Fed. Proc.* **17**, 1175.

WELSH, J. H. and PROCK, B. 1958. Quarternary ammonium bases in the coelenterates. *Biol. Bull.* **115**, 551.

WIENER, S. 1956. The Australian red back spider (*Latrodectus hasseltii*). I. Preparation of antiserum by the use of venom adsorbed on aluminum phosphate. *Med. J. Austr.* **1**, 739.

WIENER, S. and DRUMMOND, F. H. 1956. Assay of spider venom and antivenene in *Drosophila.* *Nature* **178**, 267.

WIENER, S. and FRASER, A. N. 1956. Red back spider bite treated with antivenene. *Med. J. Austr.* **1**, 858.

WIENER, S. 1957. The Sydney funnel-web spider (*A. robustus*). I. Collection of venom and its toxicity in animals. *Med. J. Austr.* **2**, 377.

WIENER, S. 1959. The Sydney funnel-web spider (*A. robustus*). II. Venom yield and other characteristics of spider in captivity. *Med. J. Austr.* **2**, 679.

WIENER, S. 1961a. Red back spider bite in Australia: An analysis of 167 cases. *Med. J. Austr.* **2**, 44.

WIENER, S. 1961b. Observations on the venom of the Sydney funnel-web spider (*A. robustus*). *Med. J. Austr.* **2**, 693.

WIENER, S. 1961c. The Sydney funnel-web spider (*A. robustus*). III. The neutralization of venom by haemolymph. *Med. J. Austr.* **2**, 449.

THE CURRENT STATUS OF NECROTIC ARACHNIDISM IN TEXAS

Don W. Micks*

Until recently, the black widow spider, *Latrodectus mactans*, has been considered to be the only species of spider of medical importance in this country. Even now, there is comparatively little published information on the association of other kinds of spiders with human disease. It was of interest therefore when Atkins *et al.* (1957 and 1958) suggested that the brown spider, *Loxosceles reclusa*, was the probable cause of necrotic spider bite in Missouri and proceeded to demonstrate that it produced a powerful necrotoxin. That this spider may create a medical problem in other areas is pointed out in a review of envenomation in Kansas by Schmaus (1959). An account of poisoning from *Loxosceles* bite in the same state had been published 30 years earlier by Schmaus (1929).

In South America, Macchiavello (1937) showed that the bite of another species of *Loxosceles*, *laeta*, was associated with cutaneous arachnidism in Chile. He also reported that renal disease was an additional clinical feature of certain cases (1947). Schenone and Prats (1961) have recently summarized the epidemiological, clinical and therapeutic findings in 40 cases of necrotic arachnidism in Chile.

Our interest in this problem in Texas began in 1958 when pediatricians drew our attention to an 8-year-old male patient in whom an " insect bite " was followed by anaphylactic shock and a hemolytic crisis, in addition to a necrotic lesion at the site of the bite. This and a similar case which occurred the following year, and was reported by the same group, James *et al.* (1961), led us to examine the prevalence of necrotic spider bite in Texas. As a part of a survey of physicians practicing in 57 counties throughout the state, it was determined by Micks (1960) that at least seventeen patients had sought medical attention during the period 1955–1959, following the bite of an unknown species of brown spider. A more recent evaluation of the problem of necrotic arachnidism in Texas has elicited information concerning forty-seven additional cases, making a total of sixty from 25 counties. (Fig. 1) for the period 1955–1960. Detailed clinical information was obtained concerning forty of these patients, and provides the basis of this report.

*Laboratory of Medical Entomology, Department of Preventive Medicine and Public Health, The University of Texas Medical Branch, Galveston, Texas.

RESULTS

Two-thirds of the cases occurred in adults and were divided equally between the sexes. The majority of bites took place outdoors during the daytime and in the vicinity of houses and barns. Seventy-eight per cent of the bites involved extremities and 90 per cent of the lesions became necrotic. The majority of patients experienced only a local reaction although several exhibited moderate to severe systemic reactions.

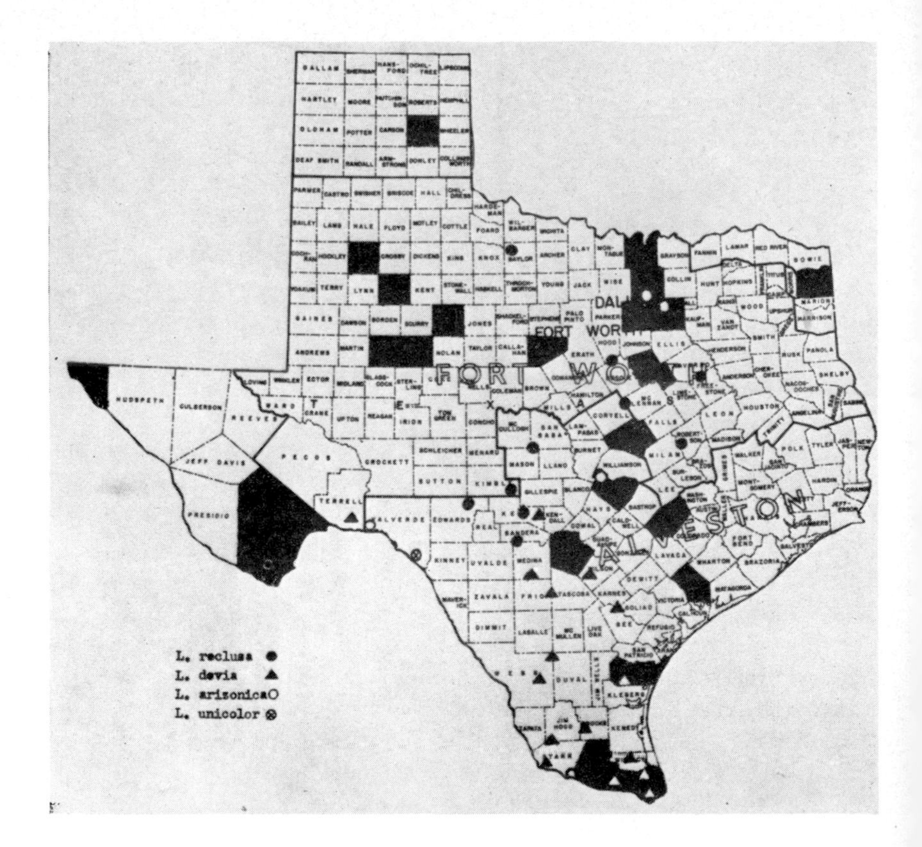

FIG. 1. Areas shown in black represent the 25 counties where brown spider bite cases originated. The distribution of various species of *Loxosceles* is also shown.

Local Reaction

Typically, the bite was followed by moderate to intense pain and was associated with a brown spider. A blister-like reaction followed in at least six cases (Fig. 2A). The entry points of the chelicerae were rarely visible.

A large area of erythema ranging from 3 to 14 cm in diameter (usually about 5 cm) formed, with induration in the center. On the third or fourth day in most instances, the central area, averaging 1.5 cm in diameter became necrotic (Fig. 2B) and sloughed, leaving an ulcer. Several physicians referred to this lesion as " dime-sized ". In most cases, there was little pain associated with the lesion, however, nine patients experienced a dull pain for several days. The time required for healing ranged from 2 to 6 weeks and averaged 3 weeks. The lesions did not respond to antibiotic therapy and skin grafts were necessary in four cases. In six instances, there was no necrosis nor evidence of local tissue reaction after three days.

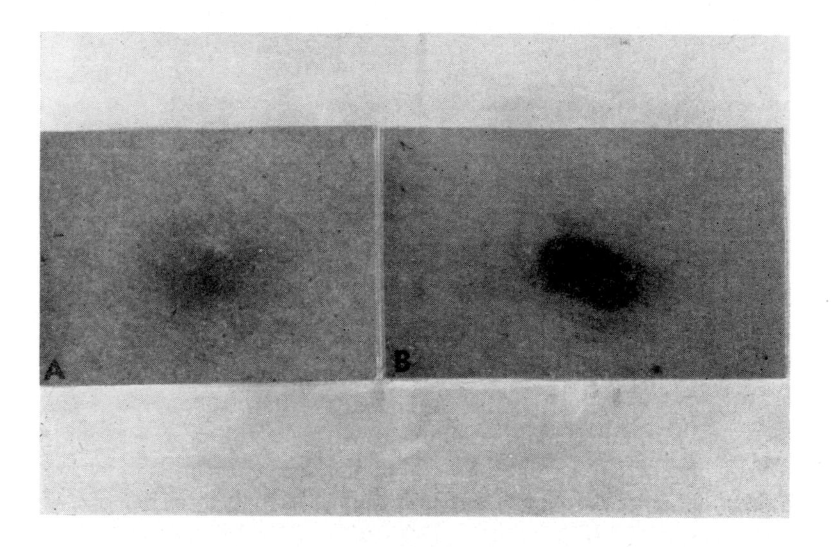

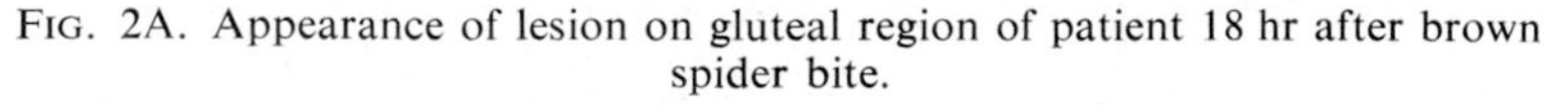

FIG. 2A. Appearance of lesion on gluteal region of patient 18 hr after brown spider bite.

FIG. 2B. Typical appearance of lesion with necrotic center several days after the bite.

Systemic Effects

In addition to the local reaction, symptoms included: generalized aching (4 cases), chills (6), fever (15), weakness (2), edema (3), urticaria (6), lymphadenitis and/or lymphagitis (10), jaundice (2), hemoglobinuria (4), leucocytosis (1), convulsive seizures (1), anaphylactic shock (1), and phlebitis leading to pulmonary infarct (1). Each of the four severely affected patients exhibited hemoglobinuria.

Treatment

The majority of patients (41) included in this study were treated with steroids, usually in combination with antihistamines or antibiotics, although a number received antibiotics alone, especially where the bite effects were localized. A few physicians reported a good response to steroid therapy, however, a uniform observation was that the lesions did not respond to antibiotics.

REPORT OF CASES

The following case summaries are presented below since each has certain features differing from the others:

Case 1. A 24-year-old Latin American female was bitten on the dorsal surface of the left arm, just above the olecranon, while picking cotton. When the patient was seen approximately 30 hr after the bite, there was an oblong area of erythema measuring 14 × 10 cm, local tenderness and heat. There was also central induration, gradually decreasing toward the periphery.

She was started on systemic penicillin and sulfa drugs, but within another 48 hr, the erythema had spread to include the entire arm. There was fluctuance of the central area, axillary and cervical adenopathy, some evidence of embarrassed circulation (forearm and hand edematous) and marked leucocytosis. Incision and drainage yielded approximately one cupful of purulent material. Following this, there was a decrease in the erythema, which now covered the posterior surface of the arm, a decrease in toxic symptoms and general improvement.

The central area then necrosed and left a baseball-sized defect after the slough, which did not respond to successive courses of topical sulfa drugs, neomycin-bacitracin, or furacin. The patient was then started on parenzyme, which appeared to have little if any effect on the healing rate. This wound required some 6 weeks to fill to about the size of a pea and was still ulcerated when last seen.

Case 2. A 67-year-old white female was hospitalized and examined approximately 16 hr after a spider bite. Along the right inguinal flexure, there was a bright red oval area approximately 4 in. long and 2 in. wide, beneath which there was marked induration. In the central zone, there was a purplish, almost black area approximately 1 cm in diameter. The patient stated that since the bite, she had had headache, was decidedly nervous, and had experienced some transient weakness and also had a sensation of chilling.

She was hospitalized approximately 5 days, during which time she was given buccal varidase, triamcinolone, and delvinal with aspirin. Sixteen days after the bite, the patient still exhibited a zone of hard infiltration, although considerably smaller, and still a dusky red color. The central area of necrotic tissue had still not sloughed.

Case 3. A 27-year-old male received a bite from a brown spider on the dorsal surface of the forearm, near the wrist. There was a slight erythema following the bite, which developed into an area of cellulitis. On the third day, a blister appeared, which continued to progress to an area of echymosis and tissue necrosis. This area was approximately ½ in. in diameter, and extended nearly ½ in. deep into the subcutaneous tissues, involving the fascia overlying the muscle. The lesion required 4 weeks to heal.

There were no generalized symptoms other than aching, malaise and low grade fever. The lesion did not respond in the slightest to antibiotics.

Case 4. A 25-year-old male construction worker was bitten by a brown spider on the anterior aspect of the right lower leg. He experienced considerable local reaction, with an ensuing 5 cm area of necrosis. He had chills, and fever to 103°F and tender inguinal nodes. He was treated with chymar ointment locally and antibiotics parenterally. He required empirin and codeine for pain and fever. He suffered 2 weeks' loss of work and the lesion required 5 weeks to heal.

Case 5. A 60-year-old Latin American female was bitten while out sitting in the grass. There was no pain during the bite and the patient was first aware of it when she felt a large raised, hard area several hours later. She awakened the following morning with her eyes swollen shut and with edema of the face.

Upon examination in the hospital several hours later, her face was still somewhat puffy and a rash was noted over much of her body, and was particularly distinct on the inner aspect of her lower arms. The bite, which was on the left gluteal region was approximately 1 cm in diameter, red and somewhat raised. The patient felt somewhat dizzy and generally uncomfortable. However she showed considerable improvement after being given benadryl and epinephrine and was sent home. It was learned later that no slough occurred at the site of the bite.

DISCUSSION

In no instance was any specimen involved in the biting of patients included in this study actually recovered and identified. Therefore, as in other cases of necrotic arachnidism or loxoscelism seen in this and other countries, the evidence that the bites were due to species of *Loxosceles* is largely circumstantial. Nevertheless, in reviewing details of the various case reports, one is struck by the great similarity in the lesions produced, even to the point where many physicians in widely scattered areas use the same descriptive phrases.

The fact that a few (six) individuals exhibited no appreciable necrosis following the spider bite may indicate a degree of immunity to the venom. For example, a physician who has treated cases of brown spider bite reported that he has been bitten a number of times by an arthropod which produced a lesion strikingly similar to that seen in typical necrotic arachnidism. Although his lesions became hard, very red and tender within 24 hr and also had a bluish, discolored area in the center, recovery was complete within 1 week's time without sloughing. The physician considered that his lesions and those of his patients were the same except for an immunity which he stated also extends to wasp and bee stings in his case.

Inasmuch as Atkins, *et al.* (1958) demonstrated in animal experiments that the amount of the venom injected was apparently proportional to the length of time the chelicerae remained in the skin, it is conceivable that spiders may occasionally be dislodged immediately following the piercing of the skin by the chelicerae, with a corresponding reduction in the severity of the local tissue reaction. There is still another possibility, namely, that the necrotoxin may vary qualitatively and/or quantitatively from species to species, and likewise its necrotizing properties. According to Gertsch (1958), at least four species of *Loxosceles* (*reclusa*, *devia*, *arizonica* and *unicolor*) are known to occur in Texas. Distribution of these species is shown in Fig. 1. The scanty data collected to date do not permit any conclusions to be drawn as to the relationship between species and severity of symptoms. In fact, James *et al.* (1961) collected specimens of *L. unicolor* from a barn where one of their patients was bitten to provide the only such circumstantial relationship known to the author in this state.

It is interesting that Schenone and Prats (1961) reported approximately the same percentage of severe reactions (viscerocutaneous arachnidism) following bites of *Loxosceles laeta* as seen in the present series of cases. Hemoglobinuria was a prominent feature in both cases. Their series of cases included one death as the result of a severe reaction to a brown spider bite. In this connection, there is evidence that necrotic arachnidism has terminated fatally in Texas. The records of the Texas State Department of Health list four deaths during the past 10 years, the symptoms of which are compatible with brown spider bite, the cause of death being listed as follows:

1951: 78-year-old white female—gangrene, left leg, spider bite.

1958: 6-year-old white male—spider bite, left chest, severe hemolytic reaction.

1960: 65-year-old white female—acute cavernous sinus thrombosis probably due to spider bite on forehead.

1960: 46-year-old Latin American male—acute uremia due to fulminating septicemia, and due to cellulitis with deep necrosis in both gluteal regions caused by " insect bite ".

The fact that the data included in this study were obtained from less than 5 per cent of the practitioners in Texas would lead to the conclusion that necrotic arachnidism is a greater medical problem than previously recognized.

ACKNOWLEDGEMENTS

Sincere thanks are extended to the many Texas physicians, who, through their kind cooperation, have made this study possible. Photographic and other materials supplied by Dr. Ray Bullard, Dr. B. LeBlue and Dr. Richard V. Price are particularly appreciated.

Grateful acknowledgment is also due the Division of Vital Statistics of the Texas State Department of Health for information kindly supplied.

REFERENCES

Atkins, J. A., Wingo, C. W. and Sodeman, W. A. 1957. Probable cause of necrotic spider bite in the midwest. *Science* **126**, 78.

Atkins, J. A., Wingo, C. W., Sodeman, W. A. and Flynn, J. E. 1958. Necrotic arachnidism. *Am. J. Trop. Med. & Hyg.* **7**, 165.

Gertsch, W. J. 1958. The spider genus *Loxosceles* in North America, Central America, and the West Indies. *Am. Museum Nov.* No. 1907, 46 pp.

James, J. A., Sellars, W. A., Austin, O. M. and Terrill, B. S. 1961. Reactions following suspected spider bite. *Am. J. Dis. Child.* **102**, 395.

Macchiavello, A. 1937. La *Loxosceles laeta*, causa del aracnoidismo cutaneo, o mancha gangrenosa, de Chile. *Rev. Chilena de His. Nat.* **41**, 11.

Macchiavello, A. 1946. Cutaneous arachnoidism or gangrenous spot of Chile. Puerto Rico. *J. Pub. Hlth. Trop. Med.* **22**, 424.

Micks, D. W. 1960. Insects and other arthropods of medical importance of Texas. *Tex. Rep. Biol. and Med.* **18**, 624.

Schenone, H. and Prats, F. 1961. Arachnidism by *Loxosceles laeta*. *Arch. Dermat.* **83**, 139.

Schmaus, L. F. 1929. Case of arachnoidism (spider bite). *J.A.M.A.* **92**, 1265.

Schmaus, J. W. 1959. Envenomation in Kansas. *J. Kansas Med. Soc.* **60**, 237.

CENTIPEDES AND MILLIPEDES AS PESTS IN TROPICAL AREAS

HUGH L. KEEGAN*

CENTIPEDES are well-known pests in the warmer portions of the Pacific region. These venomous creatures will sometimes enter houses to feed upon insects and, if touched, will usually bite immediately. Large specimens may attain a length of 10 in. or more and are of spectacular appearance because of size and coloration. Adults of several species have shining greenish or blackish bodies and orange or red legs and head. A centipede bears a pair of legs on each segment of the body except the last two and the one just behind the head. When the centipede bites, venom is injected into its prey through modified appendages on the first body segment. The specimen shown in Fig. 1 was collected on Ishigaki Island in the Southern Ryukyus.

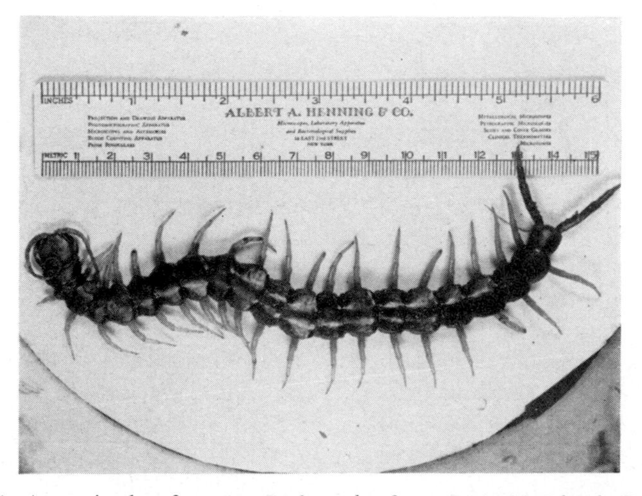

FIG. 1. A centipede of genus *Scolopendra* from Ishigaki Island, Southern Ryukyus.

Clinical reports on effects of centipede bite in man were reviewed by Remington (1950), DeCastro (1921), and Bücherl (1946). Based on experience in the Philippines, Remington concluded that centipede bites were not

*Entomology Branch, Department of Preventive Medicine, Medical Field Service School, Brooke Army Medical Center, Fort Sam Houston, Texas.

M

potentially deadly to man. Bites by large centipedes on Leyte Island were followed by intense local pain which was quickly relieved by local anesthetics. Kopstein (1932) reported that centipede bite on New Guinea and in the Mariana Islands was not serious and produced transitory pain. He did note that bite of a large Javanese centipede was fatal for small birds in less than a minute. Effects of the bite of this species on man were not known. A large centipede kept in the laboratory of the Medical Field Service School of the U.S. Army was allowed to bite two mice which were held with forceps. On one occasion the mouse was bitten on the abdomen, on the other on the back. Both mice succumbed within 15 sec after the bite. After studying effects of venoms of Brazilian centipedes on laboratory animals and man, Bücherl (1946), was of the opinion that bites by any of these species would not cause serious toxicity or danger to life in either adults or children.

More serious effects were reported by DeCastro (1921) who was writing of his experiences with cases in India, Burma, and the Andaman Islands. In patients observed by this author, recovery from centipede bites was slow, sometimes as long as three months. Every case seen in his hospital developed intense lymphangitis with edema, as well as inflammation of the skin and subcutaneous tissues. In most instances a localized necrotic process developed at the site of the bite. In some cases this progressed to a condition not unlike phagedenic ulceration. Most serious results followed bites by large centipedes from the Andaman Islands. Some of these specimens were as long as 13 in., and ranged from light yellow to dark, greenish blue in color.

Little is known concerning potency of the venoms of many of the tropical centipedes. Without describing symptoms, Reid (1956), remarked that he had seen one extremely severe centipede bite in Malaya. Symptoms in this case were more striking than after some viper bites.

In areas where centipedes abound, persons sleeping in the open or in tents should make certain that mosquito nets are properly tucked in and should exercise caution in handling clothing which has been lying on the ground overnight. Centipede infestation in houses may be prevented by proper screening and use of insecticides. Scott and Pratt (1959) advised that *Scutigera cleopatra*, a house-infesting species of the United States, could be controlled with 2 per cent chlordane, 1 per cent lindane, or 2 or 4 per cent malathion applied as spot treatments.

MILLIPEDES

Millipedes differ from centipedes in possessing two instead of one pairs of legs on each body segment. They are sometimes mistaken for centipedes, and may attain a length of several inches. Millipedes will not bite, and the great majority of species are entirely harmless. Their only defense is a secretion which is exuded or even squirted through pores on the body surface. This fluid may cause intense burning if it gets into the eyes, or may produce blisters on the skin. Secretions of some species may cause skin eruption as well as intense pain. Halstead and Ryckman (1949) reported that in Haiti the venomous secretions of a millipede found there causes permanent blindness in chickens and other small animals. Kopstein (1932) stated that one large species of genus *Spirostreptus* is much feared in the Sunda Islands, and that a species of *Julus* was considered to be very venomous on Ambon. He mentioned that other venomous species were known to occur in Malaya.

Scott and Pratt (1959) stated that 2 per cent chlordane emulsions or solutions as spot applications, 5 per cent chlordane dust, or 2 to 5 per cent malathion dusts have given good control of millipedes.

ACKNOWLEDGEMENT

Figure 1 is a U.S. Army Photograph taken at the Clinical Photography Section, Pathology Service, Brooke General Hospital, Brooke Army Medical Center, Fort Sam Houston, Texas. The photograph has previously appeared in 1960 in a U.S. Army publication, *Some Venomous and Noxious Animals of the Far East*.

REFERENCES

BÜCHERL, W. 1946. Acao do veneno dos escolopendromorfos do Brasil sobre alguns animais de laboratorie (Action of Brazilian *Scolopendronorpha* Venom on Mice, Guinea Pigs, and Pigeons.) *Mem. Inst. Butantan.* **14**, 181.

DECASTRO, A. B. 1921. The Poison of the Scolopendridae—Being a special reference to the Andaman species. *Indian Med. Gaz.* **56**, 207.

HALSTEAD, B. W. and RYCKMAN, R. 1949. Injurious effects from contacts with millipedes. *Med. Arts and Sciences* **3** (1), 16.

KOPSTEIN, F. 1932. Die gifttiere Java's und ihre Bedeutung für den Menschen. *Med. v. d. Dienst d. Volksgezondheid in Ned. Indie.* **21**, 222.

REID, H. A. 1956. Personal communication.

REMINGTON, C. L. 1950. The bite and habits of a giant centipede (*S. subspinipes*) in the Philippine Islands. *Am. J. Trop. Med.* **30**, 453.

SCOTT, H. G. and PRATT, H. D. 1959. Scorpions, spiders, and other arthropods of minor public health importance and their control. Training Guide, Insect Control Series. U.S. Department of Health, Education, and Welfare, Public Health Service Communicable Disease Center, Training Branch, Atlanta, Georgia.

CATERPILLARS AND MOTHS AS PUBLIC HEALTH PROBLEMS

HUGH L. KEEGAN*

CATERPILLARS, cocoons, and adult moths of many species may cause irritating dermatitis, severe pain, and a variety of systemic manifestations upon contact with the skin of man. Such accidents are not confined to the tropics, but are almost world-wide in distribution. One of the most notorious caterpillars, from a medical viewpoint, occurs in the United States, and is particularly numerous in the State of Texas. Other species of medical importance are known from Europe, Africa, Asia and Australia. Ubiquity of this problem is evidenced by recent papers by McGovern *et al.* (1961) describing a series of 2130 cases of caterpillar sting occurring in Texas during 1958; Zipkrkowski *et al.* (1959) describing a single outbreak of 600 cases of caterpillar dermatitis in Israel; and a series of three papers by Ogata (1958) concerning the morphology, ecology, and medical importance of *Euproctis flava*, the Far Eastern urticating moth. Basic monographs giving information on geographic distribution of medically important species, and on the various types of venom apparatus possessed by moth caterpillars are given by Gilmer (1924) and Weidner (1937).

Venom of a caterpillar is carried in modified hairs and spines on the body surface of the insect. These may occur singly, or in clusters on tubercles of the body surface. Upon contact with the skin the venom may emerge through an opening at the tip of the spine, or a portion of the hair or spine may break off in the wound, thus releasing the venom. In all cases the venom glands are believed to consist of single cells. These are located at the bases of modified hairs, or may actually be located outside of the body wall proper in the hollow spines. This type of venom is not a secretion, but consists of the actual protoplasm of the venom gland.

Pathology of the dermatitis produced by the caterpillar of *Automeris io* was described by Jones and Miller (1959). The most characteristic feature was a rapidly developing edema of the corium and subcutaneous tissue, without necrosis. This action was of approximately six hours duration. The urticating substance was not analyzed, but the reaction seemed compatible

*Entomology Branch, Department of Preventive Medicine, Medical Field Service School, Brooke Army Medical Center, Fort Sam Houston, Texas.

with one caused, at least in part, by histamine, or a histamine release phenomenon. These authors listed numerous papers on this subject, including several describing ophthalmia nodosa due to urticating hairs of caterpillars, and others describing extraction of histamine from setae of urticating species.

Each summer in Japan considerable attention is given in the newspapers to infestations with a venomous moth, *Euproctis flava*. Unlike the situation in many areas, most accidents caused by this species are through the adult rather than the caterpillar. In the summer of 1956 it was estimated that over

FIG. 1. The " yamangi " an urticating caterpillar from the Sakashima Islands.

250,000 persons on Honshu Island were affected by this moth. *Euproctis flava*, also known as the Oriental Tussock Moth, occurs in China, Siberia, and Korea, as well as Japan. Recent papers on this species, and dermatitis caused by it have been published by Masuyama, Oshima, and Goto (1956) and Ishizaki and Nagai (1956). Additional species of medical importance occur in Japan and neighbouring areas. It is the opinion of most authorities that the venomous hairs and spines are produced only by the larvae, and that moths cause dermatitis only if they are carrying some of the larval hairs on their bodies or wings. These hairs often adhere to the moth when it emerges from the cocoon. Sakai and Toshioka (1956) have given a list of references to the irritating lepidoptera of Japan (in Japanese). Reid (1958) gave two reports of trouble from adults and caterpillars of species of *Euproctis* in Malaya. One incident, involving a large number of troops and civilians at Port Dickson, in 1957, was due to adults of *Euproctis flavociliate*. The other report concerned a small number of persons at Ipoh, who came in contact with caterpillars of *Euproctis funeralis*, which were feeding in a Banyan (fig) tree close to an office window.

On Ishigaki and Iriomote islands, about 240 miles south of Okinawa a large caterpillar, known as the " yamangi " is held in considerable respect. The islanders believe that, after contact with this species, the skin will slough and serious systemic effects will occur. During September of 1956 a number of these larvae, one of which is shown in Fig. 1, were collected on Ishigaki Island. All of the specimens taken were resting on the bark of trees along

FIG. 2. A moth of genus *Dendrolimus*. The "yamangi" is the larva of this species.

streams. Because of their coloration they are difficult to see and most accidents occur when persons put their hands on tree trunks to steady themselves in the rough terrain of that island. Laboratory tests, using white rabbits, failed to confirm the dire consequences predicted by persons in Ishigaki. A slight redness and very slight swelling were the only effects noted. The rabbit did not seem to be in distress, and no symptoms whatsoever could be found on the following day. The " yamangi " is a larva of a moth of genus *Dendrolimus*. The specimen shown in Fig. 2 was reared from the larval stage.

The following interesting notes regarding relatives of the " yamangi " were contained in a letter from Mr. John Reid of the Institute for Medical Research, Kuala Lumpur, Malaya.

" The picture of the ' Yamangi ' reminds me of the largest caterpillar I ever saw (6 in. measured by ruler)—turned out to be *Suana concolor* (Lasiocampidae)—closely related to *Dendrolimus*. Filled my fingers with large, sharp, black hairs when I was foolish enough to pick it up but I carefully picked them out one by one and suffered no irritation or after effects.

" This cryptic coloration and habit of resting on tree trunks must be common in this family of moths. More recently I saw a group of three or four big ones (not *S. concolor*) resting by day on the trunk of a large meranti tree in the forest ".

The outbreak described by Ziprkowski *et al.* (1959) was unique in that no living caterpillars were discovered in the pine grove where the incident occurred, and the dermatitis was produced by contact with dead larvae and cocoons of the moth, *Thaumatopoea wilkinsoni*. These cocoons and dead larvae mixed with debris on the forest floor were contacted unkowingly by the soldiers who slept on the ground.

Symptoms produced by contact with venomous caterpillars are much the same wherever they occur. Typical symptoms in a series of 18 cases reported by Randel and Doan (1956) included sudden, burning pain at the point of contact, followed by erythema, swelling, lymphangitis, leukocytosis, and eosinophilia. Numbness, lymphadenopathy, and vasiculation occurred in some cases. The most interesting feature in this series was the rapidly developing eosinophilia, which ranged from 8 to 22 per cent. In cases reported by Micks (1952) it was noted that there was a definite relation between severity of the reaction, size of the caterpillar, and amount of pressure on contact: in each case an intense, burning pain at site of the sting was felt, followed in a matter of minutes by an area of erythema of 3 cm or less in diameter. In several patients white spots appeared in this area of inflammation. The most characteristic symptom was presence of " shooting pains ". When the sting occurred on a limb, pain extended proximally to adjacent axillary or inguinal regions. Although nausea, vomiting and localized swelling occurred in several patients, the majority were not affected in this way. Regional lymph nodes were palpable in some patients. Most patients exhibited a mild dermatitis, which lasted for 48–72 hr. In reporting on effects of contact with the adult of *Euproctis flava*, Masuyama and his co-workers (1956) noted that the chief effects were reddening of the skin, blisters, and temporary severe pain. Similar results were reported by Ishizaki and Nagai (1956), who found that 37 per cent of 81 patients had papule-like eruptions, and 63 per cent had urticaria-like signs. Four patients in this series had fever. Most patients were cured within one week. As a departure from the usual symptoms, one patient in the series observed by Micks (1952) went into shock, and exhibited some respiratory embarrassment.

Among the 2130 cases of sting by *Megalopyge opercularis* reported by McGovern *et al.* (1961) major signs and/or symptoms included: severe local pain (98.3 per cent); local swelling (92.2 per cent); lymphadenopathy (31.9

per cent); headache (29.4 per cent); shock-like symptoms (4.9 per cent); convulsions (0.24 per cent—5 cases). Eight of these patients were hospitalized. There were no deaths. Similar findings were reported by Micks (1960), who discussed a series of 54 cases of stings by the same caterpillar, also in Texas.

In contrast, the clinical picture reported by Ziprkowski *et al.*, (1959) consisted only of severe itching of the arms, thighs, abdominal region and back, accompanied by a nodular, urticarial and erythematous rash.

As pointed out by Randel and Doan (1956) the main problem in cases of caterpillar sting are proper diagnosis, relief of pain, and reassurance of the patient. These workers found oral codeine most satisfactory for relief of pain after contact with Panamanian caterpillars. Diphenhydramine orally did not seem to relieve symptoms significantly. Warm bicarbonate of soda soaks, followed by administration of tetracaine ointment was without apparent effect. In the series of patients studied by Micks (1952) 100 mg of tripelennamine orally gave no appreciable relief, but i.v. administration of 10 ml of a 10 per cent solution of calcium gluconate gave quick relief from pain. Flecker and McSweeny (1944) applied fomentations with 1 per cent Dettol followed by calamine lotion. This brought speedy relief from pain. If urticaria was severe, 10 minims of 1 : 1000 adrenalin were injected subcutaneously twice a day for 2 days. D'Avanzo (1952) found calamine lotion excellent for local application, and recommended sodium thiosulphate for disensitization. Mills (1925) found that local applications of cold water, soda and ammonia were without effect.

McGovern *et al.* (1961) found that immediate, light application of adhesive tape over the area of contact helped remove broken spines in the skin. These authors noted that early application of ice packs had been of slight help in relieving pain of several patients, but that antihistaminics had been of questionable value. Calcium gluconate, given intravenously, was of benefit to patients with severe generalized reactions, and epinephrine hydrochloride was helpful in controlling symptoms in several cases. Meperidine, morphine sulphate, or codein was usually required to control intense pain resulting from these stings. Mild analgesics such as aspirin generally failed to control pain and associated headaches. The milder symptoms produced by *Thaumatopoea wilksoni* in Israel, reported by Ziprkowski *et al.* (1959) were relieved by treatment with anti-histaminics.

Because of the sporadic, although widespread, distribution of urticating moths, it is difficult to give practical advice concerning avoidance of accidents. Only when local venomous caterpillars are known to feed on certain types of shrubbery can an attempt at control be made through use of insecticides or such vegetation avoided. Contact with moths is usually not a problem for persons in screened buildings. Many of the accidents reported in Japan occurred at night when moths, attracted by electric lights, entered buildings through unscreened windows or doors.

ACKNOWLEDGEMENTS

Figs. 1 and 2 are U.S. Army photographs taken at the 406th Medical General Laboratory, Camp Zama, Japan. Both Figs. have previously appeared in 1958 and 1960 versions of a U.S. Army publication, *Some Venomous and Noxious Animals of the Far East.*

REFERENCES

D'Avanzo, G. 1952. La dermatitis da contatto provacata de farfalle del genere Hylesia (" Yellow-tail Moth Dermatitis or Caripito Itch "). *Med. D. Lavoro.* **43** (12), 439–452.

Flecker, H. and McSweeny, A. 1944. Irritation produced by the Procession Caterpillar (*Ochrogaster contraria*). *Med. J. Australia* **2** (6), 137–138.

Gilmer, P. M. 1924. A Comparative Study of the Poison-Apparatus of Certain Lepidopterous Larvae. *Ann. Ent. Soc. Am.*, **18**, 203–239.

Ishizaki, T. and Nagai, R. 1956. Clinical Studies on Dermatitis Due to *Euproctis flava* (Report I). *Japanese Journal of Sanitary Zoology* **7** (2), 113.

Jones, D. L. and Miller, J. H. 1959. Pathology of the Dermatitis Produced by the Urticating Caterpillar, *Automeris io. A.M.A. Archives of Dermatology* **79**, 81–85.

Masuyama, T., Oshima, K. and Goto, J. 1956. Investigation of So-Called Dermatitis Due to *Euproctis flava. Japanese Journal of Sanitary Zoology* **7** (2), 113.

McGovern, J. P., Barkin, G. B., McElhenney, T. R. and Wende, R. 1961. *Megalopyge opercularis.* Observations of its life history, of its sting in man, and report of an epidemic. *J.A.M.A.* **175**, 1155.

Micks, D. W. 1952. Clinical Effects of the Sting of the " Puss Caterpillar " (*Megalopyge opercularis* S. & A.) on Man. Texas *Repts. on Biol. and Med.* **10** (2), 399–405.

Micks, D. W. 1960. Insects and other arthropods of medical importance in Texas. *Texas Repts. on. Bol. Med.* **18**, 624.

Mills, R. G. 1925. Some Observations and Experiments on the Irritating Properties of the Larvae of *Parasa hilarat.* Staudinger. *Am. J. Hyg.* **5**, 342–363.

Ogata, K. 1958. Studies on the Far Eastern urticating moth *Euproctis flava* Bremer, as a pest of medical importance. With English summary. *Japanese J. Sanitary Zoology* **9** (3), 116–121 (I) Morphological Notes; **9** (4), 203–227 (II) Ecological Notes; **9** (4), 228–234 (III) Epidemiological Notes.

Randel, H. W. and Doan, G. B. 1956. Caterpillar Urticaria in the Panama Canal Zone, Report of Five Cases. Venoms. E. E. Buckley and N. Porges, editors. Pub. No. 44 of A.A.A.S., Washington, D.C., pp. 111–116.

Reid, John. Personal correspondence. 8 December 1958.

Sakai, M. and Toshioka, S. 1956. References of the irritating lepidoptera of Japan. *Japanese J. Sanitary Zoology* **7** (2), 107–108.

Weidner, H. 1937. Beitrage zu einer Monographie der Raupen mit Gifthaaren. *Zeits. f. Angewandte Ent.* **23**, 432–484.

Ziprkowski, L., Hofshi, E. and Tahori, A. S. 1959. Caterpillar dermatitis. *Israel Med. J.* **18**, 36.

SECTION V

FISHES

A REVIEW OF THE VENOMOUS FISHES OF THE PACIFIC AREA*

BRUCE W. HALSTEAD and LOIS R. MITCHELL†

THE Pacific marine fauna is especially rich in venomous fishes. The only venomous fish group of major importance not represented are the European weeverfishes of the family Trachinidae. Most venomous fishes are inshore or reef inhabitants. Representative species of some of the groups such as stingrays, chimaeroids, scorpionfishes, star-gazers, etc., are found in deep waters, but they are few in number and are largely bottom dwellers. With very few exceptions venomous fishes are for the most part slow swimmers and prefer a protected habitat, spending much of their time buried in the mud or sand, in crevices, around rocks, kelp beds, or corals.

Poisonous fishes are of two general types: those which are poisonous to eat and those which produce envenomation. The former are usually referred to as *poisonous fishes*, whereas the latter are designated as *venomous fishes*. Venom is a product of specialized glandular cells and is generally conveyed to the victim by a dentinal or bony apparatus, which in certain fishes is highly developed. Since fish venoms are readily destroyed by heat and gastric juices they are not oral poisons, but are effective only by the parenteral route.

Despite the fact that some of the earliest literature in biotoxicology deals with venomous fishes, the bulk of our knowledge on the morphology of the venom organs of fishes has been published during the past two decades. The field of piscine venomology offers a vast field of untapped opportunity to the budding researcher since less than 5 per cent of the venom organs of fishes have been described to date, and even less is known about the pharmacology and chemistry of these venoms.

The purpose of this paper is to review the Pacific venomous fishes and briefly describe the venom organs of some representative species. The meager amount of chemical data that is available will be discussed. Mention will be made of the medical aspects, but no attempt has been made to deal with the subject at length. Only those species which have been reported in the literature as venomous species are listed. Obviously the list is incomplete,

*All illustrations are borrowed from *Dangerous Marine Animals*. The authors are indebted to the Cornell Maritime Press for their use.

†World Life Research Institute, Colton, California.

but it is nevertheless representative of what is known about the subject.

HORNED SHARKS

Venomous sharks are limited to those species which possess dorsal fin spines, namely, members of the families Heterodontidae, Squalidae, and Dalatiidae. Although a number of species within these three familes are suspected of having venom organs, only two species, *Heterodontus francisci* and *Squalus acanthias*, have been studied to even a limited extent. Clinical reports from horned sharks are largely based on the single species *S. acanthias*, and the bulk of these reports are from Europe.

Species Reported as Venomous

Heterodontidae. Bullhead or Horned Sharks:

Heterodontus francisci (Girard)

California coast from Point Conception to Lower California and into the Gulf of California.

Heterodontus philppi (Schneider)

Australia, Tasmania and New Zealand.

Squalidae. Spiny Dogfish:

Squalus acanthias Linnaeus (Fig. 1A)

Both sides of the North Atlantic and North Pacific.

FIG. 1A. Spiny dogfish. *Squalus acanthias* Linnaeus (Shirao). [The name in parentheses is the artist's name.]

Venom Apparatus

The venom apparatus of horned sharks is comprised of the dorsal fin spines and the associated glandular tissue. The dorsal stings are situated adjacent to the anterior margins of each of the two spines in most of the horned sharks. Some of the dalatiid sharks have only a single somewhat rudimentary fin spine or the spines are entirely absent. Therefore, there is some question as to whether a true venom organ is present in this latter group.

The anterior fin spine (Fig. 1B) in *Squalus acanthias* is only slightly curved antero-posteriorly, whereas the posterior spine is more curved and in lateral view is somewhat sabreshaped. The two sides are slightly convex and the longitudinally grooved posterior aspect of the spine forms the base of the

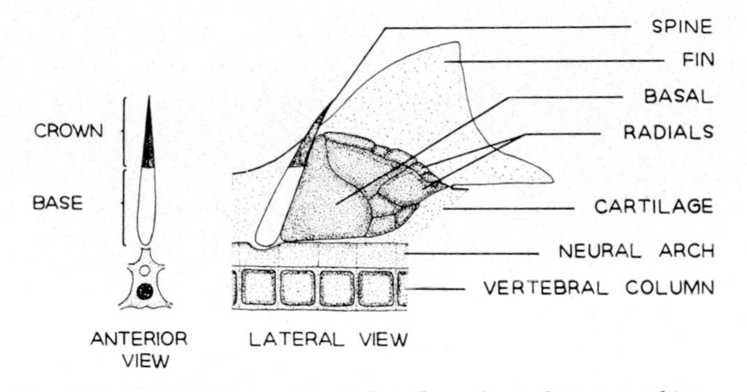

FIG. 1B. Lateral view of anterior fin spine of *S. acanthias*.

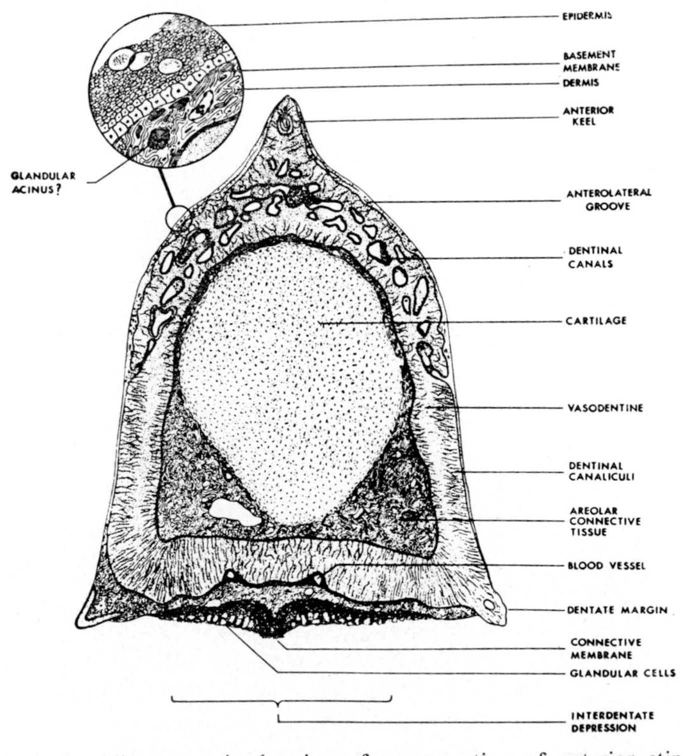

FIG. 1C. Semidiagrammatic drawing of cross section of anterior sting of *S. acanthias*. Note the heavy concentration of glandular cells in the interdentate depression. Enlarged approximately 53 times.

triangle. The spine is grooved only in its exposed portion, and the groove becomes more shallow toward the tip. The glandular tissue appears as a glistening white substance situated in the shallow posterior groove, or interdentate depression, of the spine.

Microscopic examination of the sting in cross section reveals it to be trigonal in shape and comprised of three principal layers: an outer layer of integument which covers a thick wall of hard vasodentine and an inner core of cartilage (Fig. 1C). Careful examination of the structure reveals that the glandular cells are situated in the epithelial portion of the integumentary layer in the area of the anterolateral glandular grooves and in the interdentate depression. The glandular cells are sparsely scattered in the anteroglandular-groove area, but are heavily concentrated in the interdentate depression. The glandular cells are of two basic types. Some of these are polygonal-shaped, clear, finely granular cells having slightly pycnotic nuclei, which appear to be of the mucin type. However, the venom cells in hematoxylin and triosin preparations are oval-shaped, containing homogenous brown-staining material with accumulations of finely granular material. Venom production is apparently by a holocrine type of secretion. Morphological studies on *Squalus* have been conducted largely by Evans (1921, 1923, 1943).

Pharmacology and Chemistry of the Venom

To the best of our knowledge no study has been conducted on the nature of the venom. The action of the venom is based entirely upon clinical reports.

STINGRAYS

Stingrays constitute an important group of venomous fishes in that they are probably the most common cause of fish stings. The Suborder Myliobatoidea includes the seven ray families: Dasyatidae, stingrays or whiprays; Potamotrygonidae, river rays; Gymnuridae, butterfly rays; Urolophidae, round stingrays; Myliobatidae, eagle or bat rays; Rhinopteridae, cow-nosed rays; and Mobulidae, devil rays or mantas. (The caudal spines of the Mobulidae, when present, are generally quite rudimentary and will not be considered further in this presentation). With the exception of the Potamotrygonidae, which are confined to the rivers of South America, most stingrays are marine, inhabiting shallow coastal waters, bays, brakish water lagoons, but may enter river mouths and freshwater rivers. Most reports on stingray attacks and venom organs are based on either European or North American species. Very little is known regarding the venom organs of most of the stingray species of the tropical Pacific.

Species Reported as Venomous

Dasyatidae. Stingrays or Whiprays:

Dasyatis akajei (Müller and Henle)
Southern Japan, China Seas, Korea.
Dasyatis brevicaudatus (Hutton)
Indo-Pacific Region.
Dasyatis brevis (Garman)
San Diego, California to Galapagos Islands.
Dasyatis dipterurus (Jordan and Gilbert) (Fig. 2)
British Colombia to Central America.

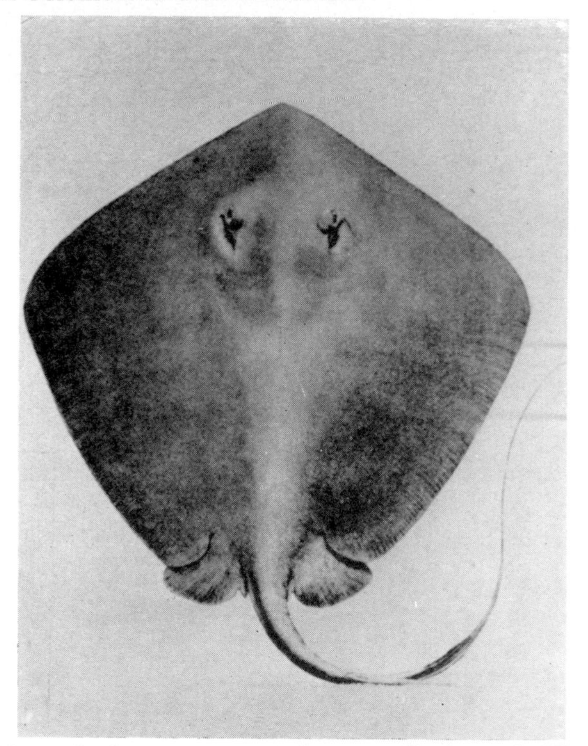

FIG. 2. Diamond stingray. *Dasyatis dipterurus* (Jordan and Gilbert) (from Walford).

Dasyastis gerrardi (Gray)
Samoa, Indonesia, India.
Dasyatis granulatus (Macleay)
Melanesia, Indonesia, Australia.
Dasyatis imbricatus (Bloch and Schneider)
Malaya and Indonesia.
Dasyatis kuhlii (Müller and Henle)
Samoa, Japan, Indonesia to India.
Dasyatis latus (Garman)
Hawaiian Islands and Australia.

Dasyatis ponapensis (Günther)
Caroline Islands
Dasyatis sephen (Forskål)
Micronesia, Melanesia, Philippines, Australia, Indian Ocean and the Red Sea.
Dasyatis uarnak (Forskål)
Indo-Pacific region westward to the Red Sea.
Dasyatis zugei (Müller and Henle)
Japan, China, Malay Peninsula and Indian Ocean.
Taeniura lymma (Forskål)
Indo-Pacific region westward to the Red Sea.
Urogymnus africanus (Schneider)
Indo-Pacific region westward to the Red Sea.

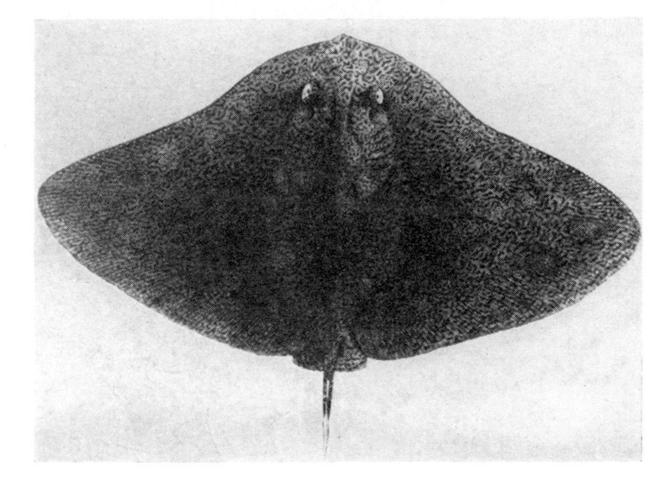

FIG. 3. Butterfly ray. *Gymnura marmorata* (Cooper) (from Hiyama).

Gymnuridae. Butterfly rays:
Gymnura japonica (Temminck and Schlegel)
Japan, Korea, China.
Gymnura marmorata (Cooper) (Fig. 3)
Point Conception, California, south at east to Mazatlan, Mexico.
Gymnura poecilura (Shaw)
Polynesia, Japan, Indo-Pacific region, China, westward to the Red Sea.
Myliobatidae. Eagle or Bat Rays:
Aetobatus narinari (Euphrasen)
Warm temperate and tropical belts of the Atlantic, Indo-Pacific region, westward to the Red Sea.

Aetomylaeus nichofii (Bloch and Schneider)
Western Pacific, Australia, Indonesia, Indian Ocean.
Myliobatis californicus (Gill) (Fig. 4)
Oregon to Magdalena Bay, Lower California.
Myliobatis peruvianus Garman
Peru to China.
Myliobatis punctatus Macleay and Macleay
Admiralty Islands.
Myliobatis tobijei Bleeker
Japan, Korea, China.

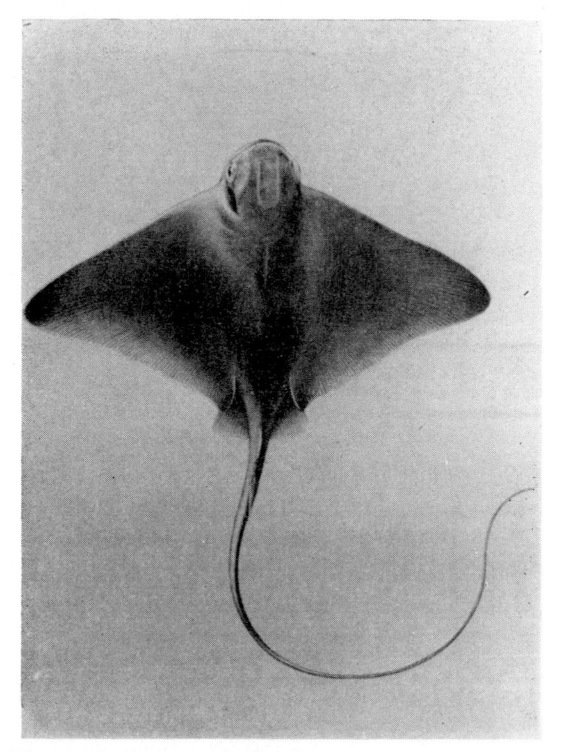

FIG. 4. California bat ray. *Myliobatis californicus* (Gill) (Shirao).

Urolophidae. Round Stingrays :
Urolophus aurantiacus Müller and Henle
Japan and Korea.
Urolophus halleri Cooper (Fig. 5)
Point Conception, California to Panama Bay.
Urolophus testaceus (Müller and Henle)
Queensland south to Victoria, Australia.

Venom Apparatus

The venom apparatus of stingrays is an integral part of the caudal appendage. The venom organs of stingrays have been divided into four anatomical types based upon their adaptability as a defense organ. This subject was discussed by Halstead and Bunker (1953).

1. *Gymnurid type* (Fig. 6). This is the most weakly-developed type of stingray venom apparatus. The caudal appendage in gymnurid rays are cylindrical, tapering, and greatly reduced in size. The sting is small, seldom exceeding 2.5 cm in length, and usually situated in the middle or proximal third of the tail. The striking ability of the organ is relatively feeble.

FIG. 5. Round stingray. *Urolophus halleri* Cooper (Shirao).

2. *Myliobatid type* (Fig. 6). The venom organs of myliobatid rays are better adapted as a striking organ than those found in gymnurid rays. The caudal appendage is cylindrical and tapers out to a long whip-like tail. The sting is generally situated on the proximal portion of the basal third of the tail and is moderate to large in size, ranging from about 5 to 12 cm or more in length. Although myliobatid rays can inflict serious wounds, the striking force of the sting is less than that of the dasyatid rays largely because of the proximal location of the sting on the caudal appendage.

3. *Dasyatid type* (Fig. 6). The venom organs of dasyatid rays are better adapted as a striking organ than are those of myliobatid rays. The caudal appendage is cylindrical and tapers out to a long whip-like tail. The sting in some species may be very large, attaining 37 cm or more in length, and is located in the distal portion of the basal or middle third of the tail. The more distal location of the sting improves the striking force of the sting.

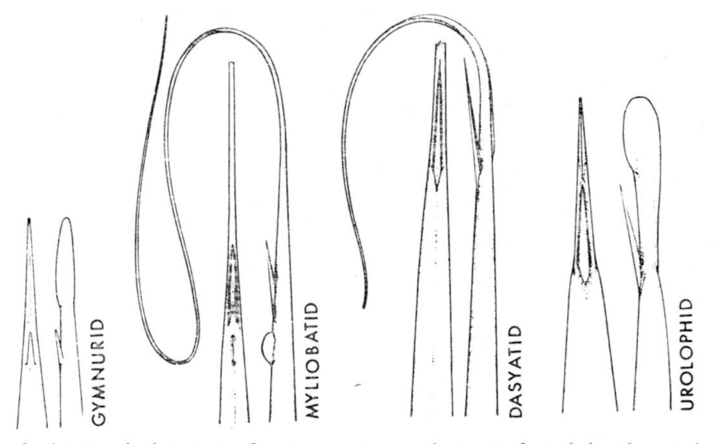

FIG. 6. Anatomical types of venom organs that are found in the various species of stingrays. The striking power of the ray varies according to the muscular development of the tail and the placement of the sting.

4. *Urolophid type* (Fig. 6). The venom organs of urolophid rays are probably the most highly developed of any of the sting rays. The caudal appendage is relatively short, very muscular, and is not produced as a whip-like structure, but rather the tail becomes compressed distal to the sting and forms a more or less distinct caudal fin. The sting is usually located in the middle or distal third of tail and moderate in size, seldom exceeding 5 cm in length. The powerful muscular structure of the tail and the distal location of the sting make this a highly efficient defensive weapon.

Although there is considerable variation in the morphology of the venom organs of various stingray species there is a basic pattern which all of the species examined thus far appear to follow. For the purpose of this review only a general description of the stingray sting will be given.

The venom apparatus of stingrays consists of a bilaterally retroserrate spine and its enveloping integumentary sheath. The spine is an elongate tapering structure that ends in an acute sagitate tip. The spine is composed of an inner core of vasodentine which is covered by a thin layer of enamel. It is firmly anchored in a dense collagenous network of the dermis on the dorsum of the caudal appendage. The dorsal surface of the spine is marked by a number of shallow longitudinal furrows. These furrows are usually more pronounced on the basal portion of the spine and disappear distally.

The serrate edges of the spine are termed the dentate margins. Medial to each dentate margin, on the ventral side, is a longitudinal groove, the ventrolateral-glandular groove. The grooves are separated from each other by the median ventral ridge of the spine. Contained within the grooves of an " unsheathed " or traumatized sting is a strip of gray tissue. The tissue lying within the ventrolateral glandular grooves consists of glandular epithelium and blood vessels. This is the primary venom producing area of the sting. In most stingray species there is a thickened wedge-shaped portion of the integument on the dorsum of the caudal appendage ventral to the sting which is known as the cuneiform area. Toxicological studies of the cuneiform integument indicate that the glandular cells of this area also secrete venom.

Microscopic examination of histological cross sections of an intact sting reveals that it is roughly diamond shape and consists of a broad T-shaped dentinal structure completely enveloped by a layer of integument. The integument is comprised of two layers. The inner layer, the dermis, consists of areolar connective tissue and vascular channels. The outer layer, the epidermis, is composed of modified squamous epithelium containing many glandular cells. A cross section of the ventrolateral-glandular groove has been termed the glandular triangle (Fig. 7). Glandular activity is generally most concentrated in the epidermis in the immediate vicinity of the ventro-

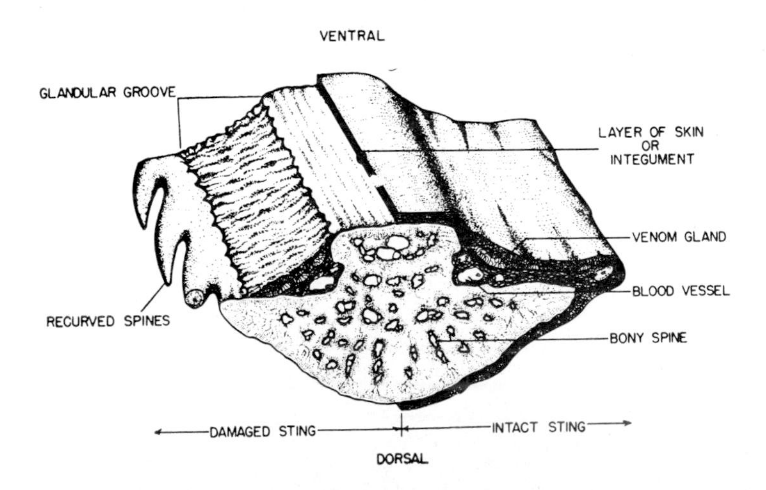

FIG. 7. Cross-section of a stingray sting showing both damaged and intact stings.

lateral-glandular grooves which is believed to be the principal site of venom production. There is no histological evidence of a venom duct. Venom production is by a holocrine type of lysis.

Pharmacology and Chemistry of the Venom

The only published account on the pharmacological properties of stingray venom is by Russell and van Harreveld (1954), who worked on the cardiovascular effects of the venom of the round stingray, *Urobatis halleri.* They found that in the smallest active concentrations the venom gives rise to vasodilation followed by vasoconstriction, or vasoconstriction without preliminary dilation. In larger and massive amounts the toxin evokes only vasoconstriction. These observations were noted in the large arteries and veins as well as in the smaller peripheral components of the vascular system. The venom has a direct effect on the heart. It provokes both an auricular and ventricular standstill which in turn were followed by contractions of lesser amplitude and slower rate. A new rhythm was evoked from a focus outside the sino-auricular node.

VENOMOUS CHIMAEROIDS

The members of the Order Chimaerae, which includes the ratfishes and elephantfishes, are a group of cartilagenous fishes having a single external gill opening on either side covered over by an opercular skin fold with cartilagenous supports leading to a common branchial chamber into which the true gill clefts open. Chimaeroids are more or less compressed laterally, tapering posteriorly to a slender tail. The snout is rounded or conical, extended as a long pointed beak, or bearing a curious hoe-shaped proboscis. The first dorsal is a large triangular-shaped fin edged by a strong sharp-pointed bony spine which serves as a venom apparatus. Only a single species has been reported as venomous in the Pacific area.

Species Reported as Venomous

Chimaeridae. Ratfish:

Hydrolagus colliei (Lay and Bennett) (Fig. 8)

Pacific coast of North America.

FIG. 8. Ratfish. *Hydrolagus colliei* (Lay and Bennett) (Shirao).

Venom Apparatus

The venom apparatus of chimaeroids consists of the dorsal spine, the glandular epithelium of the spine and connecting membrane, and the enveloping integumentary sheath. The mature spine is elongate, tapers to an acute point and is composed of a cartilaginous core covered by a sheath of vasodentine. In cross section the spine is roughly trigonal in outline with a pronounced anterior keel and a shallow posterior depression, termed the interdentate depression. Lying within this depression is a strip of soft, grayish, sparsely pigmented tissue, the glandular or venom-producing tissue. The spine is covered externally by a thin layer of integument which consists of two layers—an outer epidermis and an inner dermis. The epidermis is avascular, comprised of squamous epithelium and rests on an aceullar basement membrane. Scattered throughout this epithelium are large glandular cells, in addition to mucus cells, which give evidence of their secretory activity as evidenced by vacuolation, increased cytoplasmic area, and phantom nuclei (Halstead and Bunker, 1952).

Pharmacology and Chemistry of the Venom

Tissue extracts prepared from the glandular tissue of the spines of *Hydrolagus colliei* and injected introperitoneally into laboratory mice revealed in one series of tests mild agitation, paralysis of the hind legs, inactivity, erection of the hair, jerking motions of the body and death. Similar extracts prepared from the skin taken from the dorsum of the same fish failed to produce any symptoms. There is no other data available regarding the pharmacological or chemical nature of the venom.

CATFISHES

The suborder Siluroidea includes a group of fishes having a wide variety of sizes and shapes. Their body shape may vary from short to greatly elongate, or even eel-like. The head is extremely variable, sometimes very large, wide or depressed, again very small. The mouth is not protractile but the lips are sometimes greatly developed, usually with long barbels, generally with at least one pair from rudimentary maxillaries, often one or more pairs about the chin, and sometimes one from each pair of nostrils. The skin of these fishes is thick and slimy, or with bony plates. There is an absence of true scales. About one thousand species are included within this group, most of which are found in the fresh-water streams of the tropics, but a few species are marine. Considering the large number of catfish species amazingly little is known regarding the morphology of their venom organs or the nature of their venom. Most of the published literature on catfish venom organs deals with North American fresh-water species. Papers on these species have been published by Reed (1900, 1906, 1907, and 1924), and Halstead, Kuninobu and Hebard (1953). Tange (1953) has reported on the venom of the single Indo-Pacific form, *Plotosus lineatus*.

Species Reported as Venomous

Ariidae. Catfish:

Arius maculatus (Thunberg)
Philippines, Indonesia, China, India.

Osteogeneiosus militaris (Linnaeus)
Indonesia, India.

Bagridae. Catfish:

Mystus gulia (Hamilton-Buchanan)
Vietnam, Indonesia, India.

Pseudobagrus aurantiacus (Temminck and Schlegel)
Japan.

Clariidae. Catfish:

Clarias batrachus (Linnaeus)
Philippines, Indonesia, India.

Pimelodidae. Catfish:

Cnidoglanis megastomus (Valenciennes)
New South Wales, Australia.

Cnidoglanis nudiceps Günther
Arafura Sea, Australia.

Paraplotosus albilabris (Valenciennes)
Philippines, Malaya.

Plotosus lineatus (Thunberg) (Fig. 9)
Indo-Pacific region.

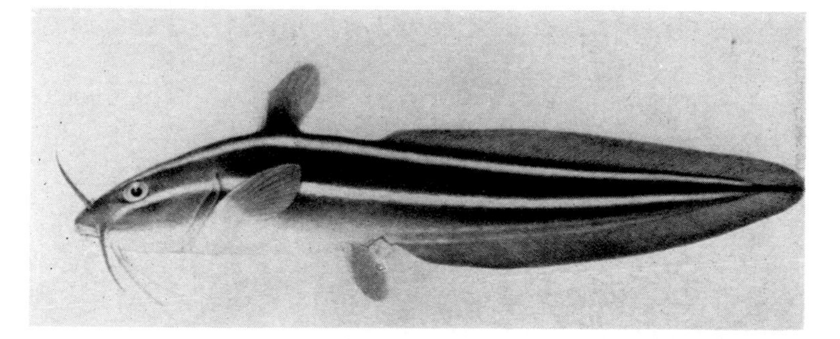

FIG. 9. Oriental catfish. *Plotosus lineatus* (Thunberg) (Shirao).

Siluridae. Catfish:

Parasilurus asotus (Linnaeus)
Japan, Korea, Manchuria and China.

Venom Apparatus

The venom apparatus of catfishes consists of the dorsal and pectoral stings and the axillary venom glands. The dorsal and pectoral spines are comprised of modified or coalescent soft rays which have become ossified, and so constructed that they can be be locked in the extended position at the will of the fish. The mature dorsal spine is a stoutly-elongate, compressed, tapered, slightly arched, osseous structure bearing a series of retrorse dentations along the anterior and posterior surfaces, and having an acute sagittate tip. The spine is generally enveloped by a thin layer of sparsely pigmented skin, the integumentary sheath, which is continuous with that of the soft-rayed portion of the fin. There is no external evidence of a venom gland. The shaft of the pectoral spine is similar to the dorsal spine in its general morphology.

Microscopic examination reveals that the level of the middle third, the sting may be divided into three distinct zones; a peripheral integumentary sheath, an intermediate osseous portion and a central canal. The integumentary sheath is comprised of a relative thick outer layer of epidermis and a thin layer of dermis. The glandular cells which comprise the venom gland are most concentrated at the anterolateral and posterolateral margins of the sting where they are sometimes clumped two or three cells deep within the epidermal layer. The venom glands of most of the catfish species that have been studied appear as a cellular sheet wedged between the pigment layer and the stratified squamous epithelium of the epidermis. The microscopic anatomy of the dorsal and pectoral stings are similar in appearance. The axillary pore, which is the outlet of the axillary gland, is located just below the vertical center of the posthumeral process of the cleithrum. The gland is enclosed within a capsule of fibrous connective tissue, and is divided into three or four lobes which are further subdivided into a variable number of lobules. The lobules are composed of large secretory cells. It is believed that this gland may contribute to the venom supplied to the pectoral stings in those species of catfishes in which the axillary gland is present.

Pharmacology and Chemistry of the Venom

One of the few published reports on the venom of a catfish is that by Toyoshima (1918) on *Plotosus lineatus.* Extracts were prepared from the stings of the catfish and injected intravenously, subcutaneously, and intramuscularly into rats, beavers, dogs, rabbits, sparrows, frogs, snakes, newts, carp, loaches, chickens and pigeons. Intravenous injections resulted in the immediate development of symptoms, consisting of musclar spasm, respiratory distress, and death. Similar results were obtained from intraperitoneal and subcutaneous injections. *Plotosus* was found to have both neurotoxic and hemotoxic properties. Bhimachar (1944) has reported similar findings for the venom of *Heteropneustes fossilis,* a fresh-water Indian catfish. The pharmacological and chemical properties of these venoms have not been described.

MORAY EELS

Brief mention should be made concerning the status of moray eels, members of the family Muraenidae, as venomous fishes. The meager amount of research that has been conducted on so-called " venomous eels " is concerned with the single European species, *Muraena helena* (Linnaeus), which is distributed along coastal areas of the eastern Atlantic Ocean and the Mediterranean Sea. Bottard (1889), Porta (1905) and Pawlowsky (1909) have discussed this species. Other species have bcen listed as venomous by modern authors, but their work is purely presumptive. The teeth of *M. helena* have been considered as constituting a venom apparatus from earliest times, but recent anatomical studies fail to show any evidence of venom glands in a large series of both European and Pacific muraenid eels that were examined.

SCORPIONFISHES

The vast family of Scorpaenidae closely resemble the sea basses from which they are distinguished by a suborbital stay which is present in the scorpionfishes. The suborbital stay joins the other bones of the head to form a coat of mail which covers the whole head. The excessive number of spines about the head are characteristic of the members of this family. Scorpionfishes vary greatly in their form and coloration. A few species may attain large size and many are considered to be valuable food fishes. Representatives of the family are widely distributed throughout all tropical and temperate seas, and several species occur in Arctic waters. The family Scorpaenidae, as the name implies, includes some of the most dangerous species of venomous fishes known.

The venomous members of the family Scorpaenidae can be classified into three basic types on the basis of the morphology of their venom organs: (1) *Pterois* or *zebrafish type*; (2) *Scorpaena* or *scorpionfish type*; and (3) *Synanceja* or the *stonefish type*.

Species Reported as Venomous

Scorpaenidae. Scorpionfishes:

I. Scorpionfishes having the *Pterois*-type of venom apparatus;

Dendrochirus brachypterus (Cuvier)

Hawaii, Samoa, Australia, Indonesia, Indian Ocean.

Dendrochirus zebra (Quoy and Gaimard)

Polynesia westward throughout the Indo-Pacific area.

Pterois antennata (Bloch)

Polynesia westward throughout the Indo-Pacific area and Indian Ocean.

Pterois lunulata (Schlegel)
Malaya, Philippines, Japan.
Pterois miles (Bennett)
Melanesia, Indian Ocean, Red Sea.
Pterois radiata Cuvier
Polynesia, Melanesia, Indian Ocean, Red Sea.
Pterois russelli Bennett
Philippines, Australia, Indonesia, Indian Ocean.
Pterois sphex Jordan and Evermann
Hawaii.
Pterois volitans (Linnaeus) (Fig. 10)
Polynesia westward throughout the Indo-Pacific region, China, Japan, Indian Ocean, Red Sea.

FIG. 10. Zebrafish. *Pterois volitans* (Linnaeus) (Shirao).

II. Scorpionfishes having the *Scorpaena*-type of venom apparatus:
Apistus carinatus (Bloch and Schneider)
Philippines, Australia, Indonesia, China, Japan, Indian Ocean.
Apistus cottoides Cuvier
Indonesia, New Zealand, China.
Apistus evolans Jordan and Starks
Japan.
Centropogon australis (White)
New South Wales and Queensland, Australia.
Gymnapistes marmorata (Cuvier)
Northern Territory and South Australia.
Hypodytes rubripinnis (Temminck and Schlegel)
Japan.
Notesthes robusta (Günther)
New South Wales and Queensland, Australia.

Scorpaena cardinalis Richardson
New South Wales and Queensland, Australia, Tasmania.
Scorpaena guttata Girard (Fig. 11)
Central California south into the Gulf of Calfornia.

FIG. 11. Scorpionfish. *Scorpaena guttata* Girard (Shirao).

Scorpaena izensis Jordan and Starks
Japan.
Scorpaena neglecta Temminck and Schlegel
Japan.
Scorpaena plumieri mystes Jordan and Starks
Pacific coast of Mexico, Central America to Peru.
Scorpaenodes littoralis (Tanaka)
Japan.
Scorpaenopsis cirrhosa (Thunberg)
Polynesia, southern Japan, Indonesia, Philippines, Red Sea.
Scorpaenopsis diabolus (Cuvier)
Polynesia, Melanesia, Australia, Indonesia.
Scorpaenopsis gibbosa (Bloch and Schneider)
Polynesia, Micronesia, Philippines, Indonesia, Indian Ocean.
Sebastapistes bynoensis (Richardson)
Polynesia, Micronesia, Red Sea.
Sebasticus marmoratus (Cuvier)
Philippines, China Sea, Japan.
Sebastodes inermis (Cuvier)
Japan.
Sebastodes joyneri (Günther)
Japan.

Sebastolobus macrochir (Günther)
Japan.
Snyderina yamanokami Jordan and Starks
Japan.

III. Scorpionfishes having the *Synanceja*-type of venom apparatus:
Choridactylus multibarbis Richardson
Polynesia, Philippines, China, India.
Erosa erosa (Langsdorf)
Japan.
Inimicus barbatus (De Vis)
Queensland, Australia.
Inimicus didactylus (Pallas)

FIG. 12. Deadly stonefish. *Synanceja horrida* (Linnaeus) (Arita).

Melansia, Philippines, Indonesia, Malaya.
Inimicus filamentosus (Cuvier)
Polynesia, Indonesia.
Inimicus japonicus (Cuvier)
Japan.
Leptsosynanceja asteroblepa (Richardson)
Indonesia.
Minous adamsi Richardson
Philippines, Japan, India.
Minous inermis Alcock
Philippines, Japan, India.
Minous monodactylus (Bloch and Schneider)
Indo-Pacific area, Japan, China.
Synanceja horrida (Linnaeus) (Fig. 12)
Philippines, Indonesia, Australia, China, India.
Synanceja verrucosa Bloch and Schneider
Micronesia, Philippines, Indonesia, Indian Ocean, Red Sea.

Venom Apparatus

The venom organs of scorpionfishes vary markedly from one genus to the next. An analysis of these venom organs reveals that they can be divided into three groups. A comparison of the venom organs of characteristic genera of these groups appears in Table 1.

TABLE 1.* COMPARISON OF THE VENOM ORGANS OF *Pterois*, *Scorpaena*, AND *Synanceja*

Structure	*Pterois*	*Scorpaena*	*Synanceja*
Fin spines	Elongate, slender	Moderately long, heavy	Short, stout
Integumentary sheath	Thin	Moderately thick	Very thick
Venom glands	Small-sized, well-developed	Moderate-sized, very well-developed	Very large, highly developed
Venom duct	Not evident	Not evident	Well-developed

I. *Pterois-type of venom apparatus.* Members of the genera *Pterois* and *Dendrochirus* possess a venom apparatus consisting of 13 dorsal spines, 3

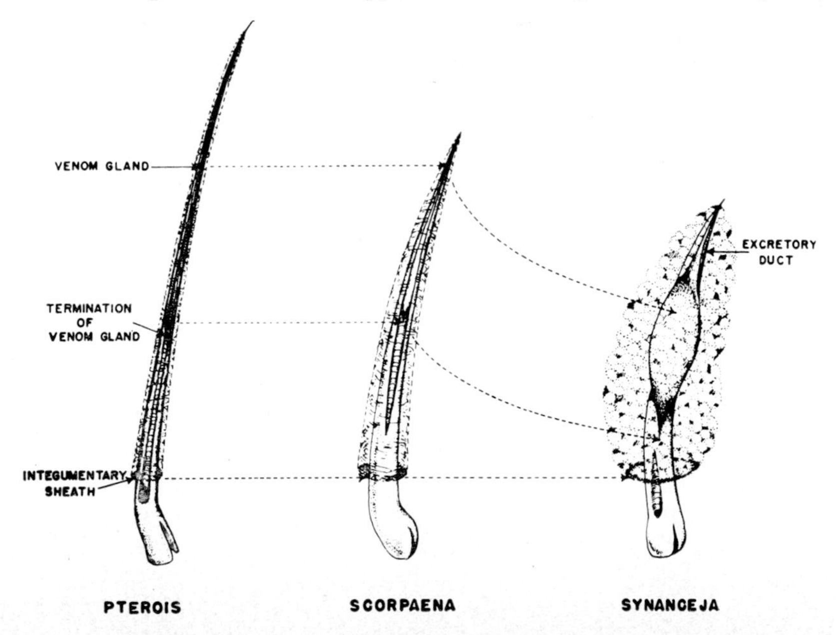

FIG. 13. Showing a comparison of the three types of scorpionfish dorsal stings.

*From *Dangerous Marine Animals*. The authors are indebted to the Cornell Maritime Press for the use of the illustration.

anal spines, 2 pelvic spines and their associated venom glands which are enveloped in their respective integumentary sheaths. The integumentary sheaths on these genera are gaily colored, having bands of white alternating with dark red to black. The light-colored areas are relatively transparent in preserved specimens, and through them can be observed, on either side of the spine, a slender, elongate, fusiform strand of grey or pinkish tissue lying within each of the glandular grooves. The tissue within these grooves is the glandular epithelium or venom-producing portion of the sting (Fig. 13). Halstead, Chitwood and Modglin (1955) found through microscopic examination of cross sections of venom glands that a cluster of large polygonal glandular cells with pinkish-grey, finely granular cytoplasm was located in the dermal layer within its anterolateral glandular grooves. The large venom-producing cells have a pinnate, heart-shaped arrangement, and vary greatly in size and morphology.

II. *Scorpaena-type of venom apparatus.* Members of the genera *Apistus, Centropogon, Gymnapistes, Hypodytes, Notesthes, Scorpaena, Scorpaenodes, Scorpaenopsis, Sebastapistes, Sebastodes, Sebastolobus* and *Snyderina* have venom organs which closely resemble each other in their morphology. The venom apparatus of *Scorpaena guttata*, the California scorpionfish, which is typical of this group, includes 12 dorsal spines, 3 anal spines, 2 pelvic spines, their associated venom glands and their enveloping integumentary sheaths (Figs. 11, 13). If the integumentary sheath is removed, a slender, elongate, fusiform strand of grey or pinkish tissue can be observed lying within the glandular grooves on either side of the spine. The spines are moderately long and heavy in comparison with those of *P. volitans.* The microscopic anatomy of the venom glands, described by Halstead, Chitwood, and Modglin (1955), is similar to that of *P. volitans.*

III. *Synanceja-type of venom apparatus.* Members of the genera *Choridactylus, Erosa, Inimicus, Leptosynanceja, Minous* and *Synanceja* have venom organs which closely resemble each other in their morphology. The venom apparatus of *Synanceja horrida* the stonefish, which is typical of this group, includes 13 dorsal spines, 3 anal spines, 2 pelvic spines, their associated venom glands, and their thick warty enveloping integumentary sheaths. The fin spines are relatively short, stout, and straight. Extending throughout the entire length of the spine, one on either side, are two anterolateral-glandular grooves. The venom glands appear as two large masses, bilaterally situated, attached by tough strands of connective tissue to the middle or distal thirds of the spine. The distal ends of the glands terminate in duct-like structures lying within the glandular grooves. These ducts extend to the distal tips of the spine. The microscopic anatomy of the venom gland of *Synanceja* differs quite markedly from either *Pterois* or *Scorpaena.* The spines in cross section appear as an inverted " T ". Packed between the vertical and horizontal limbs of the " T " is a circular mass of round and oval-shaped, closely packed, variably-sized, granular, tan bodies. These bodies have definite outlines suggesting cell membranes. Nuclei are absent, but there are " ghost-like " membranes suggesting nuclear membranes. These bodies are enclosed within this area by a thin sheet of dense fibrous connective tissue which extends between the distal tips of the vertical and horizontal limbs of the " T "-shaped dentinal structure, thus forming a closed duct. Many of the bodies are filled with brown granules of about 15μ in their greatest dimension. Scattered among the bodies are irregular patches of yellowish, homogeneous, amorphous secretion. Halstead, Chitwood and Modglin (1956), expressed the belief that these clusters of bodies are the areas of venom production.

Pharmacology and Chemistry of the Venom

The pharmacological investigations of Saunders (1959) suggest that the venoms of *Pterois volitans*, *Scorpaena guttata* and *Synanceja horrida* produce similar effects in experimental animals. The venom contains considerable quantities of protein, and the active material is non-dialyzable and heat labile, indicating that it is either a protein or is in close association with proteins. Moderate doses in rabbits resulted in hypotension, increased respiratory rate, and myocardial injury. Fatal doses produced respiratory arrest when the blood pressure declined to very low values. The mean LD_{50} of freshly prepared extracts injected intravenously into mice was 180μg of protein per kg and the mean lethal dose in anesthetized rabbits was approximately 15μg of protein per kg. There was found to be little change in potency in venom that had been stored for almost a year at $-20\,^{\circ}$C.

TOADFISHES

The Batrachoididae, or toadfishes, are small bottom fishes which inhabit the warmer waters of the coasts of America, Europe, Africa and India. Only two species have been incriminated as venomous in the Pacific area. Toadfishes present a somewhat repulsive appearance with their broad depressed heads and large mouths. Most batrachoids are marine, but some are estuarine or entirely fluviatile, ascending rivers for great distances. They may be found hiding in crevices, in burrows, under rocks, debris, in seaweed, or buried in the mud or sand. Contact with their dorsal or opercular spines can produce painful wounds.

Species Reported as Venomous

Batrachoididae. Toadfishes:

Thalassophryne dowi (Jordan and Gilbert)

Pacific coast of Central America, Punta Arenas, Costa Rica to Panama.

Thalassophryne reticulata (Günther) (Fig. 14)
Pacific coast of Central America.

Venom Apparatus

The venom apparatus of toadfishes consists of two dorsal fin spines, two opercular spines, and their associated venom glands. In the case of *Thalassophryne dowi*, which can be considered as typical of the group, there are two dorsal spines which are enclosed together within a single integumentary sheath. The dorsal spines are slender and hollow, slightly curved, and terminate in acute tips. At the base and tip of each spine is an opening through which the venom passes. The base of each dorsal spine is

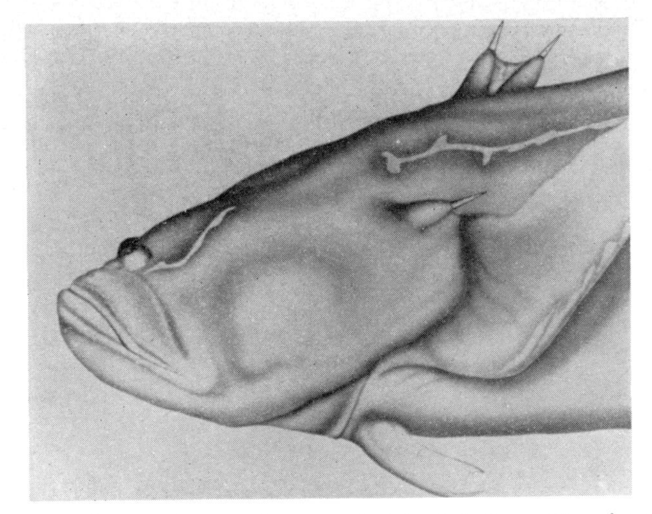

FIG. 14. Toadfish. *Thalassophryne reticulata* Günther (Kreusinger).

surrounded by a glandular mass from which the venom is produced. Each gland empties into the base of its respective spine. The operculum is also highly specialized as a defensive organ for the introduction of venom. The horizontal limb of the operculum is a slender hollow bone which curves slightly, and terminates in an acute tip. Openings are present at each end of the spine for the passage of venom. With the exception of the extreme distal tip, the entire opercular spine is encased within a glistening, whitish, puriform mass. The broad rounded portion of this mass is situated at the base of the spine, and tapers rapidly as the tips of the spine is approached. The pyriform mass consists of a tough sac-like outer covering of connective tissue in which is contained a soft, granular, gelatinous-like substance having the appearance of fine tapioca. This mass is the venom gland. The gland empties into the base of the hollow opercular spine which serves as a duct.

Microscopic examination of the venom glands shows strands of aerolar connective tissue, large distended polygonal cells filled with finely granular secretion, and vascular channels. In some instances the polygonal cells will appear to have undergone complete lysis and there remain only areas of amorphous secretion. The microscopic anatomy of the dorsal and opercular venom glands are essentially the same.

Pharmacology and Chemistry of the Venom

The only published reports on toadfish venom are those by Froes (1933). Injections of the venom into guinea pigs and chicks resulted in mydriasis, ascites, paralyses, necrosis about the injection site, convulsions and death. The author believes that the venom of *Thalassophryne* has both proteolytic and neurotoxic properties.

SURGEONFISHES

The surgeonfishes are a group of reef fishes which are characterized by the presence of a single sharp, lance-like, folding spine, or pair of fixed spines on the side of the caudal peduncle (Fig. 15). When the fish becomes excited,

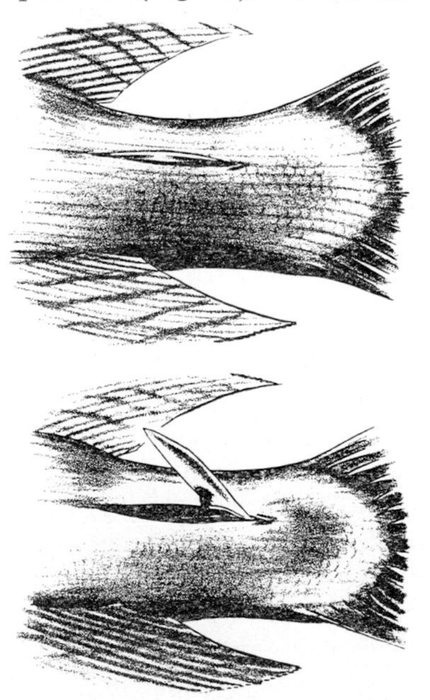

FIG. 15. Tail of the surgeonfish, *Acanthurus*. Top: Caudal peduncular spine in the contracted position. Bottom: Caudal peduncular spine in the extended position.

the folded spine, whose point is directed anteriorly, can be extended at right angles from the body of the fish. With a quick lashing movement of the tail and the extended spine, large surgeonfishes are able to inflict a deep and painful wound. The venomous properties of the caudal spines of surgeonfishes has been the subject of discussion by Beebe (1926), Souche (1935), Harry (1953), Monrod (1959), and Randall (1959). The symptomatology of stings inflicted by certain species of surgeonfishes strongly suggests the presence of a true venom apparatus in at least some species. However, there is insufficient morphological and toxicological evidence at this time to warrant a firm conclusion regarding the matter.

Tange (1955) has found that the dorsal, pelvic and anal spines of *Xesurus scalprum* are associated with venom glands. This was the first report of a venom apparatus in the fin spines of a surgeonfish.

Species Reported as Venomous

Acanthuridae. Surgeonfishes:

Acanthurus bariene Lesson
Tropical Indo-Pacific.

Acanthurus lineatus (Linnaeus)
Central Pacific to East Africa.

Acanthurus triostegus (Linnaeus)
Indo-Pacific.

Ctenochaetus striatus (Quoy and Gaimard)
Tropical Indo-Pacific to the Red Sea.

Ctenochaetus strigosus (Bennett)
Indo-Pacific.

Prionurus laticlavius (Valenciennes)
Tropical eastern Pacific.

Xesurus scalprum (Cuvier and Valenciennes)
Japan and Ryukyu Islands.

Venom Apparatus

The morphology of the venom apparatus of the spines of the caudal peduncle, if present, has not been described in the published literature in a conclusive manner.

According to Tange (1955) the venom apparatus of the fin spines of *Xesurus scalprum* consists of 9 dorsal spines, 2 pelvic spines, and 3 anal spines, and their associated venom glands. The dorsal fin spines, which are morphologically representative of the others, are elongate, slightly arched in the cranial direction, and terminate distally in a sharp point. The anterior surface of each spine bears a median ridge which contributes to the formation of the two anterolateral-glandular grooves, situated one on either side of the ridge. The venom glands lie within these grooves. The grooves are well-developed in the proximal portion of the spine, but become progressively shallower as they approach the distal tip of the spine where they completely disappear. The venom gland is elongate and prismatic in shape becoming attenuate at either end. The distal end of the gland terminates just proximal to the spine tip, and the proximal end of the gland extends to about the junction of the middle and distal third of the spine. The length of each venom gland varies somewhat according to the individual sting.

Microscopic examination of the sting in cross section reveals an inverted " T "-shaped dentinal structure, with the venom glands situated in the antero-lateral-glandular grooves on either side of the median dentinal ridge. The spine is surrounded by an integumentary sheath which is similar to that found in *Scorpaena* and *Pterois*. The glandular cells are irregular in their grouping, but are clumped together. The glandular cells vary in appearance from ovoid, to stick-like, or polygonal in outline. The glandular cells are relatively small, numbering 10–40, and measure 12–18μ by 23–33μ. The cytoplasm of the cells is acidophilic and vacuolated. The vacuoles are frequently observed to contain many round colloidal bodies of varying sizes. The nuclei of the cells are excentric in outline and contain a minimal amount of chromatin. Most cells are uninuclear. There is no evidence of a glandular duct.

Pharmacology and Chemistry of the Venom

Unknown.

JACKS OR POMPANOS

Carangids are medium or large-sized, metallic, silvery or golden-colored fishes which are usually adapted for fast swimming. Members of this group are characterized by the presence of two free spines preceding the anal fin and four to eight generally weak spines in the first dorsal fin. Most of the members of the family have the straight portion of the lateral line armed with scutes. Several species have been reported as possessing venomous spines, but work by Kobert (1902), Engelsen (1922) and Phillips and Brady (1953) offer little supportive morphological or toxicological data on the subject.

Species Reported as Venomous

Oligoplites saurus (Bloch and Schneider)

Eastern Tropical Pacific.

Trachurops crumenophthalmus (Bloch)

Circumtropical.

Venom Apparatus

Not described.

Pharmacology and Cehmistry of the Venom

Unknown.

RABBITFISHES

The siganids are a group of spiny-rayed fishes which closely resemble the surgeonfishes in their outward appearance. The differ from all other fishes in that the first and last rays of the pelvic fins are spinous. Rabbitfishes are of moderate size, usually valued as food, and abound about reefs from Polynesia to the Red Sea. Despite the fact that numerous authors have reported on the venomous properties of this group very few have attempted to describe the actual venom organs.

Species Reported as Venomous

Siganidae Rabb itfishes:

Signaus fuscescens (Houttuyn)
Indo-Pacific.

Siganus lineatus. (Valenciennes)
Ryuku Islands, Philippines, Melanesia, Australia.

Siganus puellus (Schlegel) (Fig. 16)
Philippines, Indonesia, Micronesia, Melanesia.

Siganus spinus (Linnaeus)
Indo-Pacific to the Red Sea.

Siganus sutor (Valenciennes)
Philippines to the Indian Ocean.

FIG. 16. Rabbitfish. *Siganus puellus* (Schlegel) (from Hiyama).

Venom Apparatus

Our knowledge of the venom organs of siganids is based largely on the observations of Bottard (1889) who described incompletely the venom apparatus of *Siganus lineatus*, and Amemiya (1921) and Tange (1955) who described the venom organs of *S. fuscescens*. The following description is based on the latter species.

The venom apparatus of *Siganus* consists of 13 dorsal, 4 pelvic, and 7 anal spines, and their associated venom glands. The dorsal spine is slightly curved, with the convexity pointing anteriorly. The distal end is sharp, and the proximal one thickened, and divided into two asymmetrical condyles.

The median line of the anterior surface of the spine is quite pronounced. A groove extends along both sides of the median line for almost the entire length of the spine. This paramedian groove or anterolateral-glandular groove is very deep, particularly so in the distal one-third, where the venom gland is located. The gland is thick, elongate, and prismatic in form, slowly becoming attenuate both proximally and distally. The venom gland is comprised of very large cells, similar to those found in scorpaenids. There is no evidence of a glandular duct.

Pharmacology and Chemistry of the Venom

Unknown.

STAR-GAZERS

Uranoscopids are a group of small carnivorous, bottom-dwelling, marine fishes. They are characterized by having a large cuboid head, an almost vertical mouth with fringed lips, and an elongate, conic, subcompressed body. Their eyes are small and anteriorly situated on the flat upper surface of the head. Star-gazers are of medical importance by virtue of their venomous cleithral, or shoulder spines.

Species Reported as Venomous

Uranoscopidae. Star-gazers:

Uranoscopus duvali (Bottard)

Indo-Pacific.

Uranoscopus japonicus (Houttuyn)

Philippines, Japan, China, Southern Korea, Malaya.

Venom Apparatus

The only published description of the venom apparatus of *Uranoscopus* is by Bottard (1889). The description is incomplete, but is presently being re-described by the senior author. The venom apparatus of *Uranoscopus* consists of the two cleithral or shoulder spines, situated one on either side, their associated venom glands, and their enveloping sheaths. There is no evidence of any venomous fin spines. There are no data presently available regarding the microscopic anatomy of the venom gland.

Pharmacology and Chemistry of the Venom

Unknown.

MISCELLANEOUS FISHES REPORTED AS VENOMOUS

The following fish families have been reported as containing venomous species. However, morphological and toxicological data are too meager to arrive at any conclusions as to the exact nature of their venom apparatus.

Chaetodontidae—Butterflyfishes.

Histiopteridae—Buglerfishes.
Holocentridae—Squirrelfishes.
Lophiidae—Anglerfishes.
Lutjanidae—Snappers.
Scatophagidae—Spadefishes.
Serranidae—Seabasses.

CLINICAL CHARACTERISTICS OF VENOMOUS FISH STINGS

Venomous fish injuries vary according to the causative agent, type of venom apparatus involved, nature and quantity of the venom introduced into the wound, mechanical trauma produced, the area of the body involved, and the physical condition of the patient. Stingrays and catfishes frequently produce severe lacerations because of their retroserrate fin spines. Lacerations of this type may result in the surrounding tissues becoming severely traumatized, swollen and infected in addition to the damages produced directly by the venom. Wounds from most other types of venomous fishes are of the puncture-wound type. The character and intensity of the pain are variable. The pain may amount to only a prick or stinging sensation or it may be intense, causing the victim to cry out in extreme anguish and resulting in loss of consciousness. Stingray, oriental catfish, scorpionfish, zebrafish, and stonefish stings are said to be especially severe. Stonefish wounds can be very dangerous, resulting in numbness about the area of the wound, paralysis of the limb, sloughing of the tissues about the wound site, delirium, cardiac failure, convulsions and death. The most common findings in fish stings are swelling, redness, and cyanosis in the area about the wound. Shock and secondary infections, together with a variety of more generalized symptoms, are not uncommon.

TREATMENT OF VENOMOUS FISH STINGS

The treatment of venomous fish stings is concerned with the alleviation of pain, combating the effects of the venom, and the prevention of secondary infection. Whenever possible bleeding should be encouraged, and particularly so in puncture wounds. It is desirable to irrigate the wound when possible to do so. The injured member should be soaked in hot water for 30 min to 1 hr. The water should be maintained at as a high a temperature as the victim can tolerate without injury. Infiltration of the tissues about the wound with 0.5 to 2 per cent procaine has been used with good results. Demerol may be required to control the pain. Supportive therapy, antibiotics, and a course of tetanus antitoxin may be required. An antivenin for stonefish stings has recently been developed at the Commonwealth Serum Laboratories, Department of Health, Parkville, Victoria, Australia. This is the only fish antivenin that has been developed to date and is reputed to be efficacious in treating stonefish stings.

ACKNOWLEDGEMENT

The authors are grateful to the Cornell Maritime Press for permission to republish illustrations presented in this paper.

REFERENCES

AMEMIYA, I. 1921. On the structure of the poison sting of Aigo (*Siganus fuscescens*). *Suisan Gakkai Ho.* **3** (3), 196.

BEEBE, W. 1926. *The arcturus adventure.* New York: G. P. Putnam.

BHIMACHAR, B. S. 1944. Poison glands in the pectoral spines of two *Heteropnuestes fossilis* (Bloch) and *Plotosus arab* (Forsk.), with remarks on the nature of the venom. *Proc. Indian Acad. Sci.*, Ser. B, **19**, 65.

BOTTARD, A. 1889. *Les Poissons Venimeaux.* Paris: Octave Doin.

ENGELSEN, H. 1922. Om giftfish og giftige fisk. *Nord, Hyg. Tidskrift.* **3**, 316.

EVANS, H. M. 1921. The poison organs and venoms of venomous fish. *Brit. Med.* **2** (3174), 690.

EVANS, H. M. 1923. The defensive spines of fishes, living and fossil, and the glandular structure in connection therewith, with observations on the nature of the fish venoms. London: *Philosoph. Trans. Roy. Soc.*, Ser. B, **212**, 1.

EVANS, H. M. 1943. *Sting-fish and seafarer.* London: Faber and Faber.

FROES, H. P. 1933. Peixes toxiforos do Brasil. *Bahia Med.* **4**, 69.

HALSTEAD, B. W. 1959. *Dangerous marine animals.* Cambridge, Maryland: Cornell Maritime Press.

HALSTEAD, B. W. and BUNKER, N. C. 1952. The venom apparatus of the ratfish *Hydrolagus colliei. Copeia* (3), 128.

HALSTEAD, B. W. and BUNKER, N. C. 1953. Stingray attacks and their treatment. *Am. J. Trop. Med. Hyg.* **2** (1), 115.

HALSTEAD, B. W., CHITWOOD, M. J. and MODGLIN, F. R. 1955. The venom apparatus of the California Scorpionfish, *Scorpaena guttata* Girard. *Trans. Am. Micrscop. Soc.* **74** (2), 145.

HALSTEAD, B. W., CHITWOOD, M. J. and MODGLIN, F. R. 1955. Stonefish stings, and the venom apparatus of *Synanceja horrida* (Linnaeus). *Trans. Am. Micrscop. Soc.* **75** (4), 381.

HALSTEAD, B. W., CHITWOOD, M. J. and MODGLIN, F. R. 1955. The anatomy of the venom apparatus of the zebrafish, *Pterois volitans* (Linnaeus). *Anat. Rec.* **122** (3), 317.

HALSTEAD, B. W., KUNINOBU, L. S. and HEBARD, H. G. 1953. Catfish stings and the venom apparatus of the Mexican catfish, *Galeichthys felis* (Linnaeus). *Trans. Am. Micrscop. Soc.* **72** (4), 297.

HARRY, R. R. 1953. Ichthyological field data of Raroia Atoll, Tuamotu Archipelago. *Atoll Res. Bull., Nat. Res. Council* (18), 151.

KOBERT, R. 1902. Über Giftfische und Fischgifte. *Med. Woche.* **19**, 199; **20**, 209; **21**, 221.

MONROD, T. 1959. Notes sur l'épine latero-caudale et la queue de l'*Acanthurus moroviae. Bull. Inst. Franc Afrique Noire* **21**, Ser. A. (2), 710.

PAWLOWSKY, E. N. 1909. Contribution to the question of poisonous skin glands of certain fishes. *Trav. Soc. Imp. Nat., St. Petersburg* **40** (1), 109.

PHILLIPS, C. and BRADY, W. H. 1953. *Sea Pests: Poisonous or Harmful Sea Life of Florida and the West Indies.* Miami: Univ. Miami Press.

PORTA, A. 1905. Ricerche anatomiche sull'apparecchio velenifero de alcuni pesci. *Anat. Anz.* **26**, 232.

RANDALL, J. E. 1959. Report of a caudal-spine wound from the surgeonfish *Acanthurus lineatus* in the Society Islands. *Wasmann J. Biol.* **17** (2), 245.

REED, H. D. 1900. The structure of the poison glands of *Schilbeodes gyrinus*. *Proc. Amer. Assoc. Advanc. Sci.* 49th meeting: 232.

REED, H. D. 1907. The poison glands of *Noturus* and *Schilbeodes*. *Amer. Natur.* **41**, 553–566, 5 figs.

REED, H. D. 1924. The morphology of the dermal glands in Nematognathous fishes. *Zschr. Morph. u. Anthrop.* **24**, 227.

SOUCHE, G. 1935. Contribution à l'étude des épines de l'*Acanthurus chirurgus* Bloch. *Bull. Stat. Biol. d'Arachon, Univ. Bordeaux* **32**, 31.

TANGE, Y. 1953. Beitrag zur Kenntnis der Morphologie des Giftapparates bei den Japahischen Fischen, nebst Bemerkungen über dessen Giftigkeit. II. Über den Giftapparat bei *Pterois lunulata* Temminck et Schlegel. *Yokohoma Med. Bull.* **4** (3), 178.

TANGE, Y. 1955. Beitrag zur Kenntnis der Morphologie des Giftapparates bei den Japanischen Fischen. XI. Über den Giftapparat bei *Siganus fuscescens* (Houttuyn). *Yokohoma Med. Bull.* **6** (2), 115.

TANGE, Y. 1955. Beitrag zur Kenntnis der Morphologie des Giftapparates bei den Japanischen Fischen. XII. Über den Giftapparat bei *Xexurus scalprum* (Cuvier et Valenciennes). *Yokohoma Med. Bull.* **6** (3), 171.

TANGE, Y. 1957. Beitrag zur Kenntnis der Morphologie des Giftapparates bei den Japanischen Fischen. XVI. Zusammenfassende Betrachtung über den Giftapparat. *Yokohama Med. Bull.* **8** (1), 62.

TOYOSHIMA, T. Serological study of toxin of the fish *Plotosus anguillaris* Lacepede. *J. Japan Protozool. Soc.* **7** (1–5), 45–270.

MARINE BIOTOXINS. III.
THE EXTRACTION AND PARTIAL PURIFICATION OF CIGUATERA TOXIN FROM *LUTJANUS BOHAR* (FORSKÅL); USE OF SILICIC ACID CHROMATOGRAPHY

DONALD W. HESSEL*

THE toxic substance or group of closely-related substances responsible for the ciguatera-type of fish poisoning has never been isolated, purified, and precisely defined chemically. This paper reports on the fractionation of a crude toxic extract from the somatic muscle of *Lutjanus bohar* (Forskål), the red snapper, a species of fish frequently implicated in ciguatera intoxications.

METHODS

Materials

The red snapper muscle used in this investigation was from the same batch as that reported previously by Hessel (1961). The methanol was reagent grade material distilled through a 1-meter column packed with coiled stainless steel ribbon. The anhydrous ether, also reagent grade, was used without further purification. The silicic acid adsorbent, Mallinckrodt, 100 mesh, " Suitable for chromatography by the method of Ramsey and Patterson ", was activated by heating at 110 °C for 14 hr. Storage was in jars closed with tightly fitting screw tops.

Bioassay

As a biological test for the determination of toxicity, the frog sciatic nerve test of Hessel *et al.* (1960) was employed. The basic action potential for a nerve was considered to be the average of three readings taken periodically after the nerve had been placed in the test emulsion, the first reading being taken after the nerve had been bathed in the emulsion for a few seconds. The next two readings were made at 1 min intervals. In a limited number of cases, particularly with highly toxic extracts, the action potential began to decrease immediately upon placement of the nerve in the test solution. In

*Bio Laboratories, 1742 D Street, San Bernardino, California.

these cases the basic action potential was considered to be that of the untreated nerve.

Basic Extraction and Low Temperature Precipitation Procedures

These were conducted as previously described by Hessel (1961).

Pretreatment with Silicic Acid

Previous chromatographic work of Hessel (1961) indicated that ciguatera toxin, when once adsorbed on silicic acid, could not be removed by anhydrous ether. Based upon this information a procedure for rapidly accomplishing a further purification of the crude toxin resulting from the low temperature precipitation step has been worked out. In this procedure an anhydrous ether solution of the toxic extract is added to a slurry of silicic acid and anhydrous ether. The mixture is then suction filtered on a sintered glass filter (medium porosity) and washed several times with anhydrous ether. The toxin is than stripped from the silicic acid by washing the silicic acid with several portions of ether-methanol, 1 : 1, v/v. Removal of the solvent on a rotary evaporator recovers the toxin.

In a typical application 8.4 g of silicic acid was made into a slurry with 21 ml of anhydrous ether (tap water cooling and slow addition of ether). The silicic acid was allowed to settle and the excess ether was withdrawn with a medicine dropper. To the slurry was added 8.4 ml of anhydrous ether containing 2.106 g of extract from the basic extraction and low temperature precipitation steps. A small portion of ether (4.2 ml) was used to wash out the sample flask. This wash was also added to the slurry. The mixture was swirled to insure thorough mixing, allowed to stand for a few moments, and then suction filtered on a sintered glass filter of medium porosity. The silicic acid was washed with stirring on the filter with five portions of anhydrous ether (8.4 ml each). The filtrate was discarded. The toxic material was then desorbed from the silicic acid with one 30 ml portion of ether-methanol, 1 : 1, v/v (no stirring of silicic acid), and five 13 ml portions (with stirring). Removal of the solvent from the filtrate on a rotary evaporator produced 330.5 mg of a dark yellow, viscous oil—a yield of 0.13 per cent from 250 g of red snapper muscle.

Silicic Acid Chromatography

Forty-one grams of silicic acid was made into a slurry under tap water cooling by the slow addition of 103 ml of anhydrous ether. The column, 40 cm × 21 mm, was fitted with a sintered glass disk at the bottom and a side tubulature near the top for pressurization. About 40 ml of anhydrous ether was poured into the column and the silicic acid slurry added rapidly through a funnel with a stem extension that ended near the sintered plate and below the surface of the added ether. The funnel was removed and the excess ether run through under 3 psig of nitrogen. Periodically the sides of the column were tapped with a small wooden hammer to aid in settling the adsorbent and in eliminating air bubbles. After most of the excess ether had been run through, a disk of filter paper (presoaked in ether to eliminate air) was carefully placed on top of the silicic acid; the disk was held down by a small ring of copper wire. The height of the adsorbent column was 18.6 cm. When the level of the excess ether had just reached the top of the silicic acid, 62 ml of anhydrous ether for washing was added to the column and run through under 4 psig N_2. At the completion of the washing the extract from the pretreatment step (330.5 mg representing 250 g of red snapper muscle),

TABLE 1. ETHER–METHANOL SOLVENT SYSTEMS USED TO FRACTIONATE CRUDE CIGUATERA TOXIN ON SILICIC ACID

Solution	Volume ratio Ether-Methanol	Volume (ml)
A	39 : 1	154
B	19 : 1	92
C	37 : 3	123
D	9 : 1	92
E	22 : 3	62
F	43 : 7	62
G	21 : 4	62
H	41 : 9	62
I	4 : 1	62
J	7 : 3	123

dissolved in 3 ml of anhydrous ether, was carefully added to the column by means of a medicine dropper. The sample was run on to the column under 4 psig N_2. Three ml of anhydrous ether was used to wash out the sample flask and to wash down the sides of the column; this also was run on to the silicic acid. The sample band width was about 5 mm. The column was then thoroughly washed with 123 ml of anhydrous ether under 4 psig N_2 and the eluate discarded. Development was then begun.

During the development, the room temperature was maintained fairly constant by a mechanically refrigerated air conditioner. There was, however, a slow increase in the room temperature. During the first half of the development the temperature averaged 24.8 $\pm$ 0.3 °C and during the second half 25.7 $\pm$ 0.1 °C. The extremes were 24.1 °C and 26.0 °C. Flow rate was maintained between 1.4 and 1.7 ml/min by the application of nitrogen pressure—4 psig through fraction 14 and 5 psig for the remainder of the development. All solvents were added through a separatory funnel attached to the top of the column. This funnel was pressurized during solvent addition, and at no time was the pressure in the column released. To follow the course of the development and to locate bands of material on the column, the column was periodically examined in visible and ultraviolet light (long wavelength).

The solvents used for development are listed in Table 1.

The first and last fractions (1 and 54) contained all the material removed from the column by solvents A plus B and J respectively. Fractions 2–53 each represented a 10 ml aliquot of the other solvents.

Solvent was removed from each fraction by use of a rotary evaporator operated at a pressure of 20 mm Hg; a water bath for heating was maintained at 50 °C. Storage of fractions was at −20 °C.

RESULTS

The fractions collected are shown in Fig. 1.

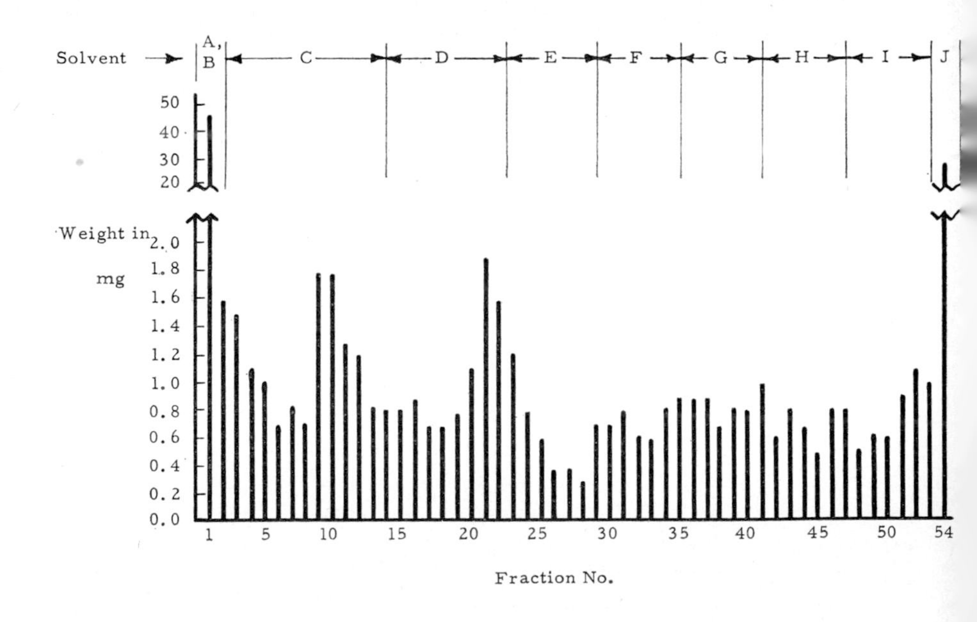

FIG. 1. Fractions from silicic acid chromatographic separation of crude ciguatera toxin. The solvent compositions are given in Table 1.

Fractions 2 and 3 represented the main portion of a band that was distinctly fluorescent on the column under ultraviolet light. The band produced a pale yellow eluate and was composed of a pale yellow oil.

Fractions 9 and 10 contained a band of material that was invisible on the

TABLE 2. TOXICITY OF FRACTIONS FROM SILICIC ACID CHROMATOGRAPHIC FRACTIONATION OF CRUDE CIGUATERA TOXIN

Fraction no.	No. of tests	Average fractional loss of action potential at 70 min[a]	Average deviation
2	1	0.06	—
3	1	0.05	—
4	2	0.11	±0.01
5	1	0.00	—
6	1	0.00	—
7	1	0.00	—
8	1	0.02	—
9	1	0.02	—
10	2	0.17	0.01
11	3	0.41	0.27
12	2	0.52	0.21
13	3	0.50	0.18
14	3	0.77	0.11
15	2	0.55	0.41
16	3	0.17	0.13
17	5	0.43	0.29
18	3	0.44	0.29
19	2	0.02	0.01
20	1	0.00	—
21	3	0.32	0.30
22	2	0.42	0.11
23	3	0.48	0.25
24	2	0.58	0.12
25	1	1.00	—
26	1	1.00	—
27	1	1.00	—
28	2	0.98	0.02
29	2	0.75	0.22
30	2	0.59	0.39
31	3	0.57	0.27
32	2	0.47	0.47
33	2	0.48	0.42
34	3	0.22	0.29
35	3	0.75	0.11
36	1	0.42	—
37	2	0.25	0.25
38	1	0.27	—
39	1	0.20	—
40	2	0.28	0.28
41	2	0.25	0.17
42	1	0.00	—
43	1	0.00	—
44	1	0.00	—
45	2	0.30	0.30
46	1	0.00	—
47	1	0.00	—
48	2	0.21	0.21
49	2	0.15	0.15
50	1	0.16	—
51	1	0.00	—
52	1	0.00	—
53	1	0.00	—

[a]Frog sciatic nerve test.

column but which yielded a distinctly yellow eluate. The material was a yellow oil.

Fractions 18–24 were composed of a white solid containing minute needle crystals. This material was invisible on the column.

In the region of fractions 28–30 a band was eluted that was visible on the column as a diffuse fluorescence. The material responsible was an oil.

Fractions 32–35 contained the bulk of a white solid that appeared as a white film in the chromatographic tubes. This material tailed off into fractions 36–38. It was invisible on the column.

Finally, fractions 51–53 appeared to be a mixture of oil and cloudy white solid.

All of the fractions not mentioned above were composed of small amounts of oily material that formed a thin coating on the sides of the sample tubes.

Each fraction was tested one or more times by the frog sciatic nerve test described by Hessel (1960). The results are presented in Table 2. Fractions 1 and 54, which checked out nontoxic, are not included for these were tested at dose levels of 10 and 20γ of material per ml of emulsion. The other fractions were all tested at a level of 5γ/ml. Samples for testing were prepared by dissolving the main fraction in 10 ml of ether-methanol, 1 : 1, v/v, and removing the proper size of aliquot. The solvent was removed on the rotary evaporator and the aliquot material emulsified into 10 ml of frog Ringer's solution by ultrasound.

DISCUSSION

Despite the fact that some of the average deviations of the test results are high, probably because of possible chemical changes in the samples, dosage variation, physiological variation in the nerves, or some other factor, the toxicity pattern is clear. Fractions 25–28 contained the material of highest toxicity. As these fractions came off the silicic acid column in the relatively narrow " dip " between two bands of white, solid—and probably non-toxic—material, further refinement of the chromatographic technique must be carried out. Without question the toxin is still contaminated by non-toxic substances, particularly in those fractions representing the extremities of the band.

Definite toxicity was also found in the region of fractions 11–18, but the number of discrete toxic substances is in doubt because of the variability in the bioassay data. Further work along the lines of fractionation and testing must be done.

All other fractions showed no toxicity or levels of toxicity so low that they were not considered significant.

The determination of the precise role and importance of each component responsible for the ciguatera syndrome must await future research into the physiological and pharmacological aspects of the problem.

SUMMARY

The poisonous substance or complex of substances responsible for ciguatera, a form of ichthyosarcotoxism with serious gastrointestinal and neurological effects, has never been isolated in pure form and chemically characterized. This paper is concerned with the use of silicic acid as a chromatographic adsorbent for the partial purification of the toxic principles.

ACKNOWLEDGEMENT

This research was done while the author was a member of the World Life Research Institute, Colton, California. This paper is Contribution Number 9 from the World Life Research Institute.

This work was supported by the United States Army Chemical Corps through contract no. DA18–108–405–CML–800 and grant no. DA–CML–18–108–61–G–19.

REFERENCES

HESSEL, D. W., HALSTEAD, B. W. and PECKHAM, N. H. 1960. Marine Biotoxins. I. Ciguatera Poison: Some biological and chemical aspects. *Ann. N.Y. Acad. Sci.* **90**, 788.

HESSEL, D. W. 1961. Marine Biotoxins. II. The extraction and partial purification of ciguatera toxin from *Lutjanus bohar* (Forskål). *Toxicol. and Appl. Pharmacol.* **3**, 574.

SOME EXPERIMENTS ON ICHTHYOTOXIN

F. Ghiretti and E. Rocca*

According to the common classification, given by Phisalix (1922), toxic fishes can be grouped in three categories:

1. Fishes which are toxic because of a poison secreted by special glands or by certain regions of the skin.
2. Fishes which do not have any poisonous apparatus, the toxin being a component of the blood plasma.
3. Fishes which become poisonous at certain periods or are toxic all the time, the poison being located in the tissues.

This classification, however, is purely empirical. It is still accepted because it simplifies description of a subject as large as toxic and venomous fishes. In the case of organisms possessing special organs or glands which manufacture a poisonous secretion, the toxicity has a biological significance for both the species and the individual. These organs and glands have indeed a survival value. On the contrary, a component of the blood plasma which shows strong or feeble toxic action when injected into another organism has no significance at all for the organism which possesses it. The third case, known also under the name of Ichthyosarcotoxism, is purely an accidental phenomenon and its importance is mainly ecological. In this case, it is generally recognized that the fish becomes poisonous as a result of its diet, the toxic food cycle being initiated by a marine plant or microorganism. Certainly, knowledge of the agent or agents which start the cycle is of great importance, theoretically and practically.

All these groups of toxic fishes, whether the poison is used for attack or defence, or is located in the blood or occasionally in the tissues, present a number of challenging problems in terms of chemistry, physiology and pharmacology of biotoxins. The numerous investigations which are devoted today to toxic substances produced by marine and terrestrial organisms are an indication (and this Conference is a witness of it) of the revival of interest in naturally occurring active substances.

We have restricted our work to the second group of toxic fishes, that is those having a poisonous compound in the blood plasma. Within this group we have selected three species belonging to the Family Muraenidae: *Anguilla vulgaris*, *Muraena helena* and *Conger vulgaris*. Each of these species

*Department of Physiology, Stazione Zoologica, Naples, Italy.

is known to possess a toxic compound called ichthyotoxin. But, whereas *Anguilla* and *Conger* have no poisonous organ or gland in the mouth or under the skin, and never produce ichthyosarcotoxism, the moray eel fits into all the three groups, although ichthyosarcotoxism in *Muraena*, which has been described for the Pacific area by Klentzos (1951), and Halstead (1954, 1955) has never been observed in the Mediterranean sea. According to Phisalix (1922) the moray eel possesses poisonous skin in the palate, as well as ichthyotoxin in the blood. The toxic secretion produced there lines the buccal cavity and can be injected when the animal bites with its pointed teeth. A crude preparation of the poison can be made from the buccal mucosa. Its activity on mammals is very similar to that of ichthyotoxin. This is an indication that the two toxins may be identical. Angelo Mosso (1888) first observed that the serum from fishes belonging to the family Muraenidae is toxic for laboratory animals. This discovery started from the trivial observation of the bitter taste of eel serum. This serum, when injected parenterally into dogs, rabbits and guinea pigs, resulted in hemolysis, decreased sensitivity to pain, hypersalivation, respiratory distress, clonic convulsions, paralysis and death. Mosso called the toxic factor of eel serum ichthyotoxin. Later it was found that the toxin is destroyed by heating at 58°C for 15 min, by irradiation with ultraviolet light and by proteolytic enzymes. Buglia (1919a–d, 1920) and Kopaczewski (1918) have shown that freezing and dessication have no effect on the toxin.

After Mosso, interest in ichthyotoxin lasted for more than 30 years, and the literature includes more than one hundred publications by various authors. Most of the work, however, was done using the whole serum and under the influence of theories of blood coagulation and the mechanism of immunological phenomena Therefore, very little or nothing was added to the knowledge of the chemical nature of the toxin. Perhaps the most important conclusion that we can draw today from these studies is that there are probably several active substances beside ichthyotoxin in eel serum.

Drilhon (1954) has reported that, as in many other fishes, sera of conger and moray eels contain large amounts of lipids. Another feature is the great quantity of the globulin components as compared with the albumin fraction. Drilhon (1953) also found a large amount of γ globulin in eel serum. Drilhon (1954, 1955) and Fontaine (1932) have studied the electrophoretic pattern of the lipid and protein components of eel serum. Great variations were observed also from one species to another, and even in the same individual, depending on the physiological conditions of the animal (sexual maturity, starvation, etc.). The albumin fraction, particularly, showed great increase and reduction perhaps indicated the nutritional state of the animal.

Eel serum is known to contain a number of 17–corticosteroids in much greater amounts than in other bloods. Fontaine and Callamand (1949) reported that it also contains a lipolytic enzyme of great activity as compared with that of mammalian sera. According to Jaques (1955), in addition to serotonin, there is also an active substance which causes slow delayed contractions of the isolated guinea pig ileum and which bears some resemblance to the substance present in wasp venom or in cat plasma after injection of thalassine. Fontaine and Callamand (1947) reported that eel serum shows a high antigonadotropic activity towards mammals. When rats are treated with eel serum at subtoxic doses, no gonadotropic hormone activity can be observed.

Figure 1 shows the electrophoretic pattern of eel serum as compared with that of human serum.

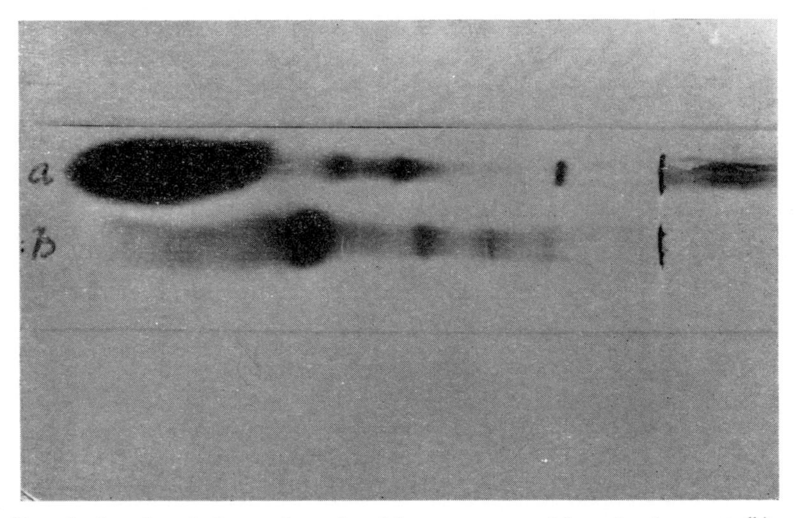

FIG. 1. Starch gel electrophoresis of human serum (a) and eel serum (b).

Ichthyotoxin has been purified from the serum of *Anguilla*, *Conger* and moray eels. Several methods have been worked out, based upon different fractionating procedures of the proteins contained in the sera. Most of the inactive proteins were precipitated with 0.1 M zinc acetate-glycine buffer at pH 6.9. The supernatant was passed through a Dowex column and contains 100 per cent of the original activity. Rivanol can also be used to remove inactive proteins from the serum when added in proper concentrations and at a proper pH. However, after several attempts, a fractionation method based on ammonium sulphate precipitation was found to give the best results and was applied to all kinds of sera. This method is outlined in Fig. 2. Fifty ml of serum containing 49 mg of proteins per ml was treated with $AmSO_4$ 25 per cent saturation. To the supernatant more $AmSO_4$ was added till 35 per cent saturation. The precipitate was dissolved in water, dialysed against NaCl 0.15 M, the pH adjusted to 5.5 and the volume brought to 50 ml. This fraction, which is as active as the original serum, contains 2 mg of protein per ml. Further fractionation with ethyl alcohol 25 per cent at −5°C. gave a fraction which contained 0.48 mg of protein and retained almost all of the original activity. The solution was lyophilized without a loss of activity.

At the ultracentrifuge (Spinco Mod. L, temperature 23.8°C; 7.7 mg of protein per ml in NaCl 0.15M) three components were observed.

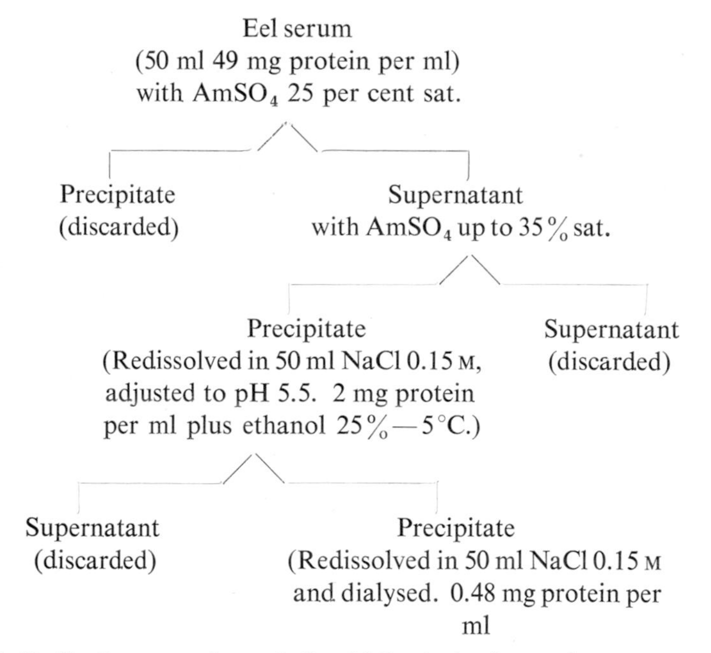

FIG. 2. Purification procedure of the Ichthyotoxin from eel serum.

The first component, which corresponded to about 70 per cent of the total proteins, had a sedimentation constant of 6.43. The two other components had S_{20} values equal to 10.59 and 14.97, respectively.

In the course of the purification procedure the activity of the protein was tested both on mammals (rabbits) and invertebrates, mainly crabs. Of the many effects shown by the whole serum—hemolysis, decreased sensitivity to pain, hypersalivation, respiratory distress, clonic convulsions, paralysis and death—only the effects upon the nervous system, followed by death, were observed when purified ichthyotoxin was injected into a rabbit. Death followed invariably by fibrillation of the heart after 30 sec when 0.2 mg per kilo were used. More striking effects were observed when the protein was injected into crabs. For most of these experiments species of the crustacean decapod, *Eriphia spinifrons*, were used, but the same effects were observed with other species. As shown in Figs. 3 and 4, immediately after the injection (from 15 to 30 μg of protein per 100 g of body weight) the animal presented clonic convulsions followed by paralysis and death.

FIG. 3. Effect of the injection of purified Ichthyotoxin into *Eriphia spinifrons*. Clonic convulsions (a). Paralysis and death (b).

ACKNOWLEDGEMENT

This study was aided by a grant of the Italian National Research Council.

REFERENCES

BUGLIA, G. 1920. Recherches sur la nature du venin de l'anguille. *Arch. Ital. Biol.* **70**, 77.

DRILHON, A. 1953. Etude de quelques diagrammes électrophorétiques de plasma de Poisson. *C.R. Acad. Sci.* **237**, 1779.

DRILHON, A. 1954. Etude des lipoprotéides sériques chez quelques poissons au moyen de l'électrophorèse sur papier. *C.R. Acad. Sci.* **238**, 940.

DRILHON, A. 1955. Euglobines chez les poissons. *C.R. Soc. Biol.* **149**, 2124.

FIRLY, S. and FONTAINE, M. 1932. Sur la teneur en protéines du sérum d'anguille et ses variations au cours des changements de salinité. *C.R. Acad. Sci.* **194**, 1854.

FONTAINE, M. and CALLAMAND, O. 1947. Sur l'activité antigonadotrope du sérum de l'anguille. *C.R. Acad. Sci.* **225**, 143.

FONTAINE, M. and CALLAMAND, O. 1949. La lipase sérique chez un Cyclostome (*Petromyzone marinus* L.) et divers poissons téléostéens. *Bull. Inst. Ocean. Monaco N.* 943.

HALSTEAD, B. W. 1954. Poisonous fishes and ichthyosarcotoxism. *U.S. Armed Forces Med. J.* **5**, 157.

JAQUES, R. 1955. A substance from eel serum producing slow contractions. *Nature* **175**, 212.

KLENTZOS, C. T. 1950. Seventeen cases of poisoning due to ingestion of an eel *Gymnothorax flavimarginatus*. *Am. J. Trop. Med.* **30**, 785.

KOPACZEWSKI, W. 1918. Recherches sur le sérum de la murène (*Murena helena*). *Ann. Inst. Pasteur*. **32**, 584.

MOSSO, A. 1888. Un venin dans le sang des Murénides. *Arch. Ital. Biol.* **10**, 141.

PHISALIX, M. 1922. *Animaux venimeux et venins.* Paris: Masson et Cie.

RALLS, R. J. and HALSTEAD, B. W. 1955. Moray eel poisoning and a preliminary report on the action of the toxin. *Am. J. Trop. Med. and Hyg.* **4**, 136.

Section VI

SNAKES

VENOMOUS SNAKES OF THE PACIFIC AREA‡

JOHN E. WERLER* and HUGH L. KEEGAN†

INTRODUCTION

Even in areas where venomous snakes are numerous, deaths from snakebite are surprisingly few. Aside from the improbability of being bitten by a venomous snake, this low death rate may be explained by several contributing factors. These are: (1) Use of potent antivenins in treatment of snakebite. (2) The fact that a dangerously venomous snake does not always deliver a lethal injection of venom with its bite. (3) Protection offered against snakebite by boots and shoes. (A good proportion of the bites in tropical areas are received while the victims are working barefooted in the fields.) (4) Bites by snakes of several species of genus *Trimeresurus* are numerous in portions of the Pacific area, but seldom produce fatalities, even in absence of modern treatment.

The fact remains that snakebite can be a severe personal problem, particularly if efficient medical aid is not available. This paper includes keys and illustrations to help in identification of dangerous species, and information on distribution and habits which might prove useful to persons traveling or working in regions where venomous snakes occur. Use of technical terms has been unavoidable, but an illustration is provided for many of the key characteristics.

SYMPTOMS OF SNAKEBITE

Symptoms following snakebite vary according to the size and species of the snake involved. Location of the bite, as well as the size and physical condition of the person bitten are also important factors. While it is commonly believed that snake venoms must be either hemorrhagic or neurotoxic in effect, this is not entirely true. Many venoms have both neurotoxic and hemorrhagic elements, and considerable variation in symptoms follows bite by most venomous snakes.

*Curator, Zoological Gardens, Houston, Texas.

†Chief, Entomology Branch, Department of Preventive Medicine, Medical Field Service School, Fort Sam Houston, Texas.

‡Arthur Loveridge, author, and the Macmillan Company, publishers, kindly granted permission to use numerous keys from their book, *Reptiles of the Pacific World.* All of the keys in this paper are taken from the Macmillan publication.

VIPER AND PIT VIPER BITES

An excellent description of symptoms following viper bite, based on a series of cases in Israel, was given by Efrati and Reif (1953). Local signs included swelling, discoloration, sanguinolent and serous cutaneous blebs, fang punctures, and toxic lymphangitis. Hemorrhages were seen in the skin, both near and distant from the bite, as well as in the mucous membranes. There was also hematemesis and hematuria. Melena, epistaxis and anemia were noted. Anaphylactoid syndromes included urticaria, Quincke's edema, mild to severe shock, eosinophilia, and thrombocytopenia.

Purananda (1956) described viper bites in Thailand as causing marked systemic symptoms, such as local petechial hemorrhages, epistaxis, and bleeding from mucous membranes and body openings. In fatal cases, death was due to circulatory failure. Symptoms following bites by *Agkistrodon halys*, the mamushi, were described by Roppongi (1928). These were: stinging pain locally with sanguineus edema, skin discoloration, spreading swelling, dull pain along the courses of the lymphatics, fever, headache, faintness, diminished urine with albuminuria, and damage to blood vessel walls. Two American physicians have published reports of bites by the habu, *Trimeresurus flavoviridis*, which occurred among military personnel during the invasion of Okinawa by U.S. Forces during World War II. Martin (1946) reported rapid onset of symptoms. There was brief local anesthesia in some cases, followed by pain, swelling, and systemic disturbances. Sonnenborn (1946) found systemic effects unexpectedly mild, but local reactions severe. In a patient bitten on the face twice in rapid succession, there was immediate swelling. In 5 min one eye was swollen shut, and in an hour both eyes, the entire face and neck were badly swollen. This patient suffered no headache, dyspnea, vomiting, or diarrhoea. The site of the bite was anaesthetic. The speech became thickened because of the swelling of the lips, face, and tongue. This swelling persisted for some time, and became discolored.

Effects produced by bite of the Taiwan habu, *Trimeresurus mucrosquamatus*, were described by Wu and Tsui (1945). These symptoms were: intense local pain, extensive swelling of the entire limb, (in patients bitten on the hand and foot), edema, ecchymosis, and blister formation. Kopstein (1928) stated that bites by the bamboo snake, *Trimeresurus gramineus*, resulted in edema, excruciating pain, and sometimes necrosis and gangrene.

Clinical observations on a series of 24 cases of snakebite due to *Trimeresurus elegans*, the Sakishima habu, were presented by Keegan and Yoshino (1959). Symptoms include hemorrhagic spots at fang punctures, pain, swelling, and cyanosis. Localized necrosis was severe in some patients. Only two of the patients in this series developed general symptoms.

Similar effects are produced by bites of North American pit vipers.

Excellent discussions are given in recent papers by Parrish (1958), Deichmann *et al.* (1958), and by Limbacher and Lowe (1959). Such symptoms, which may be seen in cases bitten by Asian as well as North American pit vipers, include: pain, swelling and discoloration, weakness and giddiness, respiratory difficulty, nausea and vomiting, circulatory disturbances, anemia, necrosis, bleb and vesicle production. Difficulties with vision have also been reported, and secondary infection may occur. Some differences of opinion exist over the importance of secondary infection. Parrish *et al.* (1956) studied the bacterial flora of mouths and venom glands of 11 Eastern diamondback rattlesnakes, four timber rattlesnakes, and 10 cottonmouth moccasins. Twenty-eight per cent of venom cultures were sterile. Most commonly found organisms in this survey were *Paracolon bacterium* sp. and *Streptococcus* sp. Reid (1958) stated that " My experience is that bacterial contamination is rare in Malayan viper bites. When it occurs, it is probably always due to treatment given after the bite, particularly incision ".

Parrish (1959) pointed out that bites by venomous snakes do not always result in venom poisoning. In this paper, Dr. Parrish presented case histories of four patients who received fang wounds from North American pit vipers, but who did not develop symptoms of envenomation. Such isolated incidents in unfamiliar territory could possibly lead to erroneous conclusions regarding medical importance of a species of venomous snake.

COBRA, KRAIT AND CORAL SNAKE BITES

Effects of cobra bite have been well reviewed by Ahuja and Singh (1956). Symptoms listed were: pain at site of bite, and affecting the surrounding area to some extent, swelling extending up the affected limb, numbness, lassitude, drowsiness, and intoxication associated with difficulty in breathing. Initial symptoms may be followed by a sense of receding consciousness. Eyesight becomes dim, and there is marked dropping of eyelids. The pulse is weak, heart action is speeded, and speech becomes labored. There is dribbling of saliva and mucous as well as paralysis of the tongue and laryngeal muscles associated with difficulty in respiration. In later stages there may be paralysis of limbs and loss of sphincter control. The interval between occurrence of the bite and onset of paralysis and other neurotoxic symptoms is seldom more than two or three hours, and frequently less.

A similar picture was given by Purananda (1956). Characteristic symptoms seen in patients suffering from cobra bite in Thailand were difficulty in breathing and swallowing; weak pulse; drooping of eyelids; stiffness of the jaws; coma; death due to respiratory and cardiac failure. Tweedie (1956) noted that cobra bites were less painful than viper bites. Swelling is usually slight, and blood rarely oozes from the fang marks. There is progressive weakness of arms and legs, the jaws feel stiff, and there may be difficulty in opening the mouth. The eyelids may droop, and the patient starts breathing heavily and rapidly. If the patient does not die, there are no permanent ill effects. Onset of paralytic symptoms may be delayed. (*Note*: Reid, elsewhere in this volume, has reported that cobra bite in Malaya is *not* characterized by neurotoxic effects, but by local effects, with a high incidence of necrosis.)

Symptoms following bites by any of the kraits are similar to those caused by cobra bite. Ahuja and Singh (1956) mention this fact, and also note that there is initial lack of pain following krait bite. There is little or no local edema or discoloration, but there may be abdominal pain. Coral snake bites are exceedingly rare. Symptoms following a bite by a specimen of *Maticora intestinalis*, the banded Malaysian coral snake, were described by Harrison (1957).

SEA SNAKE BITES

Most of the current information on sea snake bite is the work of Reid (1956a, b, c and 1959). The following informative paragraph was included in a letter from Dr. Reid to the writer on 4 December 1958:

> In sea-snake poisoning two outstanding clinical anomalies were trismus yet flaccid paresis elsewhere and secondly, haemoglobinuria without further signs of excessive haemolysis. Experimentally, sea-snake venom is only feebly haemolytic and haemoglobinuria should theoretically indicate an inevitably fatal dose. However during the last 1½ years some of the discrepancies between experimental and clinical findings are resolving. It has become increasingly obvious that skeletal muscle cells are directly and primarily attacked by the venom and appear to bear the brunt of the effect in human victims. The urine pigment is myoglobin and not haemoglobin. The clinical features I would now summarise as follows: (1) No pain or local reaction at the site of the bite. (2) The first symptom is muscle pains either generalised or in the throat or jaws starting about ½–1 hour after the bite. Generalised muscle stiffness and pain on movement increase and are followed by paresis and then loss of tendon reflexes. (3) Trismus is a prominent feature. (4) Myoglobinuria is evident before paresis is marked. (5) Death may occur within hours from hyperkalaemic cardiac arrest or respiratory failure (from paresis of respiratory muscles and/or inhalation of vomit). If the victim survives the first 48 hours or so he may die from acute renal failure. Pathologically we have confirmed the myoglobinuria, myonecrosis (in material from autopsy and a biopsy from a patient with severe poisoning who recovered), toxic liver changes and tubular necrosis of the kidneys. Professor J. H. Dible recently examined some of this material and in 2 of 3 cases found changes similar to those of the " crush syndrome ". The myocardium has been histologically normal. Thus the effect of sea-snake venom in human beings appears to be multifactorial acting primarily on skeletal muscles but also on the liver, kidneys and neuromuscular junctions.

According to Reid (1959), mortality due to sea snake bites is about 5 per cent of those bitten. In the same paper, Reid reported that three-quarters of the victims dying from sea snake bite do so within 24 hr after the bite. The most rapid death recorded was 2½ hr after the bite—the most protracted was 12 days. Recovery in a severe case may take up to 6 months. Improvement in power (from paresis) starts solely during the third week. Tendon reflexes return during the third or fourth week. In moderate cases, full recovery is achieved in 3 or 4 weeks; in trivial cases, in a few days. Permanent kidney damage has been reported, but no long-term damage to muscle, nerve or liver tissue has been found.

TREATMENT OF SNAKE BITE

During the past several years there has been considerable controversy over treatment of snake bite. This has involved both first aid measures and definitive treatment in the hospital. Specific questions have been raised concerning therapeutic value or harm of the tourniquet, incision, suction, antivenins, cold, and antihistamines in the treatment of snake bite.

Among the first to present arguments against the time-honored tourniquet, incision, and suction as first aid measures were Efrati and Reif (1953). Personal experience, and a careful study of the literature convinced these physicians that use of the tourniquet did not help the patient; that excision of the bitten area was impractical unless done immediately; and that incision and suction were of little or no value. As a result of their experiences with a series of 65 cases of viperbite, the following recommendations were made: *first* and *foremost*—achieve absolute immobilization of the bitten limb by a splint if possible; administer a *specific* antivenin: watch for shock (saline, plasma and blood may be needed); antihistamines may be helpful (their own experience with antihistamines in treatment of snakebite was meagre at this time).

This study by Efrati and Reif stimulated research on treatment of snakebite, with particular emphasis on first aid measures. The resulting number of papers and obvious differences of opinion have made it difficult to establish recommendations for snakebite which would be acceptable to all authorities. Since these various approaches to the problem have been reviewed by Genaro elsewhere in this volume, they will not be discussed in detail in this paper.

Because of the lack of agreement among military and civilian authorities on the subject of first aid for snakebite, the Armed Services of the United States requested that the National Research Council of the National Academy of Sciences investigate the problem and present recommendations for a policy on first aid for snakebite. In 1959 an *Ad Hoc* Committee of ten members was appointed to study the problem, and late in 1960, recommendations were forwarded to the Military Services. These recommendations formed the basis for a policy statement on first aid for snakebite which was approved by The Surgeon General of the Army in 1961. This policy distinguishes between measures to be applied by nonmedical personnel, and action to be taken by trained personnel of the Medical Service. Essentials follow:

1. *Action by Nonmedical Personnel*

(a) Within practical limits achieve immediate, absolute immobilization of the affected part in a position below the level of the heart.

(b) Place an improvised, lightly constricting band (tourniquet) two or four inches closer to the heart than the site of the bite and reapply the constricting band ahead of the swelling if it progresses up the arm or leg. The constricting band should be placed tightly enough to halt the flow of blood in the superficial blood vessels but *not* tightly enough to stop the pulse (arterial flow).

(c) In case the bitten person stops breathing, prolonged mouth-to-mouth or mouth-to-nose artificial resuscitation should be employed.

(d) Assistance from the nearest medical source or transportation of the patient to a treatment facility should be accomplished as soon as possible.

2. *Action by Trained Medical Service Personnel*

(a) Achieve immobilization, apply tourniquet and give necessary artificial resuscitation as described above.

(b) If the patient is seen within *one hour* following the bite, incision and suction can be instituted. Incisions must not be more than $\frac{1}{2}$ in. in length, and should be made through the skin parallel to the line of the extremity and over the site of the fang marks. Mechanical or oral suction should be instituted immediately.

(c) Every effort should be made to provide specific antivenin to the patient. In the absence of a physician and after suitable training, medical aidmen may administer antivenin after conducting sensitivity tests. Antivenin should be given intramuscularly at a site elsewhere on the body than the bite as soon as possible after it is evident that envenomation has occurred.

3. *Action by Physician*

Procedures, including those enumerated above, and to include intravenous injection of antivenin, administration of tetanus toxoid (or antitoxin where indicated), antibiotics, debridement, analgesics or other materials or methods which in the professional opinion are necessary, are reserved for the physician.

ANTIVENINS IN TREATMENT OF SNAKE BITE

Several important advances in antivenin production and research have been made during the past few years. Preparation of the first antivenin against sea snake venom was described by Carey and Wright (1960), and successful use of this product in treatment of sea snake bite was reported by Reid (1962). Preparation of an additional sea snake antivenin was described by Barme, Huard and Nguyen Xuan Mai (1962). Use of electrophoretically separated venom fractions in antivenin production was reported as a collaborative effort by scientists of the Rogoff Medical Research Institute of Petah Tiqva, Israel, and the Pasteur Institute, Paris, France. Papers describing this technique and results obtained have been published by Kochwa, Gitter, Strauss, Perlmutter-Moroz and DeVries (1959) and Kochwa, Izard, Boquet and Gitter (1959). Other research groups in different areas are following this technique in an attempt to solve the problem imposed by low antigenicity of some important venom fractions. The problem of standardization of methods for measurement of therapeutic effectiveness is also receiving widespread attention. Recent developments in this field have been discussed by Boquet (1959). The World Health Organization has noted (1960), that individuals at institutions in many countries are offering co-operation in offering samples of *Naja* antivenins and venom samples from various geographic areas in an effort to aid the establishment of a standard *Naja* antivenin. Recent preliminary studies at the Medical Field Service School have indicated that variations in venom of local subspecies of *Naja naja* may make preparation of a standard antivenin difficult. It was found that only a homologous antivenin protected white mice against lethal effects of injections of 5 LD_{50}'s of Philippine cobra venom. In this test series cobra antivenins produced in Thailand, Taiwan, India, France and Germany gave no perceptible protection to test animals. This was not surprising in view of results obtained by Keegan, Whittemore and Maxwell (1962) in tests of neutralization of ten snake venoms by homologous and heterologous antivenins. It was found that strong paraspecific action was rare, and showed no marked correlation with relationship of snake species involved. Unexpected results included neutralization of venom of the Australian tiger snake, *Notechis scutatus*, by a South American *Micrurus* antivenin, and action of *Echis carinatus* antivenin against venoms of the elapid snakes, *Naja naja* and *Ophiophagus hannah*.

Excellent antivenins against venoms of medically important snakes are produced in several laboratories in the Pacific area. Because of the proven existence of variations in venoms of snakes of the same species in different geographic areas, it is wise to procure antivenins produced in the areas in which they are to be used.

ELAPID SNAKES

Family Elapidae

The members of this large and diverse family include, at the same time, many of the world's most dangerous and innocuous venomous serpents. Some species, such as the diminutive, foot-long Hediger's snake of the Solomon Islands, are too small and rare to be considered a hazard to man. Many others are equally rare, or so secretive, that little information is available concerning their habits or life histories, and absolutely nothing is known about the effects of their venoms upon man. Also included in the family are a number of extremely venomous and dangerous snakes representing, from a medical standpoint, the most important of all Pacific area venomous serpents. Among them, the kraits and cobras cause the highest incidence of snake bite deaths in man. Two even more dangerous elapid species, the taipan and death adder, while producing a high rate of mortality among human beings, are nevertheless uncommon on the islands of the Pacific, and bites from them are rare in this area.

Although the greatest number of species is found in the Australian region, the elapid snakes are not confined to the Pacific. The family is generally distributed in Africa, through southern Asia and the Malay Archipelago, and as far east in the Pacific as the Fiji Islands. The American representatives of this group are the coral snakes.

There is no easy way by which they can be distinguished from the superficially similar but harmless snakes of the family Colubridae, except through examination of the mouth for fangs. The two families possess relatively long and slender bodies, as opposed to the heavily-built vipers and pit-vipers, and both have heads that are only a little, if any, wider than the neck. The one exception among the elapids is the death adder, which outwardly looks exactly like a viper.

It is evident that there are many widely different types of behavior among the elapid snakes. By far the majority of species are timid and inoffensive and, in the extreme, they may refuse to bite when provoked. Instead of defending itself when touched or annoyed, a krait prefers to hide its head beneath some of its coils. However, such is not the case with the taipan. Here is a large and highly venomous species that has been known to make apparently unprovoked attacks upon man, the result often being the death of a victim.

The venoms of most large elapid snakes are very potent. Those of the tapian and death adder are especially toxic. In addition to its powerful neurotoxic venom, the taipan possesses large venom sacks. But the poison glands of the long-glanded snakes are even larger. In this group of small, brightly-colored species, each venom sack begins in the head and extends posteriorly nearly a third of the length of the body.

All of the elapids possess fangs which are short, grooved and immovably fixed to the front of the upper jaw. They vary in length from the short 0.8 mm fangs of the New Guinea *Ultrocalamus preussi*, to those of the taipan, which reach a length of ½ in.

The family Elapidae, which includes about half of all the world's really venomous species, contains approximately thirty known genera, nineteen of them occurring in the Pacific area. The following key, taken from

Reptiles of the Pacific World by Arthur Loveridge, will help in their identification.

KEY TO THE GENERA OF ELAPID* SNAKES OF THE PACIFIC

1. Scales along center of back enlarged; range: Borneo south to Sumatra, east to Celebes†: (Fig. 6) . . . . kraits (*Bungarus*)
   Scales along center of back not enlarged: (Fig. 7) 2
2. Maxillary bone extending forward slightly beyond the palatine;‡ range: western Pacific east to the Moluccas: (Fig. 16) 3
   Maxillary bone not extending forward beyond the palatine; range: Pacific from Moluccas east to the Fijis: (Fig. 17) 6
3. Internasal scale bordering nostril; 15 to 25 scales around middle of body; spreads a " hood " when alarmed: (Figs. 3, 18, 19, 42) 4
   Internasal scale not bordering nostril; 13 to 15 scales around middle of body; cannot spread a " hood " 5
4. A pair of large occipital shields; 15 scales around middle of body; range: Philippines south to Indonesia†: (Figs. 18, 19, 41, 42) . . . .
   king cobra (*Ophiophagus hannah*)
   No occipital shields; (17) 19 to 25 scales around middle of body; range: Formosa south to Indonesia†: (Figs. 44, 44a hooded cobras (*Naja naja* subspp.)
5. Poison glands not extending beyond the head; range: Formosa south to Sumatra†: (Figs. 45, 46, 47) . . Oriental coral snakes (*Calliophis*)
   Poison glands extending along anterior third of body§; range: Philippines south to Indonesia‖ . . . . . . long-glanded snakes (*Maticora*)
6. Pupil vertical; body thick, short, with 21 to 23 scales around middle; tail compressed toward tip and ending in a long spine; majority of shields beneath tail in a single series; range: Obi; Ceram; and Timor Laut east to New Guinea¶: (Figs. 14, 48). . . . death adder (*Acanthophis antarcticus*)
   Pupil round or almost so; body moderate or slender; tail neither compressed nor ending in a long spine; majority of shields beneath tail in a double series *except in* 2 *species*: (Fig. 5) 7
7. Poison fangs followed by 1 to 7 small teeth 10
   Poison fangs followed by 7 to 15 small teeth 8
8. Tail short or moderate with 19 to 41 paired shields below; range: Ceram east through New Guinea and adjacent islands to Bismarck Archipelago¶
   —Müllers and Schlegel's snakes (*Aspidomorphus*)
   Tail moderate or long with 61 to 105 mostly paired shields below . . 9

---

*That is to say, land snakes with a pair of enlarged, more or less rigid, grooved open or closed, poison teeth on either side of the front of the upper jaw.

†Also Asiatic mainland, the cobras also in Africa.

‡This cranial character necessitates opening the mouth and a decision is not always easy in the case of *Calliophis* and *Maticora* of section 3, but locality will settle dilemma unless the snake comes from the Moluccas.

§In a freshly killed long-glanded snake this may be ascertained without dissection by feeling for the displaced heart in the middle third of the body, instead of in anterior third as in the corals.

‖Also Asiatic mainland.

¶Also Australian mainland.

9. Scales on back each bearing a ridge or keel; 21 to 23 scales around middle of body; 61 to 78 (pairs of) shields beneath tail; range: New Guinea*: (Figs. 2, 49, 50) . . . . ° taipan (*Oxyuranus scutellatus*)
   Scales on back quite smooth; 15 scales around the middle of body; 69 to 105 (pairs of) shields beneath tail; range: Yule Island and New Guinea*: (Figs. 1, 51) . . . . . . whip-snake (*Demansia psammophis* subspp.)
10. Belly shields more than 160 (164 to 328) 11
    Belly shields less than 160 (139 to 152) 19
11. Eye moderate or small, its diameter about equal to, or included 1½ times in, its distance from the mouth 12
    Eye very small, its diameter included 2 times in its distance from the mouth . 14
12. Belly shields more than 180 (199 to 233); eye moderate, its diameter about equal to its distance from the mouth; range: New Guinea*: (Fig. 52) . mulga snake, etc. (*Pseudechis*)
    Belly shields less than 180 (164 to 179) 13
13. Eye moderate, its diameter about equal to its distance from the mouth; back of head and nape colored uniformly with back; range: Solomons* —Guppy's and Woodford's snakes (*Denisonia*)
    Eye small, its diameter included about 1½ times in its distance from the mouth; back of head and nape much paler than snout and back; range: Aru Islands, Indonesia, west through New Guinea to islands of Torres Straits* . . . . . . brown-headed snake (*Glyphodon tristis*)
14. A preocular separating prefrontal from lip shields; belly shields 165 to 223 16
    No preocular, the prefrontal in contact with a lip shield; belly shields 230 to 328 15
15. Nostril between two nasals; 15 to 17 scales around middle of body; range: New Guinea; Woodlark and Ferguson's Islands . . . *Toxicocalamus*
    Nostril in a single nasal; 13 to 15 scales around middle of body; range: New Guinea and Seleo Island . . . . *Ultrocalamus*
16. Nostril between 2 nasals 17
    Nostril in a single nasal 18
17. Pupil said to be " vertically elliptic "; range: New Guinea . *Apistocalamus*
    Pupil round; range: New Guinea and Solomons . . . . *Micropechis*
18. Belly shields 196 to 205; anal shield divided; range: Sattelberg, New Guinea: (Fig. 4) . . . . Nyman's snake (*Pseudapistocalamus nymani*)
    Belly shields 165; anal shield entire; range: Bougainville, Solomons: (Fig. 4) . . . . . Hediger's snake (*Parapistocalamus hedigeri*)
19. Belly shields 139 to 152; anal shield divided; scales beneath tail 27 to 38 pairs; range: Fijis . . . . . Fiji snake (*Ogmodon vitianus*)

KRAITS (*Bungarus*)

The five species of kraits which inhabit the Pacific area can easily be recognized by their smooth and shiny scales, by the enlarged row of scales down the middle of the back and, often, by the alternating light and dark colored rings that circle the body. Some species possess a pointed tail; in others the tail end is blunt and knobby. They are of moderate to large size, one kind reaching a length of nearly 7 ft.

---

*Genus also on Australian mainland.

Generally they prefer open country and low elevations. Their noctural wanderings frequently take them into houses; by day they commonly find their way into agricultural areas.

All kraits have an extremely toxic venom although they seldom bite in self defense, being timid and inoffensive by nature.

KEY TO THE KRAITS OF THE PACIFIC

1. Scales around middle of body 13; back with ridge; shields beneath tail partly single, partly paired; range: Borneo; Sumatra; Java*: (Fig. 38) —yellow-headed krait (*Bungarus flaviceps*)
   Scales around middle of body 15 to 17; shields beneath tail in a single series . . . 2
2. Back with a ridge; tail ending bluntly; range: Borneo; Sumatra; Java*: (Figs. 5, 12, 39) . . . . banded krait (*B. fasciatus*)
   Back without a ridge; tail ending in a point 3
3. Back without crossbars; range: north coast Java . Javan krait (*B. javanicus*
   Back with numerous white crossbars, the center portion of each bar spotted with black 4
4. Back with 20 to 25 broad white crossbars; range: Sumatra; Java; Celebes* —Malayan krait (*B. candidus*)
   Back with 27 to 48 narrow white crossbars; range: Taiwan*: (Fig. 40) many-banded krait (*B. multicinctus*)

Yellow-headed Krait (*Bungarus f.aviceps*) (*Fig.* 38)

Other names. *U.ar tandjon api* (northeast Sumatra).

Distribution. The yellow-headed krait is found in Viet Nam, southern Burma, the Malay Peninsula, Nias, Sumatra, Borneo, and possibly Java.

Description. This species should not be confused with any other krait. The adult is usually shiny black above with a bright red head; the back end of the body and all of the tail are of the same scarlet color. Often an elongate black streak marks the back of the head. There may be a narrow, pale stripe or a row of yellowish dots down the middle of the back. A bluish white stripe extends along the sides near the belly. The young are colored much like the adults, but with more distinct markings.

The general color scheme of this species suggests that of the Oriental coral snakes, but it is easily identified by the more stout body, greater size, unique coloration and enlarged scales down the middle of the back.

A mountain race of the yellow-headed krait, which possesses a unique and startling coloration, is found in Borneo. This subspecies, *Bungarus f. baluensis*, is coral red with iridescent black bands on the body.

Size. This large krait grows to a length of six feet.

Habitat. While it is most often found in mountain or foothill jungle, one was collected at sea level near the coast of Perak in Malaya.

*Also Asiatic mainland.

Habits. This is a rare snake and little is known of its habits. Brongersma (1948) mentions a Sumatran specimen that had swallowed two snakes identified as *Dendrelaphis c. caudolineatus.*

Banded Krait (*Bungarus fasiatus*) (*Fig.* 39)

Other names. Ngu sam liem (Siam); *ular katam tabu* (Malaya); *oraj welang* (Sundanese); *ular welang* (Malaya).

Distribution. The banded krait ranges from northeastern India through Burma, southern China, Malaya, Thailand, Indo-China and Indonesia. In the Pacific it occurs on Sumatra, Java, Borneo and Siak.

Description. This distinctive and boldly marked snake is banded with black and yellow, the black bands about as broad as the yellow ones, or a little wider. The head is brownish at the snout and black behind, with a yellow streak on each side which extends up from the throat to a point above and behind the eye. A pronounced ridge runs down the middle of the back for its entire length, and the tail, unlike that of the other krait species, is blunt instead of pointed, sometimes even slightly expanded at the tip. The young are marked somewhat like the adults, but they are paler, the normally light colored bands being dirty white. Pope (1935) described two juvenile specimens from China whose tail tips were not nearly as blunt as those of the adults.

The mangrove snake, *Boiga dendrophila,* is sometimes mistaken for the banded krait; however, its yellow bands are much narrower than the black ones, giving it the appearance of a black snake with yellow transverse stripes.

Size. While the average length is about 4 ft., a large example from Thailand measured 6 ft. 7 in. in length.

Habitat. The banded krait is a common species, associated more often with relatively open country than with jungle. It is not confined to low elevations, for, in western Yunnan, China, according to Annandale (1911), it occurs in the mountains as high as 5500 ft elevation. In Indonesia it is found at an altitude of about 4700 ft in the Tengger Mountains of Java. De Rooij (1917) says that East Indian specimens are frequently discovered in dry places in hollows of the ground; in Java they inhabit the Sawah dikes. Their liking for water often leads them to rice fields, and according to Ridley (1899), they have been observed near the sea in tidal waters. Mr. J. Lear Grimmer of the National Zoological Park in Washington, says that kraits in the National Zoo are stimulated to feed by first sprinkling them liberally with warm water before introducing food snakes into their cage. Perhaps, like the Texas coral snake, *Micrurus f. tenere,* this species remains secreted until after a prolonged warm rain, when numbers of specimens come out of hiding to search for food.

Disposition. For such a venomous snake, the banded krait has an amazingly taciturn disposition. It is sluggish and inoffensive, rarely attempting to strike, even under extreme provocation. If annoyed, as by poking, it does not crawl away, but coils up and hides the head beneath some part of its body. Meanwhile it jerks the coils, first one way, then the other.

Food. Its diet is chiefly other snakes, but mice, lizards, toads, fish and snake eggs are occasionally eaten.

Young. Eight to twelve eggs, measuring $2\frac{1}{2}$ in. long by $1\frac{1}{2}$ in. wide, are laid beneath rubbish or deposited in holes in the ground where they are guarded by the female.

Javan Krait (*Bungarus javanicus*)

Distribution. This rare krait is known only from the north coast of Java.

Description. The top of the head, as well as the tail and neck, are blue-black; the upper lips are white. On the forward third of the body, each of the enlarged scales down the middle of the back displays a pair of small white spots. A narrow yellow line extends along each side of this scale row from the middle of the body to the tail. Beneath the last one-third of the tail, the color is dark lead grey. The back is without a high ridge, and the end of the tail is pointed.

Size. Reaches a length of about 38 in.

Habitat. Along the northern coast of Java, where the first specimen was found, the area is terraced into rice fields which, according to Kopstein (1932), is also typical of the habitat occupied by the Malayan krait. Here the elevation is nearly a thousand feet.

Medical importance. Little information is available concerning this rare krait except the account written by Kopstein (1932), in which he described this as a new species. He relates that one night in July of 1931, two natives in the village of Matahadji, on the north coast of Java, were bitten by a snake of this species as they slept in a small hut. The first one, a man 30 years of age, felt the snake crawl over his hand and, upon awakening, made a quick movement that resulted in his being bitten on the left index finger. He cried out, "A snake bit me!", and immediately threw the offending reptile away from him. Unfortunately, it fell on his 50 year-old father, who suffered a bite on the calf of his left leg close to the knee. Almost at once, as each man was bitten, he experienced difficulty in breathing and soon found himself unable to stand. Both victims demonstrated a loss of speech, possibly indicating a paralysis of the throat muscles. The older man died approximately a half-hour following the bite and his son lived until 3 p.m., 16 hr after the accident. If these represent typical cases of poisoning by the Javan krait, then this species must be considered extremely poisonous.

Malayan Krait (*Bungarus candidus*)

Other names. *Ular weling* (Malaya); *oraj weling* (Sundanese).

Distribution. The Malayan krait is widely distributed throughout southeast Asia, where it is known from India, Burma, southern China, Thailand, Indo-China, Malaya and Indonesia. Its Pacific range includes Sumatra, Java and Celebes.

Description. This snake is dark olive or black, with numerous broad, white or yellowish crossbands on the body and tail. These markings, which become wider along the sides, may be spotted with black or brown. On the forward part of the body they are much narrower than the black spaces between them; towards the back they are about the same width as the black interspaces. The head is black on top; the lips and abdomen are white. A light, sometimes indistinct, V-shaped mark occurs on the neck. The scales along the middle of the back are enlarged; however, the vertebral ridge is lacking.

The coloration of this species is very much like that of the banded krait, except that the black markings do not extend across the belly, and the tail end is pointed instead of blunt.

Size. It is not as large as either the banded or yellow-headed species, 3 or 4 ft being the usual length.

Disposition. Like the other kraits, this species appears to be sluggish and inoffensive.

Young. Six to ten eggs are deposited in holes in the ground.

Many-banded Krait (*Bungarus multicinctus*) (*Fig.* 40)

Distribution. This snake occurs in Burma, southeast China, Hainan and Taiwan.

Description. In common with the Malayan krait, this species is black with white or yellowish crossbands. However, in the many-banded krait, the white markings across the back are narrower and more numerous (27 to 48 in the many-banded krait; 20 to 25 in the Malayan krait). The white markings expand along the sides, and on the forward part of the body they are more widely separated from one another. Sometimes the white bands contain black spots. The head is dark brown or black, the lips and underside white. There is no ridge along the middle of the back.

Size. The average length is less than 3 ft, but occasional specimens may be nearly 5 ft long.

Disposition. Pope (1935), who had an opportunity to handle five live specimens in the field, gives a good account of the snake's behavior pattern. He comments that (1) none attempted to strike the way that most snakes do; (2) two of the five could not be provoked to strike. One of these only bit objects presented to it while it was held by the neck, and two of the specimens bit each other. One finally became so enraged that anything brought near it was bitten. All of the snakes showed a tendency to hold on when biting; (3) they all assumed irregular coiled positions, jerking about vigorously, and hiding the head under the body; (4) two specimens attempted to rush to freedom, two flattened the body, one threw its tail and the back part of its body violently about, and one hissed.

Food. The ophiophagous habits of this snake are well known; however, it is reported to feed also upon mice, frogs and fishes. Keegan (1960) includes an illustration of a many-banded krait that is in the process of swallowing a mammal.

King Cobra (*Ophiophagus hannah*)

This genus has only one species. In form and coloration it closely resembles the common cobra and at a glance might be mistaken for its smaller relative. However, the pair of occipital shields on the head of the king cobra will serve to distinguish it from other cobras.

King Cobra (*Ophiophagus hannah*) (*Figs.* 41, 42, 43)

Other names. Ular anang (Java); *tedong selar* (Borneo); *ular kunyett terus* (for immature specimens, Malaya); hamadryad.

Distribution. This large, widely ranging species occurs in peninsular India to the western Himalayas, eastward through Burma and the Andaman Islands, into parts of southern China, and through Thailand, Laos, Viet Nam and Cambodia, then south and east through the Malay Peninsula and Archipelago.

Description. Its variable coloration is either yellowish, brownish, olive-green or blackish above, uniformly colored or marked across the back with numerous narrow crossbands which are margined in black. On the rear of the body and on the tail, the black gradually encroaches upon the lighter color, so that in some specimens these parts are black with light crossbands. The head is colored like the body with many of the scales edged in black. The throat is nearly always yellow or orange-yellow with variable black markings. Young king cobras, more vividly marked than the parents, possess a contrasting pattern of many narrow white or yellow crossbands on a black or dark brown body color. Occasionally, each scale between the bands is light centered. Four white lines cross the head of young snakes, one over the snout, another in front of the eye, one behind the eye, and the last one over the back of the head.

Size. The king cobra is the world's largest venomous snake, a record length of 18 ft 4 in. having been reported by Smith (1930) for a specimen from peninsular Thailand. Most adults are between 13 and 15 ft long. In relation to its size, the hood of the king cobra is not nearly as wide as that of the common cobra.

Habitat. While this diurnal species prefers a jungle environment, especially near streams, it does not confine itself to wooded regions. As a matter of fact, in Viet Nam and Bengal, India, it is usually seen on the plains, and in Thailand it also inhabits rather open country. Throughout Malaya, where the snake is common, it is frequently encountered on estates bordering the jungle. On one occasion, a large specimen was discovered on the Island Golf Course in Singapore, where evidently it had spent most of its life undetected. Despite its large size, it sometimes climbs trees.

Disposition. Much has been written about the unsavoury reputation of the king cobra. It has been described as ferocious and aggressive, and several accounts tell in detail of capricious attacks made by this snake upon human beings. However, in spite of its bad reputation, the king cobra, when disturbed by man, generally makes every possible effort to avoid an encounter, sometimes even while at the nest.

A classic example of such behavior was reported in Vol. 39 of the *Journal of the Bombay Natural History Society.* In this case, fourteen people in a picnic party, and their seven dogs, twice passed within 2 yd of a king cobra nest without creating any visible response from the snake. When a stick was poked into the nest, the snake merely thrust out its head momentarily from the pile of leaves to investigate. A somewhat similar report is made by Evans (1921), who several times closely approached an adult king cobra which had been flushed from hiding by a pack of dogs. The snake in this instance was given every reason to make an attack, having been provoked repeatedly, yet time and again it sought only to escape its tormentors. Tweedie describes the recent case of a forest worker who unwittingly stood on a king cobra's tail while inspecting a rubber tree. Hearing a hissing sound nearby, the man looked around, only to find that he was standing on the snake's tail. When he lifted his foot, the cobra crawled away, but immediately the man's dog brought the snake to bay. It is significant that with all of this provocation the reptile completely failed to take the initiative and attack.

Naturalists familiar with the king cobra agree that while this snake is potentially very dangerous, and although it may on rare occasions make an apparently unprovoked attack upon a human being, such attacks are exceptional and can usually be attributed to the snake's desire to protect its nest.

We are so accustomed to seeing photos of cobras with their hoods spread that many people do not realize that normally a cobra looks like any other snake. It is only when startled or annoyed that a cobra rears the forepart of its body and, by raising the unusually long forward ribs, distends the skin to form the hood. Because of its great length, a king cobra can rear up until its head is level with a man's chest, but its hood is relatively narrower than that of other cobras.

Food. Snakes apparently constitute the main item of food in the king cobra's diet, but other reptiles are also eaten. Smith (1943), for instance, reports that monitor lizards are sometimes consumed.

Young. Most oviparous snakes deposit their eggs in a suitable medium and pay no further attention to their development. Such is not the case with the king cobra. This species makes an elaborate two-chambered nest of leaves and other vegetable debris, the lower compartment for the eggs and the one above for the brooding female. The nest, which looks much like a pile of dead leaves, may contain from twenty to forty eggs. It is carefully guarded by the female, sometimes with the help of the male. When hatched, the young snakes measure about 20 or 21 in. in length, according to Wall (1924).

Cobras (*Naja*)

This group of dangerous snakes appears to be composed of seven species, only one of which occurs on the islands of the Pacific. The others occupy the continent of Africa and the countries of southern Asia.

All of them can spread a hood by widening and flattening the neck. The lack of occipital shields will separate the members of this group from the king cobra, which also is able to produce a hood.

Common Cobra (*Naja naja*) (*Figs.* 44, 44A)

Other names. *Ular tedong sendok* (Malaya); *ular bedul* (Malaya); *oraj sinduk* (Sundanese); *ular biludah* (Padang Highlands, western Sumatra); *hantipeh pura* (Dajak name); *aguason* (of the Philippine Manobos); *alupong* or *ulupung* (of the Philippine Tagalogs); *camamalu* (of the Philippine Pampangas); *tadioko* (Pangasinan, Luzon, Philippines).

Distribution. The extremely wide ranging common cobra inhabits southern Asia from Transcaspia to China, and the Malay Peninsula and Archipelago. Pacific records include Formosa, Sumatra, Riou, Banka, Borneo, Java, Lombok, Sumbawa, Flores, Alor, Wetar and the Philippine Islands (Bohol, Leyte, Luzon, Mindanao, Mindoro, Palawan, Samar).

Description. The common cobra, typically banded and spectacled on the hood throughout much of mainland Asia, shows considerable color and pattern variation in the Pacific area, two or more color varieties often occupying one island. On Sumatra it may be totally brown or black above, with no markings on the hood. The neck is white beneath with a black transverse band and three black spots up forward. A differently colored cobra is found on Java. Here it is pale brown, grey or black above, with one or more dark transverse bands on the belly towards the head. This one also lacks a hood marking. A third variety, found on both Java and Sumatra, is black or dark brown on top and beneath, but differs from the first two in having yellow or orange on the sides of the head and on the neck. The young of this snake possess a pale U- or O-shaped marking on back of the hood; the chin and throat are whitish. In Borneo we find a very dark phase of the common cobra that is black above and below. The yellowish-white throat of this snake lacks markings. The head is brown, paler on the sides. The race, *Naja n. miolepis*, found on the nearby Philippine Island of Palawan, also occurs in

Borneo. Another variety, uniformly olive-brown above and white beneath, lives on the islands of Flores and Alor. The Chinese cobra, *Naja n. atra*, still another race of the common cobra, is also found on Formosa. On that island it is generally black or very dark brown, with widely-spaced narrow white bands, the markings sometimes narrowly separated along the middle of the back. The head is either unmarked or bears an incomplete spectacle on the upper surface. Maki (1931) reports a maximum length of 5 ft 5 in. for a Formosan specimen.

In contrast to the wide color variation that exists among Indonesian populations of the common cobra, the color and pattern differences of Philippine Islands specimens are closely correlated with distribution. As a result, three clearly defined Philippine races have been recognized.

One of these, *Naja n. philippinensis*, from the islands of Luzon and Mindoro, can be described as light brown to olive brown on top, cream to yellow brown underneath. The adults have no distinctive crossbands; however, young ones show a reticulate pattern of indistinct, light lines, with small, round or lengthwise spots along the sides. On Luzon, where it is said to be very common, this species grows to a maximum length of about 57 in. Another and a slightly smaller race, *Naja m. miolepis*, from Palawan Island in the Philippines, and from Borneo, is dark brown to black above, yellow to grey underneath. It has no marking on the hood, either above or below. Taylor (1922), who gives its maximum length as slightly more than 4 ft, states that it is easily distinguishable from other Philippine forms by the uniformly dark color of the adults and by the white markings on the young. Juvenile specimens possess a dozen or more white or yellowish crossbands on the back and a distinctive chevron-shaped crossband behind the head, its apex pointed backward. According to Griffin (1909), this cobra is common on Palawan.

The subspecies from the southern islands of Bohol, Leyte, Mindanao and Samar, is the only Philippine race with a distinct black crossbar on the throat. It is dark brown to black above, usually with a network of yellowish lines on the back and a light line low along each side. Neither juveniles nor adults have crossbands on the back. In the Agusan Valley of Mindanao, where these snakes are common, Taylor (1922) found them crawling about in the daytime, over the forest floor and even on the lawn in front of his house. The largest one collected by him was a little more than 3½ ft long.

Habitat. The common cobra tolerates a wide variety of habitats wherever it is found. It lives out on the open plains, in jungles or in regions heavily populated by man. Tweedie (1942) says that Malayan specimens prefer the thick undergrowth, where they are most often encountered when secondary jungle is being cleared. According to Loveridge (1945), they may take up residence in old termite hills, among ruins, in root systems of large trees, or in the vicinity of human dwellings. They are equally adapted to living at sea level or in mountains of some height. On Sumatra, De Rooij (1917) records this snake from the Battak Mountains at 2400 to 3000 ft elevation, and Guenther (1864) says that in Sikkim, India, it has been found at an altitude of 8000 ft.

Disposition. There is general agreement that the cobra is not aggressive and bites only when accidentally stepped on or otherwise molested. As a matter of fact, Smith (1943) claims that cobras have on occasion been picked up and handled without making any effort to bite. He explains that generally this has taken place during the day when the snakes are less apt to defend themselves than they are at night. Acton and Knowles (1914) agree with this and state that cobras, better able to see at night, make a more determined strike in darkness. Smaller specimens are said to be much more aggressive than adults, with more inclination to bite.

Despite a peaceable nature, the common cobra of the Malay Peninsula, the Philippines and Sumatra, when sufficiently aroused, may spit its venom, usually aiming at the eyes of an intruder. Specimens from Komodo Island, although equally adapted for spitting, apparently are not inclined to do so. Studies made by Bogert (1943) disclosed that the fangs of spitting cobras are modified for directing the venom outward and upward as it leaves the fang orifice. Furthermore, the forcible ejection of poison from the fangs is assisted by a hissing, which serves to spray the venom for a distance of 6 ft or more. If deposited on the unbroken skin, the poison is harmless, but, if it reaches the eyes it causes severe inflammation, acute pain and temporary blindness. According to Kauffeld (1946), permanent damage may result if the eyes are not quickly flushed with a boric acid solution or with water.

All cobras are capable of raising the long ribs of the neck to form a hood, which they do only when annoyed or frightened. While the king cobra has relatively the narrowest hood spread of any cobra, the common cobra has the widest. When displaying the hood, the common cobra is able to erect itself from one-quarter to more than two-thirds of its total length.

Habits. This is an active, mostly nocturnal snake, that shows a decided fondness for water, occasionally entering brackish bays or the salt water of the ocean.

Size. Indian specimens grow over 6 ft long, but Pacific islands races are smaller, usually 4 to 5 ft long.

Food. Unlike the king cobra, which has an exclusively reptilian diet, this species feeds on a wide variety of small animals. It has been reported to eat frogs, toads, snakes, lizards, mice and rats, and less frequently, birds and their eggs. Pope (1929) tells of finding two loaches and an eel in the stomach of one cobra from Kokow, China, where fishes are numerous in the flooded and partly flooded rice fields. Newly-hatched captive cobras have eaten tadpoles and young frogs. In India, and perhaps elsewhere, the common cobra actively searches for food in the late afternoon and early evening.

Young. As with the king cobra, the males of this species may share in guarding the incubating eggs, which hatch in from 69 to 88 days. A shorter period of incubation is mentioned by Taylor (1922), who reports the hatching, after 49 days, of twelve eggs deposited in the laboratory by a female Philippine cobra, *Naja n. philippinensis.* The number of eggs laid by a female varies from 9 to 22, with one abnormally large clutch of 45 (36 of which were infertile) reported by Smith (1943). The newly-hatched snakes measure from 9½ to 14 in. long. They grow rapidly during the first year; some that measured 12 in. in length after hatching had an average length of 2 ft 6 in. after one year. Even before they have completely left the egg, while still partially protruding from the shell, the young cobras spread their hoods, ready to follow up this intimidating gesture with a venomous bite. The fact that the bite of a 5-day-old cobra caused the death of a guinea pig 22 min later, is an indication of the young snakes' capabilities.

Oriental Coral Snakes (*Calliophis*)

This group of small, slender snakes contains a half-dozen species, five of which occur on Pacific islands, and a number of subspecies. Together with the long-glanded snakes, they make up the most colorful assemblage of venomous species in the area under consideration. Oriental coral snakes are chiefly nocturnal, remaining hidden during the day within the humus of forest floors, or beneath logs, stones and other debris in wooded areas. In view of their small size, secretive habits and docile nature, they cannot be considered very dangerous to man.

The following key will help to separate the Pacific forms of *Calliophis.*

KEY TO THE ORIENTAL CORAL SNAKES OF THE PACIFIC

1. Scales in 15 rows; anal entire; 2 preoculars; range: Philippines . . —beautiful coral snake (*C. calligaster*)
   Scales in 13 rows; 1 (rarely 2) preoculars 2
2. Anal entire; temporals 2 + 2; range: Philippines . . . . . . McClung's coral snake* (*C. mcclungi*)
   Anal divided; temporals 1 + 0, 1 + 1, or 1 + 2 3
3. Temporals 1 × 0; belly shields more than 300; range: Sumatra† . . graceful coral snake (*C. gracilis*)
   Temporals 1 + 1 or 1 + 2 4
4. Back and sides without longitudinal black lines 5
   Back and sides with 1, 3, or 5 longitudinal black lines 6
5. Temporals 1 + 1; range: Taiwan . Swinhoe's coral snake (*C. m. swinhoei*)
   Temporals 1 + 2; range: Ryukyus . Iwasaki's coral snake (*C. m. iwasakii*)
6. Black side line interrupted by vestigial black crossbars edged with yellow; range: Ryukyus: (Fig. 45) . . . Striped coral snake (*C. j. japonicus*)
   Black side line uninterrupted; range: Taiwan: (Fig. 46) . . . . Sauter's coral snake (*C. j. sauteri*)

---

*Leviton (1961) has recently designated this form as a race of *C. calligaster*.
†Also Malay Peninsula.

Beautiful Coral Snake (*Calliophis calligaster*)

Distribution. Found only in the Philippine Islands.

Description. Unfortunately, published descriptions of this snake are based entirely upon specimens that have been in preserving fluid for a considerable time. As a result, some of the true colors have been lost, particularly the lighter ones, and it is necessary to speculate on the nature of the colors in life. The following description is based upon the works of Taylor (1922) and Leviton (1959).

The general body color of blue-black is marked with many narrow, dotted crossbands of yellowish-white. On the head the blue-black color extends down through the eye and across parts of the upper lip. The snout is yellowish and the temples are blackish. Two broad, bluish bands cross the flesh-pink tail, each one divided by a very narrow light line. The belly is barred with bluish-black and cream (red in life?). Young ones are cream (red?), with dark brown body bands. The head is yellow and there is a narrow band from the eye to the mouth. Specimens from Cebu, Negros and Panay differ from those on Luzon in that each crossband on the body is divided by a narrow white stripe which extends onto the belly, and by the less heavily marked temples. The bands of the Luzon snakes are solid, and the temples more heavily marked.

Size. Adults are about 18 in. long.

Habitat. Leviton (1959) tells us that one of these snakes was found buried in the soil of the dipterocarp forest on Mt. Makiling, and Taylor (1922) reports several specimens from low altitudes at the same place. From all indications, these are snakes of the lowlands, living at or near sea level.

Food. Apparently they feed on snakes, for one specimen contained a dwarf snake in its stomach and another had eaten a blind snake. Aside from this meager information, the habits of the beautiful coral snake remain unknown.

McClung's Coral Snake (*Calliophis mcclungi*)

Distribution. This extremely rare snake is known only from Polillo Island in the Philippines.

Description. According to Taylor (1922), this species is cream-white above, marked on the back with wide, purplish crossbands, some of them partly divided by a light streak which is visible on the abdomen, partly so on the sides. The first crossband on the neck is the widest and it extends forward onto the head. A black spot occurs around the eye.

Size. The only available preserved specimen is less than 7½ in. long.

Graceful Coral Snake (*Calliophis gracilis*)

Distribution. The limited range of this snake includes the Malay Peninsula and the nearby island of Sumatra.

Description. The pattern in this species consists of stripes and spots. The reddish or pale brown body is marked with three dark stripes that run the length of the snake. The stripe down the middle of the back passes through a series of small black spots; the stripes on the sides, one on either side of the first, pass through larger spots that alternate with those above. Low on each side near the belly, two or three black lines, enclosing one or two narrow yellow lines, extend the length of the body. The abdomen is barred with black and yellow, the tail with black and red.

Size. This snake reaches a length of slightly more than 2 ft.

Banded Coral Snake (*Calliophis macclellandi*) (*Fig.* 47)

Distribution. This species, in its various forms, ranges from Assam and Burma to southern China, Formosa and the Ryukyu Islands.

Description. The banded coral snake, a boldly marked species which is somewhat reminiscent of the North American coral snake, *Micrurus fulvius*, lacks the characteristic lengthwise banding of the next species, *Calliophis japonicus*. From the eastern part of its range, the banded coral snake is red above, with narrow black crossbands bordered on each side by yellow. Sometimes black spotting occurs between the bars. The head is black above except for a broad white bar across the head; the end of the snout is frequently light in color.

Two races of this snake occur in the Pacific: Swinhoe's coral snake from Formosa and Iwasaki's coral snake from the Ryukyu Islands.

Size. The longest specimen measured by Wall (1918) was 31 in. in length.

Habitat. While found occasionally at low altitudes and in open country, this is chiefly a snake of high, forested mountains having deep humus floors. Here, at elevations between 3000 and 4000 ft, it spends nearly all of its existence beneath stones, logs and other debris. Most of the specimens collected by Maslin in China were unearthed during excavations of one kind or another.

Disposition. The temperament of this attractively marked snake is not greatly different from that of other Oriental coral snakes. Pope (1929) remarked that it behaves in a stupefied manner and cannot be made to strike or bite. Yet, a specimen that he picked up at night by the end of the tail, tried to bite him.

Striped Coral Snake (*Calliophis japonicus*) (*Fig.* 45)

Distribution. Known only from Taiwan and the Ryukyu Islands.

Description. Although it shows a considerable amount of variation in markings, this species can easily be distinguished from the banded coral snake by the longitudinal black lines on its body. The greater number of specimens is crimson red above, with a median dark brown or black stripe down the back from head to tail. Most examples have an additional dark stripe on either side of the first one; a few show indications of still another stripe below each of the second pair. Thus, they may have a total of one, three or five such stripes. A number of widely spaced black rings, sometimes edged in white, extend around the body. The top of the head is brownish-black, this color finding its way down to the level of the eyes.

Sauter's coral snake, the subspecies from Taiwan, differs from the striped coral snake in several ways. In addition to having no rings around the body, its three longitudinal stripes are much broader than they are in the Ryukyu race, the two on the sides touching the belly. Furthermore, a broad yellow band, enclosed by black, extends over the head.

Size. Adult specimens are under a foot long.

Long-Glanded Snakes (*Maticora*)

This genus and the preceding Oriental coral snakes are closely related. As a matter of fact, the two groups are so much alike that no outward characters will serve to separate them. There is, however, a marked internal difference. This involves the venom glands which, in the Oriental coral snakes are situated at the sides of the head just behind the eyes, as they are in most poisonous species. Those of the long-glanded snakes, instead of being confined to the head, extend back into the body for nearly a third of its length, becoming gradually thicker and terminating in bulbous ends. They are generally small snakes, only one kind reaching a length of 5 ft. Three species are found in the Pacific, two of which are represented by several distinct races.

KEY TO THE LONG-GLANDED SNAKES OF THE PACIFIC

1. Diameter of eye about half as long as its distance from the mouth: range: Philippines . . Philippine long-glanded* snake (*Maticora philippina*)
   Diameter of eye much more than half as long as its distance from the mouth 2
2. Shields beneath tail in 15 to 33 pairs; range: Philippines southwest to Sumatra and east to Celebes† . . . . common long-glanded snake (*M. intestinalis* and races)
   Shields beneath tail in 34 to 50 pairs; range: Borneo; Sumatra; Java and adjacent islands . red-bellied long-glanded snakes (*M. bivirgatus* and races)

Philippine Long-glanded Snake (*Maticora philippina*)

Distribution. This snake is found only in the Philippine Islands of Luzon, Mindanao and Samar.

Description. The Philippine long-glanded snake is dark yellowish-brown above, each scale edged with a darker color. A dark line runs down the middle of the back, broken occasionally by a yellowish spot. On either side of this line is another, lighter stripe, below which the body color breaks

*Leviton (1961) considers this snake a subspecies of *M. intestinalis*.
†Also Malay Peninsula.

into darker brown or black bands that encircle the belly and are separated by orange. The bands under the tail are brilliant scarlet, much wider than those on the belly, and extend high up along the sides. Indistinct, darker shading marks the head. Juveniles of this snake are differently marked than the adults. A young specimen from Mindanao is described by Taylor (1922) as having a yellow head and a light line down the back which is broken by short, black, rectangular spots. On either side of this line is a dark brown, darker-edged stripe, beginning at the eye and continuing unbroken to the tail. The belly is barred with black and yellow, the colors extending up onto the sides. The tail is reddish below with two narrow black bars.

Size. Two feet is the maximum size.

Habits. On Mindanao, Taylor (1922) found them under rotting logs. When exposed to the light they did not move, but upon being touched, immediately began their aimless writhing and jumping, a behavior common among the long-glanded and Oriental coral snakes.

Common Long-Glanded Snake (*Maticora intestinalis*)

Other names. Banded Malaysian coral snake (Malaya); *ular chabe* (Java); *ular tjabeh* (Malaya); *tadung munggu* (Borneo); *ular kapala dua* (Sumatra); *oro odto* (Palawan group, Philippines).

Distribution. Its range includes Burma, Thailand and the Malay Peninsula and Archipelago. In the Pacific it is known from Java, Sumatra, Borneo, Celebes, Nias, Riou, Banka and the Philippine Islands (Balabac, Culion, Palawan, Jolo, Luzon, Mindanao and Samar).

Description. Generally dark brown to black above, this species has a narrow yellowish or red stripe down the middle of the back, which is occasionally interrupted by brown spots. Two light brown or yellow stripes extend parallel to, and on either side of, the first. Frequently there is another longitudinal light stripe lower on the sides. The white belly is barred with black and the tail is red above and below, sometimes with and often without crossbars. A yellow or whitish patch may mark the side of the head.

The common long-glanded snake, with its considerable color variation, does not have the same appearance in every part of its extensive geographic range. Leviton (1959) describes some of the Pacific island variations as follows:

In western Sumatra the snake possesses a light median stripe bordered by brown or black, a wider light brown to reddish brown or grey stripe on either side of it.

In eastern Sumatra and Java it generally has a prominent, very narrow white or yellow stripe down the back which divides on the head. The stripes on either side of this are usually indistinct, but those lower on the sides, when present, are distinct, light and narrow.

On Borneo and in the Philippines the median stripe is black or dark brown, the stripes below it are reddish brown, light brown or grey, and very distinct.

Specimens from the Philippine Islands and Borneo can be further segregated according to their markings and by distribution. For example, those from the Palawan Archipelago differ from the typical Bornean form in the presence of a distinct white line low on the sides near the belly. Furthermore, the black crossbars on the abdomen do not reach the black of the sides, and the light stripe high on either side is narrow. The common long-glanded snake from the Sulu Islands is similar to the typical Bornean form but differs in certain minor scale characters. In this snake the black crossbars on the underside contact the black along the sides, the stripe high on the side is broad and reddish-brown, and the white line low on the sides is missing.

A dark-colored mountain race from Malaya, Borneo and Celebes does not occur below 4000 ft elevation, at least in Malaya. In this snake, the median stripe along the back, and those on the sides, are black and difficult to distinguish from the dark body color; the black bars underneath are narrow.

Size. This small species reaches a length of only 2 ft.

Habitat. Apparently secretive, it is most often discovered under logs and beneath vegetable litter. Boulenger (1912), quoting Capt. Flower, says it was encountered both in bright daylight and after dark crawling slowly about.

Disposition. When touched or otherwise provoked, this snake does not attempt to crawl away to safety, but throws its coils about, twisting and tumbling in a most unorthodox manner. During these maneuvers, the belly is often exposed. Sometimes it simply raises the tail to display the coral-red undersurface, or it may crawl away with the tail held in this position.

Red-bellied Long-glanded Snake (*Maticora bivirgata*)

Other names. Blue Malaysian coral snake (Malay); *ular sina matahari* (Malaya); *ular tedong matahari* (Singapore); *kendawang* (Dyak); *pito* (Borneo); *ular tjabeh* (Malaya); *oraj tjabeh* (Java).

Distribution. This large species is known from peninsular Thailand, and the Malay Peninsula and Archipelago. It is reported from the Pacific islands of Java, Sumatra, Borneo, Banka, Nias and the Mentawi Islands.

Description. While the color and pattern exhibit a great amount of variation, the three described races of this snake are easily distinguished from one another and fit into well-defined geographic areas. The iridescent blue or bluish-black body color contrasts with the longitudinal pale blue lines along the sides and with the bright coral-red of the head, tail and belly.

Specimens from the mainland and from the islands of Sumatra, Nias, the Mentawi group and Banka possess broad blue or purplish bands along the sides. In a few specimens a narrow, white line may divide this marking into two halves. The upper part of the tail bears a black stripe that occasionally separates into small spots.

Javan examples are blackish above, with a whitish band or line low on the sides, broadest up forward, fading or disappearing to the rear. In this race, the upper surface of the tail is brown-red, without a black stripe as in the first subspecies. It can be identified, however, by a pair of narrow, white, zigzag lines along the sides just above the white band.

Size. Large specimens are as much as 5 ft long, but the average length is 2 to 3 ft.

Habitat. Common in the lowlands and hills.

Disposition. These snakes cannot be considered a serious hazard to man. Like the common long-glanded snakes, they show a reluctance to bite in self-defense.

Food. The diet is quite similar to that of other long-glanded species, and consists primarily of snakes.

Death Adder (*Acanthophis antarcticus*)

This genus is represented by only one species and possibly two races. No other elapid snake looks so much like an adder or viper. The head of the death adder is wide, the neck is narrow, and the body is unusually short and heavy.

Death Adder (*Acanthophis antarcticus*) (*Fig.* 48)

Distribution. This species occurs throughout Australia (in all states except Tasmania) and on the Pacific islands of Obi, Ceram, Haruku, Timor Laut, Kei Islands, Aru Islands, New Guinea and the Southern Islands.

Description. The most outstanding feature of this elapid snake is the unusual viperine appearance. Unlike other members of the cobra and coral snake family, it has a broad, flat head which is set off from the short, heavy body by a small neck. The short tail terminates in a light-colored spine that has the appearance of a segmented worm. The general body color is variable and may be grey, brown, yellowish or brick red, according to the locality in which it lives. Body markings, consisting of darker crossbands with irregular edges, are most pronounced in young specimens.

Size. The average size is 18 to 24 in., but large examples may reach a length of 1 yd.

Habitat. It generally is associated with dry, scrubby areas, although not necessarily limited to this kind of an environment. Barbour (1912), for example, found them in damp, heavily forested regions on New Guinea and Ceram.

Disposition. Nocturnal in habits, the death adder is sluggish during the day, often lying half buried in loose sand or dust. Thus concealed, it remains motionless and makes no effort to move out of the way when approached. Worrell (1952), an experienced collector, says that it does not go out of its way to attack, but when closely approached, will often strike at anything within range, even if unprovoked. He states further that the strike is amazingly quick and accurate. The length of a strike is said to be about nine inches.

Habits. The remarkable manner by which the death adder attracts lizard prey is described by Worrell (1952). It illustrates how a heavy-bodied snake such as this may catch an active and swiftly moving animal which it could not possibly overtake by pursuit. The snake, lying at rest with the tail tip near the head, simply waits for its prey. At the approach of a lizard, the adder twitches the end of the tail in a peristaltic motion that simulates to a surprising degree the movement of a segmented worm. The moment the lizard attempts to seize the " bait ", it is itself captured. A death adder in the writer's care displayed such tail wiggling only a few times during its more than seven years in captivity. On one occasion, a keeper, cleaning the snake's cage, was attracted by what appeared to be a mealworm moving in the sand a short distance from the specimen. As he reached down with a pair of forceps to remove the " worm ", he realized his mistake and withdrew his hand. Closer examination showed that most of the snake's tail was buried below the sand, with only the light-colored tip exposed.

Young. The death adder gives birth to living young, twelve to fifteen at a time.

Medical importance. The death adder is a dangerous snake. Kinghorn (1956) maintains that its venom is more potent that that of the Indian cobra, and Barrett (1950) comments that recorded cases of its bite show a 50 per cent mortality rate. Death results from respiratory failure produced by paralysis of the muscles controlling the diaphragm. As in most elapid envenomations, there is little effect at the bite. The fangs are relatively short, but this deficiency is offset by the snake's toxic venom and large venom glands.

Müller's and Schlegel's Snakes (*Aspidomorphus*)

Little is known about these two closely related species. In view of their small size and rarity, it is presumed they are not dangerous to man.

Müller's Snake (Aspidomorphus mülleri)

Distribution. This species is found on the following Pacific islands: New Guinea, New Britain, New Ireland, Duke of York, Mansinam, Misool, Salawatti, Ceram, Woodlark, Fergusson and Trobriand.

Description. Specimens are uniformly grey or brown, but all have larger and smaller, light-edged, rounded spots on top of the head. Along the side of the head is a light band, broadly interrupted by an oblique dark bar below the eye. Specimens from Woodlark, Fergusson and Trobriand islands have dark lines on the back and fewer spots on the head. Brongersma (1934), who has clarified the classification of these snakes, says that specimens from the Bismark Archipelago are like those from Papua, but are smaller.

Size. This small snake may reach a length of 2½ ft.

Schlegel's Snake (*Aspidomorphus schlegelii*)

Distribution. The distribution of this snake includes New Guinea (especially the western part) and surrounding islands on the Sahul shelf.

Description. In this species, which may be either grey or brown, the top of the head is marked with only a few small spots or none at all. The light-colored band at the side of the head is not interrupted by a broad, oblique bar under the eye. A number of light and dark bands parallel the one on the head and extend backward onto the body. The throat is almost entirely black or thickly powdered with brown. Some specimens are so darkly colored that the light bands have become indistinct. One specimen, from Lake Sentani, was uniformly grey in color with only a trace of markings.

Size. This is a smaller snake than its relative, Müller's snake, 18 in. being about maximum length.

TAIPAN (*Oxyuranus scutellatus*)

One species and two races of this large and extremely dangerous snake have been described, only one of which occurs in the islands of the Pacific.

Taipan (*Oxyuranus scutellatus*) (*Figs.* 49, 50)

Other names. *Diriora* or *gobari* (Port Moresby region of New Guinea).

Distribution. In Australia the taipan is restricted to the northn part of the continent, from the Cape York Peninsula, along the Gulf of Carpentaria, to northeast Queensland. Its Pacific distribution is limited to New Guinea, where it has been found in the Fly River District at the southeastern part, and at other points along the coast to the vicinity of Port Moresby.

Description. The New Guinea race of this snake, *Oxyuranus s. canni*, differs from the Australian form in certain characters of the skull, in some scale characters and in color. It is greyish-black above, with a prominent broad, reddish-orange area on the posterior two-thirds of the back. The young are marked much like the adults.

Size. The usual length of the taipan is between 7 and 8 ft, but large specimens may reach a length of 11 ft.

Habitat. In southeastern New Guinea this snake occurs in the savannah forest and on inland plains, but it is more abundant along the coast near river banks where grasslands intercept wooded areas. It shows a preference for country dotted with boulders, and in such places, secrets itself in the burrows of animals.

Disposition. In addition to being one of the longest of all poisonous snakes, the taipan is also reported by some herpetologists as one of the most aggressive species. Ordinarily shy and retiring, the taipan under provocation becomes an extremely vicious and dangerous adversary. When preparing to attack, it flattens the head and neck vertically and raises one or two coils of the body off the ground, at the same time waving the tail back and forth in an elevated position. Thus prepared, the snake strikes with such speed and unexpectedness that a victim may receive several bites before he can take any action to defend himself. Much of the venom, according to Thomson (1933), is injected during the first assault, so that little can be milked from the snake immediately following an attack.

Medical importance. The recovery rate from the bites of this species is extremely low. Death, when it occurs, comes relatively quickly. According to Kinghorn's (1956) records, only one of at least six white persons bitten have survived. Oliver (1958) reports two recoveries among human victims. In two fatal cases, death occurred within 7 hr of the bite, despite the use of every known treatment; in another case the victim died the day following the accident. Flecker (1944) cites a case history involving a 21 year-old aboriginal girl, bitten on the back of her bare foot, who died soon after being admitted to a hospital.

The high fatality rate is not only the result of the great amount of venom injected by the snake, but is also due to the high toxicity of the venom. Morgan (1956) demonstrated that it is almost twice as toxic as that of the tiger snake.

Food. Apparently it feeds mostly on rats, which it seeks chiefly during the daytime and early evening.

Young. The number of eggs laid by a taipan varies from three to seven. The largest egg from one clutch measured slightly more than 1½ by 3 in. Oliver (1958) mentions an incubation period of 91 days. The young snakes were from 12½ to 17 in. in length a few hours after hatching.

Brown Snakes (*Demansia*)

This is an important group of snakes in Australia, where a number of different kinds occur, some of them considered deadly. Only one species, with two races, occurs in New Guinea.

Spotted-headed Snake (*Demansia psammophis*) (*Fig.* 51)

Distribution. This snake is known from Australia and New Guinea.

Description. The body color varies from orange or reddish-brown to grey or yellow; there are no markings except for the black-tipped body scales and a distinctive black-edged yellow marking around the eye. Worrell (1952) remarks that a short, black streak curving below the eye gives the marking the appearance of a comma.

Size. Average spotted-headed snakes are less than 3 ft long. The maximum length is about 6 ft.

Habitat. In Australia it prefers a sandy habitat, where it has been found hibernating under sandstone rocks and at the bases of trees.

Disposition. A normally inoffensive snake, it prefers to crawl away when annoyed. However, if greatly provoked, it delivers a number of quick snaps.

Food. The food of this terrestrial snake consists of small mammals and birds, sometimes lizards and frogs. The young eat insects.

Young. From fifteen to twenty eggs are deposited by one female.

BLACK AND MULGA SNAKES (*Pseudechis*)

In all, there are about eleven species in this group, two of which are found in New Guinea, the remainder in Australia. They are generally large and dangerous, but seldom deadly to man.

Common Mulga Snake (*Pseudechis australis*) (*Fig.* 52)

Other names. King brown snake (Australia).

Distribution. The common mulga snake is found in the northern and northeastern parts of Australia and in southern New Guinea.

Description. This species is uniformly colored and without markings. Its olive-brown to coppery-brown color is relieved only by the orange-tipped scales on the body. The lighter under-surface is yellowish, sometimes with faint orange blotches. Older specimens have less color. Sometimes confused with the more dangerous taipan, it can be distinguished from that species by its smooth, instead of keeled, scales.

Size. Worrell (1952) found a specimen in Queensland, Australia which measured 9 ft in length. This probably constitutes a record size. He states that 6 ft-long individuals are rather common on the continent.

Habitat. According to Worrell (1952), the mulga snake inhabits drier regions, as do all brown-colored species of the genus.

Disposition. This large and heavy elapid snake becomes aggressive when aroused, flattening the neck, champing the jaws and striking repeatedly. If it succeeds in biting, it will usually hold on and chew. Fortunately, it does not have a highly toxic venom.

Food. Its diet consists of rodents, bandicoots, lizards and snakes.

New Guinea Mulga Snake (*Pseudechis papuanus*)

Other names. Papuan *pseudechis*.

Distribution. This species inhabits only southeastern New Guinea.

Description. Very similar to the common mulga snake, it differs from that species in details of scalation and in color. It is blackish above and below, with a whitish chin. The scales around the middle of the body are in nineteen to twenty-one rows, in the common mulga snake they are in seventeen rows.

GUPPY'S AND WOODFORD'S SNAKES (*Denisonia*)

East of New Guinea in the Solomons are two allied snakes of the genus *Denisonia* with 15 to 17 scales around midbody; they may be separated by seeing whether

Shields under tail are mostly single; range: Faro; Guadalcanal; Howla; Melanta; Ysabel . . . . . . Guppy's snake (*Denisonia par*)
Shields under tail are paired; range: New Georgia; Rendova; Tetipara; Vanguna, etc. . . . Woodford's snake (*Denisonia woodfordii*)

Guppy's Snake (*Denisonia par*)

Distribution. Known only from the Solomon Islands of Faro, Guadalcanal, Howla, Melanta and Ysabel.

Description. The body color in this species is extremely variable; it may be yellowish-white, pink, reddish, brown, grey or black, with or without red-brown crossbars. The head is dark.

Size. Reaches a length of slightly more than 3 ft.

Woodford's Snake (*Denisonia woodfordii*)

Distribution. Known from the Solomon Islands of New Georgia, Rendova, Tetipara, Vanguna, and others.

Description. The general body color is pale sandy brown. Each scale is dark-edged, giving the effect of a fine reticulated pattern.

Size. Grows to a length of slightly more than 3 ft.

BROWN-HEADED SNAKE (*Glyphodon*)

The single species of this genus occurs in New Guinea as well as on the Australian mainland.

Brown-headed Snake

Distribution. This snake is found in northeastern Australia, and from the Aru Islands west through southeastern New Guinea to the islands of the Torres Straits.

Description. The dark brown or blackish body is unmarked except for the light-colored edges of the scales. A yellowish or pale reddish patch occupies the back of the head and nape, and the dark color of the back and sides extends onto the yellow belly.

Size. Three feet is the maximum length for this snake.

Habits. Beyond the fact that it is terrestrial, nothing is known of its habits.

ELONGATE AND MT. STANLEY SNAKES (*Toxicocalamus*)

The two species in this genus have small heads no wider than the neck, slender bodies and round eye pupils. The fangs are very short and the solid teeth that follow them decrease in length gradually from front to back. Neither species is considered dangerous to man.

The two species of *Toxicocalamus* may be recognized as follows:

Midbody scales in 17 rows; belly scales 274 to 305; range: Ferguson and Woodlark Islands, New Guinea . . . elongate snake (*T. longissimus*)

Midbody scales in 15 rows; belly scales 230 to 261; range: Owen Stanley Mountains, 2000 to 4000 ft . . . Mt. Stanley snake (*T. stanlevanus*)

Elongate Snake (*Toxicocalamus longissimus*)

Distribution. This species is found in the Woodlark and Ferguson Islands near New Guinea.

Description. It is greyish-brown above, whitish on the sides, each scale with a grey-brown streak. A reddish bar cross the snout and another crosses behind the eye, otherwise the dark color of the head forms two vertical bars across the yellow upper lip. The underside is white, marked by two grey-brown, lengthwise stripes. The tail ends in a compressed horny scale which is keeled above.

Size. Known specimens are about 2 ft long.

Mt. Stanley Snake (*Toxicocalamus stanleyanus*)

Distribution. This species is confined to the Owen Stanley Mountains of New Guinea.

Description. The general color of the body is blackish-brown. The two rows of scales on each side near the abdomen are white with black centers. As with the elongate snake, the dark color on top of the head extends down the sides to form two vertical bars across the yellow upper lip. A yellow, black-bordered collar crosses the neck. The snake is white underneath with a black spot on each side of the belly plates. Like the preceding species, this one has a compressed, horny scale on the end of the tail.

Size. This species reaches a length of approximately 2 ft.

SHORT-FANGED SNAKE (*Ultrocalamus preussi*)

This group, containing only one species and two races, is not found outside of New Guinea. Its members have slender bodies and small heads. In these snakes the fangs are short; the solid teeth that follow gradually diminish in size from front to back. Bogert and Matalas (1945) tell us that, in proportion to its length, this species has the shortest fangs of any known elapid snake. The fang of a specimen 20 in. long measured only 0.8 mm.

Short-fanged Snake (*Ultrocalamus preussi*)

Distribution. The short-fanged snake is confined to New Guinea and to the island of Seleo off its northern coast.

Description. This small, slender species has been separated into two races by Bogert and Matalas (1945), who describe it as dark brown above. The two rows of scales on each side near the belly are lighter in color, each involved scale centered with a dark spot. A cream-colored band extends across the back of the head to the lips on either side. The tail terminates in a cream-colored, blunt scale.

Size. The maximum known length is 28 in.

Habitat. Presumably these are burrowing and insectivorous snakes.

GENUS (*Apistocalamus*)

From New Guinea five species of *Apistocalamus* have been described, several from a single example. When more specimens are available, it is possible that some of these " species " will have to be united. An idea of their overlapping can be gained from the following list.

Belly shields 173 to 193; subcaudals 28 to 46; range: Mount Lamington district . . . . Mt. Lamington snake (*A. lamingtoni*)
Belly shields 190; subcaudals 41; range: Owen Stanley Mountains at 4000 ft . . . . Pratt's snake (*A. pratti*)
Belly shields 196; subcaudals 50 or more; range: Haveri, Moroka . . —Lori's snake (*A. loriae*)
Belly shields 199 to 218; subcaudals 22 to 32; range: north of Fakfak at 1700 ft . . . . Lönnberg's snake (*A. lönnbergi*)
Belly shields 207; subcaudals 27; range: Setekwa River . . . . —giant *Apistocalamus* (*A. grandis*)

Mount Lamington Snake (*Apistocalamus lamingtoni*)

Distribution. This snake is known only from the Mt. Lamington district in New Guinea.

Description. Young specimens possess a yellow neck collar which is absent in the adults.

Pratt's Snake (*Apistocalamus pratti*)

Distribution. The range of this species is confined to the Owen Stanley Mountains, where it has been found at an elevation of about 4000 ft.

Description. Pratt's snake is olive-brown above, with an oblique, yellowish streak on each side of the neck. The upper lip is yellow. The belly is yellowish and marked with a row of olive-brown spots down the middle, which combine near the middle of the body to form a band. A pointed scale, keeled above, is located on the end of the tail.

Size. It is known to reach a length of about 13 in.

Lori's Snake (*Apistocalamus loriae*)

Distribution. Known from Haveri and Moroka on New Guinea.

Description. The general body color is dark greyish-olive. The upper lips are yellowish. Three rows of small dark spots mark the yellowish abdomen, while the underside of the tail is dark, with light edges.

Size. This species is less than 2 ft long.

Lönnberg's Snake (*Apistocalamus lönnbergi*)

Distribution. The range is limited to the region north of Fakfak, New Guinea, at 1700 ft elevation.

Description. The color of this snake is dark olive-brown above, the scales along the sides bearing whitish centers. A yellow collar, and two spots of the same color, may be present on the back of the head. The belly is unmarked. The tail ends in a pointed scale, keeled above.

Giant Apistocalamus (*Apistocalamus grandis*)

Distribution. The range of this species is limited to the region about the Setekwa River in southern New Guinea.

Description. The dark brown body is marked with irregular whitish blotches. The upper lip is white, as is the belly. The tail ends in a pointed scale, keeled above.

Size. This species, the largest member of the group, is known to reach a length of 37 in.

IKAHEKA AND BANDED SNAKES (*Micropechis*)

The two species in this group, of which the larger grows to a length of 5 ft, occur in New Guinea and on the Solomon Islands.

Ikaheka Snake (*Micropechis ikaheka*)

Distribution. This species is known from the island of Bantanta and from New Guinea, where it has been collected at about 4000 ft elevation.

Description. The snake is yellow above. Irregular rows of black may cross the back; generally, however, the forepart of the body is uniform yellowish, the rear part black, each scale margined with yellow. While the head and tail are black, the belly is yellowish.

Size. This snake grows to about 5 ft in length.

Banded Snake (*Micropechis elapoides*)

Distribution. Its range is limited to the Solomon Islands.

Description. The cream-colored body is marked with black crossbands; many small, black spots form a streak down each side of the back. The end of the snout and the region about the eyes are black. Rings of black circle the tail.

Size. Smaller than the preceding species, it has a maximum length of about 30 in.

NYMAN'S SNAKE (*Pseudapistocalamus nymani*)

A single species of the genus is known. It has a small head which is depressed and scarcely distinct from the neck. The small fangs are followed by teeth that gradually decrease in size from front to back.

Nyman's Snake (*Pseudapistocalamus nymani*)

Distribution. Sattelberg, New Guinea.

Description. This snake is iridescent bronze-brown or blackish above, lighter on the sides. It shows a yellow band across the front of the head and a yellow spot on each side of the neck. The upper lips are yellowish. The blackish-brown abdomen is edged with light grey, and a pointed scale, keeled on top, is located at the end of the tail.

Size. The usual adult length appears to be 16 or 17 in.

HEDIGER'S SNAKE (*Parapistocalamus hedigeri*)

This genus contains only one species.

Hediger's Snake (*Parapistocalamus hedigeri*)

Distribution. Hediger's snake is known only from Bougainville in the Solomon Islands.

Description. Only one specimen of this 12 in.-long snake has ever been collected. It apparently is blackish-grey above, with a row of white scales low on the sides near the belly. The throat and underside of the tail are lightly washed with grey.

FIJI SNAKE (*Ogmodon vitianus*)

There is only one species in this genus.

Fiji Snake (*Ogmodon vitianus*)

Distribution. Known only from the Fiji Islands.

Description. This, the only venomous land snake in the Fijis, is too small to be of medical importance. It may be dark brown to blackish on top, somewhat lighter colored along the sides, and brown or white beneath, with indistinct black spotting. The tail is entirely black.

Size. The usual adult length is 15 in.

SEA SNAKES

Family Hydrophiidae

This family of highly specialized, exclusively aquatic serpents contains some fifty-two different species which vary in size from the small, 18 in. long Crocker's sea snake of the Solomon Islands, to the widely distributed *Hydrophis spiralis*, which occasionally grows to a length of 9 ft.

Their distribution includes the coasts of Asia from the Persian Gulf to Japan, south through the Indo-Australian seas to Australia, then east in the Pacific to the Samoan Islands. Only one, the yellow-bellied sea snake, ranges beyond these limits. It occurs from the east coast of Africa, across the

Indian and Pacific oceans to the west coast of Latin America, and from southern Siberia to Tasmania.

All of them are immediately recognizable by the unusual shape of the tail, which is greatly flattened from side to side much like the blade of an oar (Fig. 13). In this they resemble certain eels. However, the sea snakes can be identified by their normally dry, scaly covering; eels have a smooth, slimy skin. In addition to the unique tail shape, some sea snakes possess a body that is vertically flattened for nearly its entire length. In others, the back half or one-third of the snake is unusually thick, with the front part proportionately very long and slender; the small head is little, if any, wider than the neck. The broad belly scales usually found in land-dwelling species are greatly reduced in most kinds of sea snakes and may be absent in some, only a few of them having retained the full-sized ventral scales. This too is in keeping with their aquatic habits, since large abdominal scales for crawling would be of no value in the water. Their ability to tolerate the rigors of a salt water environment is explained by Leviton (1959), who points out that sea snakes possess a thickened skin, especially between the scales, and that this serves as a protection against body fluid loss or penetration of the body by salt ions. A further adaptation for an aquatic life is the position of the nostrils on top of the head (except in *Laticauda*) and their water-tight, valve-like closures.

Thus equipped, the members of this family have made their way to most parts of the warmer Pacific. A principal factor governing the distribution of nearly all sea snakes is the depth of the water in which they feed. It must be shallow enough for them to go to the bottom for food and to rise to the surface for air. Because of this limitation, sea snakes seldom venture very far out from land. They prefer the relatively shallow waters along the coasts and are especially common in the vicinity of river mouths. The outstanding exception to this rule is the yellow-bellied sea snake, an ocean-going reptile whose wanderings take it hundreds of miles from land. Occasionally sea snakes swim upriver to points one-hundred miles or more from the ocean. In Malaya, Reid (1956) has information of a boy fatally bitten at the edge of a river some five miles from the sea. Close to shore they may inhabit rock crevices, tree roots along beaches, or pilings that support houses built over the water. Fishermen in the Philippine Islands may bring in as many as a hundred with one haul of a net, and on the coast of Malaya at least one specimen is captured with each drag of a seine. The largest concentration of sea snakes ever to be reported was described by Lowe (1932). On a steamer journey that took him between the Malay Peninsula and Sumatra, Lowe observed a line of Stokes' sea snakes in the water that was 10 ft wide and fully sixty miles long. The mass of snakes, estimated to consist of millions of individuals, was presumed to be migrating or to be concerned in some way with the breeding season.

In spite of the abundance of sea snakes, relatively few people are ever bitten by them. Their disposition varies according to species. Generally, they are inoffensive and seldom offer to bite, even when provoked by rough handling. There are numerous accounts of fishermen picking up sea snakes with a complete disregard for their venomous qualities. The banded sea snake, especially, is said to be remarkably gentle, and there appears to be no record of a bite from this species suffered by a human being. A few kinds, however, are not so reluctant to defend themselves. In Malaya, the common sea snake, *Enhydrina schistosa*, was found by Reid (1956) to be much more aggressive than the other local forms observed by him. When held by the back of the head in preparation for venom extraction, specimens of this snake snapped their jaws repeatedly, even before the venom collecting spoon was within reach. The chittul, *Hydrophis cyanocinctus*, also bit readily as a rule, but held on more tenaciously. After the milking operation it was often necessary to remove the spoon forcibly from between its jaws. Some observers agree that sea snakes are more aggressive during the breeding season. In the Philippine Islands, according to Herre (1942), they retire to small, uninhabited coral or rocky islands to have their young. Here they may be seen gathered together by the hundreds, actively crawling about and prepared to bite with little provocation. At such times it would be dangerous to step ashore.

Not a great deal of useful information is available about the venoms of sea snakes. It is known that some species are deadly to man and that others can create no more serious effects in a human being than a short period of discomfort. Most present-day knowledge concerning the subject has been provided by Dr. H. A. Reid and his associates.

The fangs of sea snakes are short, grooved and immovable, just as they are in the closely related cobras and kraits. And in common with their elapid relatives, these ocean-dwelling snakes are provided with a basically neuro-toxic venom.

Of approximately fifty-two different kinds of sea snakes recognized today, about forty are found in the Pacific area. They are separated into two large subfamily groups as follows:

I. *Laticaudinae*. This small group includes the genera *Laticauda*, *Aipysurus* and *Emydocephalus*. All of these have body scales which overlap one another, and enlarged belly plates like those found in most land-dwelling snakes. They are seldom found far from shore and some of them may even leave the ocean to lay their eggs on land.

II. *Hydrophiinae*. In this group, which takes in all of the remaining sea snakes, the body scales sometimes overlap, but more often do not. They are purely aquatic species.

The family *Hydrophiidae* is a small one, containing only 2 to 3 per cent of all known species of snakes; but in spite of the relatively small number of kinds involved, they are not always easily distinguished from one another. Many different species possess the same general pattern of dark rings or cross-bands on a brown- or olive-colored body. This similarity, when it occurs, makes the separation of kinds difficult. In some cases there is also a marked degree of individual variation within one species, which renders identification even more troublesome. The following key, taken from Loveridge's *Reptiles of the Pacific World*, will be helpful in determining the genus to which a sea snake belongs.

KEY TO GENERA OF SEA SNAKES IN THE PACIFIC*

1. Belly shields large, one third to over half the body width . . . 2
   Belly shields small, not more than one quarter of the body width (except in *Hydrophis mertoni*), or absent 5
2. Nostrils open sidewards; nasal shields separated by internasals; range: Japan southwest to Sumatra east to the Fijis and Savage Islands: (Figs. 20, 21) . . . . *Laticauda*
   Nostrils open upwards; nasal shields in contact with each other . . 3
3. Upper lip bordered by 3 shields on each side; no maxillary teeth following the fangs; range: Taiwan and Ryukyus east to Loyalty Islands: (Figs. 22, 27) . . . . *Emydocephalus*
   Upper lip bordered by 6 to 10 shields on each side; 5 to 11 maxillary teeth following the fangs 4
4. Belly shields one third to half the body width; maxillary bone extending forward beyond the palatine; range: Sumatra east to New Caledonia . *Aipysurus*
   Belly shields nearly as broad as the body width; maxillary bone not extending forward beyond the palatine; range: northwest Australia . *Ephalophis*
5. Belly shields small but distinct throughout, normally entire (see also *Kerilia jerdoni*; *Lapemis curtus*) 6
   Belly scales, except on the forward portion, either divided longitudinally and usually smaller than the adjacent scales, or absent, *i.e.* not distinguishable (except in occasional specimens of *Kerilia* and *Lapemis*) (Fig. 9). . 11
6. Head shields normally regular, the nasal shields in contact with each other . 7
   Head shields more or less divided posteriorly 10
7. No preocular shield in front of eye; range: northern Australia . . *Hydrelaps*
   A preocular shield in front of eye 8
8. Chin shield very long, partly hidden in a groove; range: (? Japan); Borneo and Malay Straits east to New Guinea . . . . *Enhydrina*
   Chin shields normal 9
9. Belly shields of uniform width throughout; range: Japan southwest to Sumatra east to the Fijis . . . . *Hydrophis*
   Belly shields broad on front of body, narrower on hinder part; range: Borneo south to Java . . . . *Praescutata*
10. Body scales large, 31 to 35 around middle of body; forming regular rows; range: Borneo south to Java, east to the Moluccas. . . . *Thalassophis*
    Body scales small, 70 to 90 around middle of body; in irregular rows; range: Java seas . . . . *Kolphphis*
11. 23 scales or less (19 to 23) around middle of body; maxillary bone extending forward beyond palatine; a series of teeth following close behind fangs; range: Borneo to Malay Straits . . . . *Kerilia*
    23 scales or more (23 to 67) around middle of body 12

*Ranges extending to other oceans not included.

12. Shields above and behind eye spiny; range: (? Hong Kong) east to Torres Straits, New Guinea . . . . *Acalyptophis*
    Shields above and behind eye without spines 13
13. Less than 45 (25 to 43) scales around middle of body 14
    More than 45 (47 to 67) scales around middle of body 15
14. Head very small; body long and very slender in its forward portion; maxillary bone extending forward as far as or a little farther than the palatine; range: Hainan south to Sumatra and Java (possibly east to Australia) . —*Microcephalophis*
    Head not small; body not long nor particularly slender in its forward portion; maxillary bone not extending forward as far as the palatine; range: Japan southwest to Sumatra east to New Guinea and the Queensland coasts . . . . *Lapemis*
15. Back scales pointed and strongly overlapping; belly shields in two halves; range: China sea east to Torres Straits, New Guinea: (Fig. 9) . . *Astrotia*
    Back scales neither pointed nor overlapping but forming a mosaic: belly shields, if at all larger than the adjacent scales, with a median groove; range: southern Siberia southwest to Sumatra east to Samoa and Panama: (Fig. 10) . . . . *Pelamis*

The following sea snakes represent the more important species found in the area under discussion. Since most of them are the only species to occur within their respective genera, they are listed without generic headings.

Black-banded Sea Snake (*Laticauda laticaudata*) (*Figs.* 20, 21)

Distribution. The black-banded sea snake occurs from the Bay of Bengal to the Ryukyu Islands and south through the East Indian Archipelago to Australia.

Description. The body color is light or dark bluish-grey above. There are numerous broad, black to blackish-brown rings around the body, separated by spaces of nearly equal width, the markings sometimes incomplete on the belly. The head is black and the upper lips are yellow. A curved yellow mark occurs on top of the head, this color extending forward to cover the snout and parts of the sides. The belly is yellow and an elongate yellow mark is found beneath the lower jaw.

The body scales are smooth and overlapping; those on the belly are wide, being about four times as broad as long.

Size. The black-banded sea snake reaches a maximum length of 3 ft.

Habitat. According to Taylor (1922), this species is usually found about rocky seacoasts. Herre (1942) states that it is common in harbours, bays and on rocky shores in Philippine waters.

Banded Sea Snake (*Laticauda colubrina*) (*Fig.* 53)

Other names. *Uao-uao* (of the Philippine Misamis).

Distribution. This species is found from the Bay of Bengal to Japan and Australia, then east to the Friendly Islands and south to New Zealand.

Description. It is light or dark bluish grey above and yellowish below, with dark-brown or black bands which go nearly around the body. The markings are much the same width above and below, or a little wider along the middle of the back. The yellow color of the snout extends backward on each side of the head, crossing over the eye to the upper lips; otherwise the head is mostly black.

All of the body scales are smooth and overlapping. The belly plates are about four times as long as wide.

In this sea snake the body is nearly the same thickness for its entire length and no bigger around than the head.

Size. Five ft appears to be the greatest length attained by the banded sea snake.

Habitat. Writing of its habitat in the Philippine Islands, Taylor (1922) says it is abundant along the coast where (in the Sulu Archipelago) it was discovered in large numbers on small, rocky islands, generally in the cracks of cliffs and under rocks. They are, he reported, more terrestrial than the other poisonous water snakes. In another part of the Pacific, at Pulau Salo, a small island near Singapore, Herre (1942) observed fifteen of them in $\frac{1}{4}$ hr among the exposed root masses of trees that grow along the beaches. He remarks that the species is most active in late afternoon or at night.

Young. This is one of the few sea snakes that lays eggs.

Erabu-unagi (*Laticauda semifasciata*) (*Fig.* 54)

Distribution. The limited range of this sea snake includes the Philippine Islands, the Moluccas and the Ryukyu Islands.

Description. The color is greenish or greyish above and yellowish below. The broad, dark bands that encircle the body are widest at the middle of the back and broader than the light spaces between them. The head is dark brown with a yellow curved mark on top which connects with the yellow band at the back. Older snakes lose the markings and ultimately appear uniformly brown.

The body scales are smooth and strongly overlapping. The belly plates are nearly four times as broad as long, each with a median keel, at least in the adults.

Size. The erabu-unagi, as the snake is called in the Ryukyu Islands, is among the largest of all sea snakes. Specimens are known that measured 6 ft in length and 3 in. in diameter.

Habitat. In the Philippine Islands, according to Herre (1942), it is common on outlying reefs and rocks exposed to the open sea. Further testimony as to its abundance in these islands is given by Schmidt and Inger (1957), who state that as many as 30,000 specimens a year may have been taken from the Philippines by Japanese fishermen, who sold them for their food value and hides. It is also quite common around Erabu-shima in the northern Ryukyu Islands.

Samoan Sea Snake (*Laticauda schistorhynchus*)

Distribution. This species has an eastern Pacific distribution that takes in the Fiji Islands, Samoa, the Friendly Islands and Savage Island.

Description. The body color is greenish or yellowish on top and lighter below. On the back is a series of black or greenish crossbands; each of the markings is broadest on the middle of the back, often interrupted along the abdomen. A curved, yellow marking on top of the black-colored head usually connects with the yellow neckband. This is a smaller and more brightly colored snake than the similar *erabu-unagi*.

Size. A length of $2\frac{1}{2}$ to 3 ft is average for the Samoan sea snake.

Disposition. A naturalist who collected specimens on Savage Island reported that the snakes were constantly caught and handled by children and that they never attempted to bite.

Crocker's Sea Snake (*Laticauda crockeri*)

Distribution. This land-locked sea snake is found only in Lake Tungano on Rennell Island in the Solomons.

Description. Crocker's sea snake can be distinguished from other members of the genus *Laticauda* by its elongate head, uniform coloration and more rounded snout. Except for the yellowish colored anal plate under the tail, it is uniformly dark brown.

The head is barely distinct from the neck and the body is vertically flattened, especially to the rear. The scales are smooth.

Size. This, one of the smallest of all sea snakes, reaches a length of about 20 in.

Habitat. According to Slevin (1934), who first described this interesting species, Crocker's sea snake lives only in Lake Tungano. Barely 2 miles inland from the east point of Rennell Island, this small body of water is 10 miles long and completely separated from the sea. Although the water there is used by the natives for drinking, it is considered too salty for the average visitor to the island. Soundings made at the lake show no bottom at 30 fathoms.

Spine-tailed Sea Snake (*Aipysurus eydouxii*)

Distribution. This species inhabits the waters from the Gulf of Siam to the Malay Archipelago, New Guinea and Queensland, Australia.

Description. It is brownish or olive above with numerous crossbands composed of many yellow, black-edged scales. All of the bands become wider near the abdomen and some are interrupted on the middle of the back. The head is dark olive in adults, blackish in the young.

For nearly its entire length, the body is of nearly the same thickness. The scales on the back are smooth and overlapping, those on the belly large and with a median ridge along the center. There are one or two spines at the tip of the flat tail.

Size. This snake is generally about 2 ft long, but one that measured 3 ft in length was found at Semarang, Java.

Habits. Tweedie (1953) says that it frequents shallow waters near shore, where it is sometimes taken in seine nets.

Olive-brown Sea Snake (*Aipysurus laevis*)

Distribution. The olive-green sea snake ranges along the coast of New Guinea and tropical parts of the Australian coast.

Description. This heavily built sea snake may be uniformly olive-brown or light brown, with dark spots on the body running in lengthwise rows. Kinghorn (1956) mentions a peculiar ragged appearance of the tail end in all of the specimens that he has seen.

The body scales are smooth and overlapping, those on the middle of the back larger than the others. There is a central keel along the length of the abdomen.

Size. Large specimens of the olive-brown sea snake are 6 ft long.

Dubois' Sea Snake (*Aipysurus duboisii*)

This snake is found around New Guinea, the north coast of Australia and the Loyalty Islands.

Description. The body is either uniformly dark brown or light brown, or yellowish with dark bars or bands on the back. These markings touch one another on the middle of the back and taper along the sides. There may also be alternate yellow bands along the sides.

The body scales overlap and are smooth or bluntly keeled. The abdominal scales are about half as wide as the body; each one possesses a median keel. The head is short and flattened, dark brown in color.

Size. Dubois' sea snake reaches a length of 4½ ft.

Ijima Sea Snake (*Emydocephalis ijimae*) (*Figs.* 22, 23, 24)

Distribution. Known only from the Ryukyu Archipelago (Ishigaki, Yaeyama, Okinawa, Iriomote) and Botel Tobago Island at the south end of Taiwan.

Description. The moderately stout body of this snake shows nearly the same thickness from head to tail. It is yellowish or brownish and marked with broad, black or dark brown rings which circle the body; the edges of the markings are wavy. Its head bears a light, curved marking across the top that reaches the back of the mouth on either side. The nearly smooth body scales are large and strongly overlapping; those along the middle of the back, at least to the rear, are twice the size of the others.

Size. This snake grows to a length of nearly 3 ft.

Grey's Sea Snake (*Ephalophis greyi*)

Distribution. This species occurs off the coast of northwest Australia and possibly in the Lesser Sunda Islands.

Description. The body is light olive, with a row of dark grey, angular blotches down the back, each blotch touching every other one along the middle of the back.

Grey's sea snake differs from other species in having a tail that is narrower and more rounded vertically. The scales of the body overlap; those on the belly are very wide.

Size. This is a small sea snake, reaching a length of only 20 in.

Jerdon's Sea Snake (*Kerilia jerdoni*)

Distribution. Jerdon's sea snake is found along the east coast of India and along the coast of Ceylon to the Straits of Malacca, east as far as south Viet Nam, and south to Borneo.

Description. This snake is olive to olive brown above, yellowish or white beneath, with a series of large, black spots down the back, broadest at the top, narrow along the sides. Additional small spots or bars may occur between the larger markings. In the young the black markings go completely around the body.

The body scales are broader than they are long, overlapping and strongly keeled. The abdominal plates are slightly broader than the adjacent scales.

The short and very narrow head of this slender snake slopes downward at the snout.

Size. This species grows a little longer than 3 ft.

Common Sea Snake (*Enhydrina schistosa*)

Distribution. This snake occurs from the Persian Gulf to the Gulf of Siam, and south to New Guinea and the northern coast of Australia.

Description. It is greyish above, uniformly colored or banded with indistinct darker crossbars. Juveniles are olive or grey above, with dark grey or black bands crossing the back which are widest in the middle and come to a point on the sides. In some specimens the markings circle the body.

The body scales are keeled and overlapping. Those on the belly are only a little broader than the adjacent scales, each one bearing two keels. The end of the snout extends down over the lower jaw and there is a deep groove under the chin.

Size. Specimens may grow more than 5 ft long, according to Kinghorn (1956), but the average length is more nearly 4 ft.

Disposition. It is the opinion of Reid (1956), who has seen and handled more sea snakes than most herpetologists, that this species is more aggressive than any others living in Malayan waters.

Habits. Boulenger (1912), quoting Cantor, remarks that the common sea snake is incredibly numerous in the Bay of Bengal, at Penang and Singapore. He goes on to say that specimens can be expected with each haul of the fishing nets.

Like terrestrial species, sea snakes sometimes swallow food items with a greater diameter than their own girth. The day after it was placed in an aquarium, Reid (1956) watched a common sea snake regurgitate a fish that was twice its own diameter.

Hydrophis spiralis

Distribution. Found from the Persian Gulf to the Malay Peninsula and Archipelago.

Description. The markings of this yellowish to yellow-green snake consist of more or less complete black rings around the body which are much narrower than the spaces between them and which tend to become wider at the middle of the back. The scales in the light areas are margined with black. The head, which in young snakes is blackish and bears a yellow horseshoe-shaped marking, becomes entirely yellow with age. Both juvenile and adult possess a yellowish belly; that of the young may have a black line down the middle.

The belly plates are twice as broad as the adjacent scales. The body scales overlap each other slightly and are smooth or bear a central keel or tubercle.

This is the largest of all sea snakes, often growing to a length of 6 ft and occasionally to 9 ft.

Habits. Like certain other kinds of sea snakes, this species comes to the surface to bask in the sunlight.

Hydrophis melanosoma

Distribution. Known from the Straits of Malacca, the coast of Borneo, and Macassar.

Description. Numerous greenish-yellow bands, half as wide as the spaces between them, completely or nearly circle the body. The scales of the back are edged with black. Yellow mottling appears on the snout; otherwise the head is black.

The body scales, which in adult males are strongly keeled, overlap. Each belly plate bears two keels and is not quite twice as wide as the adjacent scales.

Size. The maximum length is 5 ft.

Chittul (*Hydrophis cyanocinctus*) (*Fig.* 55)

Distribution. The range of this widely distributed snake encompasses the area from the Persian Gulf to Japan and the Indo-Australian Archipelago. Smith (1926) reports it to be the most common sea snake in the Straits of Hainan, and Taylor (1922) describes it as common about Manila Bay. It is also well known from the Ryukyu Islands and Formosa.

Description. The markings, although variable, consist of black crossbars which terminate along the sides, or they may be black rings which encircle the body. The general color is yellowish or olive. The color of the head is dark, fading on the lips and throat. Young specimens have a black band down the middle of the belly. When first born they are colored very much like the adults, but with variable black markings on the body. In some juvenile specimens the bands are widest on the back and go completely around the body; in others, the markings are broadest on the back and become wide again low on the sides; some have barred markings that taper to a point near the abdomen. A light-colored horseshoe-shaped marking often occupies the top of the head.

The body is long but not especially slender towards the head. The overlapping scales are distinctly keeled or raised into two or three tubercles. On the forward part of the body the belly plates are small and about twice as broad as the adjacent scales; those toward the rear are not as wide.

Size. Reaches a length of about 6½ ft.

Young. From three to fifteen young are born alive at one time.

Semper's Sea Snake (*Hydrophis semperi*)

Distribution. Semper's sea snake inhabits the fresh waters of Lake Bombon (frequently called Lake Taal) on Luzon Island in the Philippines.

Description. The color is black, with many narrow, whitish bands across the back or complete rings around the body. The head is entirely black, as are the belly scales.

The scales of the body overlap one another. Each has a short keel which may be in two halves. The belly scales, each bearing two keels, are not more than twice as broad as the nearby body scales.

The head is of moderate size and the body is not especially slender toward the front, its greatest thickness being about twice that of the neck.

Size. Semper's sea snake is less than 30 in. long.

Habitat. This sea snake spends all of its life in fresh water. Another land-locked species, Crocker's sea snake, is confined to an inland lake on one of the Solomon Islands where the water is brackish. The lake inhabited by Semper's sea snake is an ancient crater, 10 to 12 miles across, that empties into the sea through a narrow, fast moving stream, 5 or 6 miles long.

Hydrophis melanocephalus (*Figs.* 25, 26)

Distribution. This species is known only from the seas around Formosa, and the Ryukyu and Pescadores Islands.

Description. The color is grey or olive above, yellowish or white beneath. A series of broad, black bands crosses the back, these markings about as wide as the spaces between them. They become broader above and below; at the slender part of the body they run together on the belly. A yellow spot behind the nostrils and a yellow streak back of the eyes marks an otherwise blackish head. In the young the black bands are wider and more pronounced.

The body scales are keeled and overlapping; the belly scales are about twice as broad as the adjacent scales, each bearing two keels.

The head is small. Toward the front, the body is long and slender; to the rear it is considerably larger and vertically compressed, the greatest thickness being from two to three times that of the neck.

Size. Reaches a length of at least 4 ft.

Hydrophis torquatus

Distribution. The three races of this sea snake occur over an area that includes the northern part of the Gulf of Siam, the Straits of Malacca, the east coast of the Malay Peninsula, and Borneo.

Description. Specimens from the Straits of Malacca are pale grey on top and yellowish beneath. Numerous poorly defined, dark grey crossbands extend over the back and reach to the abdomen. The head is grey, with yellow markings that are not clearly defined. The whitish young are ringed with distinct, black bands; the head is black, with a yellowish or whitish mark across the snout and on the sides.

The race from Malaya and Borneo is much like the first, but shows a greater number of dark body bands, well defined head markings in the adults, and a larger size.

A short keel or central tubercle occurs on the rear body scales, which are more or less hexagonal in shape. The belly plates are not twice as broad as the adjacent scales.

The head is of moderate size and the body elongate, not very slender up forward. It is compressed along the rear, the greatest diameter being two to three times that of the neck.

Size. This snake reaches a maximum length of about 3 ft.

Hydrophis ornatus

Distribution. This widely distributed species occurs from the Persian Gulf to the Ryukyu Islands and Taiwan, then south as far as New Guinea and northern Australia.

Description. There are many broad, dark bars or rhomboidal spots along the back, wide and closely spaced on top, tapering on the sides. The body color is pale greyish or olive above, sometimes almost white, while underneath it is yellowish or whitish.

The scales on the rear of the body are about as broad as they are long, with a central tubercle or short keel on each one. The belly scales are approximately twice as broad as the adjacent scales, except towards the rear, where they are narrower.

The body is robust and not especially elongate, the greatest diameter at the rear being about twice that of the neck. The head is large.

Size. The maximum size for this snake is 3 ft.

Hydrophis inornatus

Other names. *Malabasahan* (Manila, Philippines); *calabucab* (Manila, Philippines).

Distribution. The range of this snake includes the coast of China, and the seas from the Philippine Islands to northern Australia.

Description. Compared with *Hydrophis ornatus*, with which it is similar, this species has a narrower head and a more slender and much compressed body. At its heaviest part, the body is three times as bulky as the neck. Adults are greyish above and whitish below, the two colors clearly separated in an irregular line along the sides. The head is grey or olive on top; white bands occur on the tail. Young ones are marked differently than adults, being yellowish with dark crossbands on the back.

The hexagonal body scales sometimes overlap, each one bearing a short keel or tubercle. The belly scales are not twice as broad as the adjacent scales.

Size. Like *Hydrophis ornatus*, it does not grow longer than 3 ft.

Hydrophis caerulescens

Distribution. The range of this species is from Bombay, India to China, then south through the Malay Archipelago.

Description. It is bluish-grey above and yellowish beneath. The broad, black bands that circle the snake are about twice the width of the lighter spaces in between, at least on the forward part of the body. They taper toward the belly, where they may be incomplete; in older specimens the pattern is often completely faded. The head is black in young specimens, dark grey in the adults, often with a light streak behind the eye.

The head is moderately small and the body not very slender up front; it is vertically flattened at the back, its greatest diameter from two to three times that of the neck.

All the scales are strongly keeled, those at the rear of the body slightly overlapping. The belly plates are not twice as broad as the adjacent scales.

Size. Adults are under 3 ft. long.

Young. Females of this species bear from two to six live young at a time.

Hydrophis fasciatus

Distribution. This snake occurs from the Gulf of Siam to the Straits of Malacca, New Guinea and the northern coast of Australia.

Description. The head, as well as the neck and forward part of the body, are black or dark olive, marked with yellowish oval spots; otherwise, the color is greyish or dirty yellow above and white below. Dark crossbars mark the back. These are largest at the top and end in points along the sides.

Each scale on the rear of the body has a short, blunt keel or central tubercle. The belly scales are not twice as broad as the adjacent scales, and each one bears two keels.

The head is small and the body long and very slender towards the front, larger and much compressed at the back, its greatest diameter two-and-a-half to four times that of the neck.

Size. The maximum length attained by this snake is 4 ft.

Habits. Van Denburgh and Thompson (1908), who observed this snake in Manila Bay, give the following information about the race *atriceps:*

> This species is rarely seen in the daytime, and has not been observed floating on the surface during the day. . . . When it comes to the surface for air it swims directly upward at great speed, with the neck and anterior third of the body straight and the tail and posterior portion of body undulating, the head rises about a centimeter above the surface of the water, and then, instantly, the animal turns and dives vertically down out of sight. At night, in the area illuminated by the gangway lights, they are seen swimming slowly and horizontally at the surface, the neck nearly straight or curved slightly while the posterior third of the snake is in motion. . . . They are fairly easy to capture and are extremely helpless when out of the water. . . . The only food found in the stomachs of the series of nineteen snakes was four specimens of a small eel belonging in the genus *Muraenichthys.*

Two females collected in January each contained two embryos.

Hydrophis brookei

Distribution. The presently known distribution extends from the Gulf of Siam, through the Straits of Malacca to the northern coasts of Borneo and Java.

Description. This species is grey above and yellowish underneath, with darker grey crossbands. Up forward, where they go completely around the body, these markings are of uniform width and about twice as wide as the spaces between them; on the rear of the body they become narrow along the sides and may even disappear on the belly. The head is either blackish or greyish, with a curved yellow mark which crosses the snout and then extends backward along the sides of the head. In addition, there may be two connecting bands of yellow across the top of the head. These markings become obscure with age.

Brooke's sea snake characteristically has a very small head and a long body which is quite slender up front. The scales on the rear of the body are more or less hexagonal, usually with a median tubercle or short keel. The belly plates, which are not twice as broad as the adjacent scales, each have two keels.

Size. Adults of this snake are between 3 and 3½ ft in length.

Darwin's Sea Snake (*Hydrelaps darwinensis*)

Distribution. This colorful sea snake occurs on the northern coast of Australia and along the southern coast of New Guinea.

Description. It is attractively marked with numerous black crossbands, broad on the back and narrower below, which contrast sharply against the yellowish to white body color. There may be a yellow spot at the top of each black band, and the head is dark olive with yellow markings. The body scales are smooth and over-lapping.

Size. Adults of this small species are about 18 in. long.

Praescutata viperina

Distribution. This snake is found from the Persian Gulf to southeastern China and the Malay Archipelago.

Description. Two color forms of this species are commonly seen. One is grey above and lighter below, the colors sharply separated where they meet; the other is grey with a series of dark rhomboidal markings down the back, the spots widest at the top and narrower on the sides. In rare cases the bands extend completely around the body.

The belly plates up forward are half the width of the body; they gradually become narrower to the rear, where, ultimately, they are not even twice as broad as the adjacent scales.

Size. It reaches a length of about 3 ft.

Peron's Sea Snake (*Acalyptophis peronii*)

Distribution. Peron's sea snake is definitely known from Torres Strait between Australia and New Guinea. It may also occur as far north and west as Hong Kong.

Description. All specimens are greyish or pale brown above and whitish underneath. Some have dark bars across the back which taper to a point on the sides, and narrow bands or spots on the belly. A unique feature of this species are the spiny scales surrounding the top and back of the eyes, a condition which may occur also on other scales of the head.

This a bulky snake with rather loose skin on the neck. The head is short and moderately small while the neck is a third to two-fifths the greatest thickness of the body.

Toward the back of the body the scales are slightly overlapping and broader than long; in older snakes they become strongly keeled and spiny. The belly plates are the same width as the adjacent body scales, or only a little narrower.

Size. Peron's sea snake grows to a length of nearly 5 ft.

Thalassophis anomalus (*Figs.* 27, 28)

Distribution. Occurs in the Gulf of Siam and off the shores of Cambodia, Java, Sumatra and Borneo.

Description. There are numerous dark bars on each side of the back, wider than the spaces between them, and tapering along the sides. Those on opposite sides of the body often meet along the middle of the back, and they may continue around the body. Young specimens often have a pale mark across the snout which runs back along each side of the head.

The body is stout and short. The scales on the rear of the body are almost as broad as they are long, and strongly keeled; those on the belly scarcely broader than the adjoining scales, each with a pair of keels.

Size. Adults are generally between 2 and 3 ft long.

Annandale's Sea Snake (*Kolpophis annandalei*)

Distribution. This snake is found off the coasts of peninsular Siam, South Viet Nam, the Malay Peninsula and Java.

Description. The body color is pale grey to yellowish. The back is marked with dark crossbands which are narrower than the spaces between them, and which taper to a point on the sides. There are no markings on the olive-colored head.

In this snake, the scales of the body are very small, smooth or with a short keel, and slightly overlapping at the rear of the body. The belly scales are just a little, if any, wider than the adjacent scales.

Size. Three feet appears to be the greatest length of this species.

Graceful Sea Snake (*Microcephalophis gracilis*)

Distribution. This sea snake is known from the Persian Gulf to southern China, through the Malay Archipelago to northern Australia and New Guinea.

Description. Adults are grey above and whitish underneath; indistinct darker bands cross the back. Young snakes are black with whitish body bands to the rear, lateral spots or less distinct bands near the forward part of the body. Usually the head is olive yellow.

The head is small, the neck and forward part of the body are slender and the rear part of the snake is much compressed.

Size. Four feet appears to be the maximum length.

Stokes' Sea Snake (*Astrotia stokesi*)

Distribution. Stokes' sea snake occurs from the China Sea, east to Torres Straits, New Guinea.

Description. Light brown, yellowish or orange-red above, it is marked with broad, black or dark brown bands; small spots occasionally occur between these markings. In some cases the bands are separated into cross-bars above and spots below. The head is large, dark olive to yellowish in color.

This is considered the largest but not the longest of the sea snakes, the extremely stout body, according to Kinghorn (1956) reaching a girth of about 10 in.

In this species the body scales are keeled and overlapping. Nearly all of the belly plates are divided longitudinally.

Size. Adults may be nearly 6 ft long.

Young. The female produces from twelve to fourteen young at a time; they measure 14 or 15 in. when born.

Hardwick's Sea Snake (*Lapemis hardwickii*)

Other names. *Walo-walo* (Negros Island, Philippines).

Distribution. Distributed from the Bay of Bengal to Japan in the north, and to northern Australia and New Guinea in the south. Taylor (1922) says that it is very numerous in Manila Bay.

Description. This is a stout snake with a large head. The diameter of the neck is half, or more than half, the greatest body diameter. The color varies, but is generally greenish or yellowish olive above and lighter below, with pale olive to dark grey crossbars on the back. These markings taper to a point on the sides or, less often, continue completely around the body. A narrow, dark stripe may occur on the belly. The head is pale olive to blackish, with or without yellow markings.

The body scales, which may or may not have a central spine, are square or hexagonal in shape and do not overlap one another. Those nearest the belly scales are larger than the others. Except on the neck, the keeled belly scales are just a little smaller than the adjacent body scales, or they may be absent altogether.

Size. Most adults of this species are between 2 and 3 ft long.

Yellow-bellied Sea Snake (*Pelamis platurus*)

Distribution. This, the most widely distributed of all sea snakes, ranges from the east coast of Africa, across the Indian and Pacific oceans, to the west coast of Mexico, Central and northern South America, and from southern Siberia to Tasmania. Shaw (1961) mentions a specimen recently found alive on the beach at Los Angeles Bay, about 300 miles south and east of San Diego, California, that marks the northern limit of its distribution along the coast of western North America. In the area under consideration, it is known from at least the following major islands: Borneo, Celebes, Taiwan, Japan, Flores, Java, Sumatra, Sumba and New Guinea. It is also known from the Hawaiian Islands where, according to Oliver and Shaw (1953) it is uncommon.

Description. There is so much variation in the yellow-bellied sea snake, from one part of its range to another, that seven color varieties have been listed by Smith (1926). The most common ones appear to be (1) black above and yellow or brown below, with a conspicuous yellow line which separates the two colors, and (2) yellow, with a wide, black dorsal band, the two colors sharply delineated. The long, narrow head is black on top and yellow along the sides below the eye. Another variety, from the area about Singapore, Borneo, Macassar, Java and the Gulf of Siam, is yellow, with black- or brown-edged crossbars on the back, and a series of similar bars on the belly which alternate with those above. In these snakes the head is irregularly marked with black. Still another form, from Chinese and Japanese waters, is reported by Pope (1935) to have a black vertebral stripe, wavy in outline or broken up into spots along the rear of the body; they are yellow along the sides and on the abdomen. The tail may be barred with black, or marked in some other way. The body is vertically flattened, its greatest diameter being more than twice that of the neck.

Size. This is not a large species; the maximum known length is 44 in.

Young. Wall (1921) reports that near Ceylon the young are born in March and April. One female examined by him contained only two embryos. It is presumed that the females retire to isolated reefs and small islands to give birth.

VIPERS

Family Viperidae

This important family of venomous snakes is divided into two subfamily groups, the Viperinae and the Crotalinae. All of them are easily recognized by the broad, flat head, narrow neck and elliptical eye pupils. Snakes belonging to this family are further characterized by the long, movable fangs in the front of the upper jaw. These lie folded against the roof of the mouth when the snake is at rest, but during a strike the mouth is opened widely, the upper and lower jaws forming an angle of nearly 180 degrees. The fangs are then erected to point almost directly forward.

Most Pacific species possess a venom of moderate toxicity that produces a great deal of local reaction but seldom results in a human death. The principal exception, however, is Russell's viper, one of Asia's most poisonous and dangerous snakes.

In general the Viperidae are of moderate to large size. The yellow-green pit-viper (habu), the largest of all, is known to reach a length of 7½ ft.

The two subfamily groups are separated according to the presence or absence of a facial pit on either side of the head between the eye and the nostril. They are separated as follows:

I. Viperinae. This group of snakes, called the true vipers, does not occur in the Americas but ranges over central and southern Asia, most of Europe and all of Africa. It includes approximately thirty species, only two of which, *Vipera russelii* and *Vipera berus*, are found in the area under consideration. The facial pits are lacking in this group (Fig. 30).

GENUS *Vipera*

The two species of true vipers inhabiting the Pacific can be separated as follows:

KEY TO THE SPECIES OF VIPER OF THE PACIFIC

19 to 23 scales around middle of body; range: Sakhalin; Uisut; and Great Shantar Islands . . . . . . common adder (*Vipera berus*)
27 to 33 scales around middle of body; range: Formosa; Java; Komodo; Flores; Lomblen; and Endeh Island, Indonesia—Russell's viper (*Vipera russelii*)

Common Adder (*Vipera berus*) (*Fig.* 56)

Distribution. The common adder is found from England and Scotland, across northern Europe and Asia (just south of the Arctic Circle at 70 degrees north) as far east as Sakhalin Island north of Japan, and south to Sinuiju in Northern Korea. Its Pacific distribution is limited to a number of islands north of Japan, the largest being the Russian island of Sakhalin; it is also found on Uisut and the Greater Shantar Islands.

Description. Considerable variation occurs in the general body color. It is sometimes grey or olive-brown, with a prominent dark, zigzag or wavy, longitudinal band extending the length of the back, and a row of large spots along each side. In some cases the band is partly or completely broken up into spots, or it may possess straight edges. In others, the band is absent or reduced to a straight, narrow stripe. A black V- or X-shaped marking dominates the top of the head and a dark streak runs along the side of the head from the eye to the back of the mouth or onto the neck. Some of the white or yellow lip shields are conspicuously margined with brown or black. An unusual color variation involves the totally black individuals that occur rather frequently throughout the range of the species.

Size. The largest specimen on record is a 33 in. long snake from Europe. However, the usual length is from 18 to 22 in.

Habitat. This terrestrial snake has been found in the European Alps as high as 9000 ft elevation. Boulenger (1913) writes that in the north of Europe it prefers dry moors, sandy heaths and hills well exposed to the sun, while in the warmer southern regions it frequents marshy localities.

Disposition. Judging from the contradictory reports of various authors, this is evidently a snake with a diverse disposition. It is described by some as retiring and inoffensive, and by others as irascible and very ready to bite when first caught.

Food. Its varied diet includes such mammals as weasels, mice, voles, shrews, and moles, in addition to lizards, frogs, salamanders and slugs. The young feed also on insects and worms.

Young. The living young produced by this snake number five to twenty in a litter, with an average of about twelve. They are born in August and September, sometimes as early as the end of July, and at that time measure

6–8 in. in length. In the northern part of the range where temperatures are low and the summers short, two seasons are required before the embryos can fully develop, according to Schmidt and Inger (1957).

Medical importance. The common adder is of slight medical importance in the Pacific due to its limited distribution in this area. Apparently there is no published information to indicate the frequency of bites by this species on Sakhalin Island, the only major Pacific island inhabited by it.

Russell's Viper (*Vipera russelii*) (*Figs* 57–58)

Other names. *Daboia*; *tic-polonga* (Singhalese).

Distribution. This widely distributed viper is found in India (from the southern tip to Sind, the western Himalayas and the Ganges basin), Ceylon, southern Burma, Thailand (north of Bangkok), southern China (coastal province of Kwangtung), Formosa and Indonesia. In the Pacific it is known from Formosa, Java (Sepandjang and Kembang Kuning, both on the eastern part near Surabaja), Komodo, Flores (Endeh village), Endeh and Lomblem.

Description. Russell's viper is an attractively marked snake with a bold pattern. The general body color of Pacific islands' examples is greenish-brown or grey. Down the middle of the back is a row of large, reddish-brown, oval spots, each one circled by black and narrowly edged with white; adjacent spots are sometimes fused into an undulating band. The dorsal markings on the tail are connected to form a stripe. Small, dark spots or streaks generally occupy the spaces between the three rows of larger markings, and the areas between the lateral spots and the abdomen. The top of the head bears three prominent, dark markings, and a broad band extends along the side of the head from the eye to the back of the mouth.

Size. Specimens from the Pacific islands do not attain the length recorded for those from the mainland of Asia. Seven examples from Java measured approximately 3 ft in length, according to Van Hoesel (1958), and one large specimen reported by Neuhaus (1935) was 45 in. long. Those from Flores are even smaller; Van Hoesel (1958) states that only a few attained a length of more than 3 ft, although one from near the village of Bedjawa, with the end of the tail missing, measured 40 in. The maximum length for a Russell's viper from India is reported by Smith (1943) to be 5 ft 6 in. but average size adults are 4–5 ft long.

Habitat. It may be found in a variety of habitats, from low coastal plains to mountain elevations of considerable height. Smith (1943) reports that it occurs plentifully in many upland regions and that it has been met with in the Palni Hills of southern India at an elevation of 7000 ft. On Formosa, where it is uncommon, Russell's viper inhabits the mountains. At any elevation, it prefers open country and avoids dense jungle.

Disposition. Although somewhat sluggish and not apt to strike unless provoked, it is quite capable of lunging at an adversary with such energy that its body leaves the ground. It is also known to hold on after striking. Frequently it attempts to avoid contact by hissing, the noise often being loud enough to be heard 10 or 15 ft away. According to Pope (1935), the young are more vicious than the adults.

Habits. The disconcerting habits of Russell's viper to frequent roads and paths and to enter houses in search of food has resulted in a high incidence of bites by this species among humans.

Food. The diet consists of small mammals, especially rats, but birds, lizards and frogs are also eaten. Werner (1920) and Mell (1929) both report cannibalism among young Russell's vipers.

Young. The progeny of this prolific species are born alive. There may be as few as twenty or as many as sixty-three in a litter, the new-born snakes measuring 8–11 in. in length. The gestation period is said to be longer than 6 months.

II. Crotalinae. The members of this subfamily are found in the Americas, southeastern Asia and Indonesia, but are absent from Australia and Africa. Of approximately fifty known species, seventeen occur in the Pacific. They are characterized by the facial pit (Figs. 31, 33) on each side of the head between the eye and nostril, which functions as a heat-sensory organ, enabling the snake to detect the presence of warm-blooded prey, even in total darkness.

The two genera that occupy the Pacific may be separated as follows:

KEY TO THE GENERA OF PIT-VIPERS OF THE PACIFIC*

Head covered above with a few large, paired shields; range: Japan east to Marshall Islands, southwest to Formosa; Sumatra; Java: (Fig. 32) . . —ground pit-vipers (*Agkistrodon*)

Head covered above with numerous small scales; range: Luchus southwest to Sumatra, east to Celebes: (Fig. 34) . . . . —climbing and also ground pit-vipers (*Trimeresurus*)

GENUS *Agkistrodon*

The three species of this genus which range into the Pacific can be identified by their broad heads, narrow necks, relatively short tails and elliptical eye pupils. Unlike the snakes of the next group, *Trimeresurus*, which also have pits between the eyes and nostrils, they possess large plates on top of the head instead of numerous small scales.

KEY TO THE AGKISTRODON PIT-VIPERS OF THE PACIFIC†

1. Scales smooth; range: Sumatra; Java . Malayan pit-viper (*A. rhodostoma*)
   Scales ridged 2

*Both occur on Asiatic mainland; *Agkistrodon* also in Europe and Asia.
†All three occur on Asiatic mainland.

2. Snout ending in a short, pointed, upturned appendage; range: Formosa —long-nosed pit-viper (*A. acutus*)
Snout normal, not turned up; range: Japan and Luchus east to the Marshall Islands . . . . . . Pallas' pit-viper (*A. halys*)

Malayan Pit-Viper (*Agkistrodon rhodostoma*) (*Fig.* 59)

Local names. *Ular kapac daun* (of the Jalor Malays); *ular biludak* (Java; *ular tanah* (west Java); *ular gebuk* (west Java); *ular bandotan bedor* (central Java); *oelar bedoedak* (west Java); *oelar lemah* (west Java).

Distribution. This species has a curiously discontinuous range which includes, in the north, Thailand (except the northeast part), Laos, Viet Nam, Cambodia and northern Malaya (as far south as Penang). It has not been found in the southern Malay States but occurs again on Sumatra and Java.

Description. The general color is grey, reddish or pale brown, with a dorsal pattern of large, dark brown, triangular spots which extend downward from either side of the dark line on the middle of the back. They may join at the midline or alternate with one another. A broad, dark brown, black-edged stripe extends from the eye to the back of the mouth, with a light streak above it and yellow or pinkish lips below, the line of demarcation giving a scalloped effect. Smith (1943) comments that the light streak above and behind the eye is well marked in the young but may be absent in older snakes. The abdomen is dirty-white or yellowish, with or without brown specks or mottling.

Size. It reaches a length of approximately 3 ft.

Habitat. Although reported as occurring in Java as high as 5000 ft (on Mt. Willis), the Malayan pit-viper is principally a lowland snake partial to wooded country near the sea. Tweedie (1953) suggests that it probably requires a climate with a more or less marked wet and dry season for its well being.

Disposition. Reported by Tweedie (1953) as ill-tempered, and by Boulenger (1912) as sluggish, *rhodostoma* is described by Smith (1943) as rather fierce and ready to bite when provoked.

Food. Its diet is chiefly small mammals, but birds, reptiles and frogs are sometimes eaten.

Young. Although most vipers give birth to live young, this species not only lays eggs from which the little snakes hatch, but guards the eggs during incubation. Smith (1943) observed egg laying by two captive females in Bangkok, one of which laid thirteen eggs on August 1st, the other, thirty eggs on September 1st. The 6 in.-long young hatched 42 and 47 days later, respectively.

Long-nosed Pit-viper (*Agkistrodon acutus*) (*Fig.* 60)

Local names. Hundred-pace snake (Formosa).

Distribution. Known from mainland China (Chungang Hsien, Kuatun,

Hunan, Chekiang, Fukien, Kwangtung), the Chinese island of Hainan, Viet Nam (Chapa, in the northern part) and Formosa.

Description. While Loveridge (1945) notes a general similarity in color between this snake and Pallas' pit-viper, both of which occur together in some mainland areas, other herpetologists have commented on the resemblance of *acutus* to the southern copperhead of the United States. It can be immediately recognized by the pointed, upturned appendage at the end of the snout.

In the adult, a series of dark brown, hour-glass-shaped crossbands, broadly edged with black, marks the greyish-brown to light brown body color. Where these markings are interrupted at the middle of the back they form dark brown lateral triangles, the markings frequently alternating with one another. A row of large, black spots extends along the sides near the belly. In large specimens the top and upper sides of the head are uniformly black, with a black streak from the eye to the back of the mouth. The young are much lighter than the adults with essentially the same pattern; however, they are more vividly marked. In the juveniles the lateral triangles are narrowly edged with a lighter color and the top of the head is light grey instead of black, thus accentuating the dark postocular streak.

Size. This heavy-bodied pit-viper is easily the largest member of the genus *Agkistrodon* in the Pacific area. It is reported by the Japanese herpetologist, Maki (1931), as reaching a total length of 5 ft, although the same author gives the maximum length of Formosan specimens as 49 in. Within the genus, only the North American cottonmouth moccasin grows larger.

Habitat. On the Chinese mainland Pope (1929) found the long-nosed pit-viper abundant in the high, forested mountains near Sanchiang, living on boulder-strewn mountain sites and in wild ravines. In this area it was generally discovered by day neatly coiled on a bed of dry leaves among boulders. An exception was one individual found in an open, cultivated valley. On Formosa, Dasch (1952) reports specimens from the southern mountain areas about Ali San.

Disposition. In the field it is described as sluggish and disinclined to retreat. Pope (1935) has even seen it handled with impunity when unalarmed. In spite of this normally tolerant behavior, the long-nosed pit-viper strikes and bites vigorously when aroused. It is not belligerent as a captive, but shows considerable alertness, turning the head abruptly to face every nearby movement, no matter how slight.

Food. Individuals in the field and in captivity have eaten mice, rats and birds.

Young. According to Maki (1931), this species lays about twenty eggs. Pope mentions a large female from China which contained twenty-six well-developed eggs.

Pallas' Pit-viper (*Agkistrodon halys*) (*Fig.* 61)

Other names. *Mamushi* (Japan).

Distribution. This snake has a wide distribution. It is found from western Europe near the Caspian Sea (Saltan-Murat Desert and the Induski Hills), eastward across central Asia to Japan, and southward in the Pacific to Taiwan and the Pescadores Islands. In the Pacific it occurs frequently on the four main Japanese islands and is apparently common on the seven islands of Izu off the southeast coast of Honshu. It was collected on Yaeyama in 1900, according to Stejneger (1907), but has not recently been found there. Presumably it is no longer a part of the Ryukyu Island fauna. On Taiwan it must be rare, if we can judge by the infrequency of accidents on that island caused by its bite.

Description. The pattern and coloration of this widely ranging pit-viper show a great deal of individual and geographic variation. Specimens may be dull brown, reddish brown, yellowish or, at the extreme, black, with a pattern of large, oval blotches on either side of the body, meeting or alternating along the middle of the back. Some specimens lack all trace of a pattern. A broad, black band, bordered above by a narrow, white line and below by the white lip, extends from the snout to the back of the mouth. In the juveniles the colors are brighter, the pattern is more contrasting and the tail tip is yellowish. Among adult Japanese examples there is an even division between those with dark or light tail ends.

Size. This small snake, usually 18–24 in. long, reaches a maximum length of about 30 in.

Habitat. These snakes are found in many kinds of environment and at various elevations. Shannon (1956) states that in Korea it prefers the low, marshy habitat provided by rice paddies or meandering streams. He says that at times it may be found on the lower slopes of the hills, though seldom penetrating to any considerable altitude. On the other hand, Pope (1935) found that over most of its range this species is chiefly a snake of mountains and plateaus. He cites one record by Despax (1913) of a mamushi that was found in the Yalung Valley of Szechwan at an elevation of 12,467 ft. In Japan, where it is the only venomous land snake, it occurs both in wet bottomlands and in dry environments at high elevations.

Disposition. Considerable difference of opinion exists regarding the temperament of Pallas' pit-viper, but most observers agree that it has a mild disposition. Shannon (1956) reports that Korean examples collected by him were usually mild tempered, seeking to escape even when annoyed. Maslin (1950) says that disturbed specimens assume an alert attitude and face the aggressor, but that no amount of teasing can provoke them into striking. He states further that they often vibrate the end of the tail when annoyed, or flatten the entire body.

Food. They eat both warm and cold-blooded food, including a variety of animals. On Syoryuzan Island in Kwangtung and in southern Manchuria, the species is said to subsist largely on birds, according to Koba (1938). Korean specimens examined by Pope (1935) had eaten mice, rats, lizards and a frog, while several Chinese examples were reported to have consumed mice, rats and lizards.

Young. The usual litter consists of from three to twelve young.

GENUS *Trimeresurus*

Members of this genus possess numerous small, irregularly arranged scales on top of the head instead of the large, symmetrical plates seen in most other snakes. The one exception, *Trimeresurus macrolepis* of Ceylon, has large head scales. Based on color and habitat, the seventeen species living on Pacific islands are divisible into two fairly distinct, natural groups. One of these is a tree-dwelling assemblage composed of species with a prehensile tail and a body color of green, rarely brown. Those of the second group lack the prehensile tail, are generally darker in color and do not live in trees. It is agreed that the bite of the *Trimeresurus* pit-vipers, although painful in its local effects, rarely causes death in man.

KEY TO THE TRIMERESURUS PIT-VIPERS IN THE PACIFIC

1.	Scales between the eyes smooth or faintly ridged; throat scales smooth .	2
	Scales between the eye strongly ridged; throat scales ridged	20
2.	Scales around midbody 33 to 37; belly shields 222 to 231; range: Luchus yellow-green pit-viper (*T. flavoviridis*)	
	Scales around midbody 19 to 27; belly shields 127 to 218	3
3.	Tail straight, not prehensile;* chiefly ground-dwellers	4
	Tail prehensile, usually shown by its being strongly curled at tip, often slender, compressed and tapering; chiefly bush- or tree-dwellers . .	8
4.	Belly shields 182 to 219; scales between eyebrow shields 10 to 16 . .	5
	Belly shields 127 to 176; scales between eyebrow shields 4 to 9. . .	6
5.	Belly shields 182 to 191; shields beneath tail 66 to 77; range: Luchus —elegant pit-viper (*T. elegans*)	
	Belly shields 198 to 219; shields beneath tail 76 to 96; range: Formosa† —pointed-scaled pit-viper (*T. mucrosquamatus*)	
6.	Angular ridge of head from eye to above nostril sharply angular; range: Luchus . . . . Okinawa pit-viper (*T. okinavensis*)	
	Angular ridge of head from eye to above nostril bluntly angular except in young	7
7.	Scales around midbody 21 to 27; shields beneath tail 36 to 62 in pairs or single; range: Formosa† . . . . mountain pit-viper (*T. monticola*)	
	Scales around midbody 19; shields beneath tail 19 to 31 pairs; range: Borneo . . . . Chasen's pit-viper (*T. chaseni*)	

---

*See also the ashy pit-viper, with the tail prehensile in young but less noticeably so in adult snakes.

†Also Asiatic mainland.

8. First lower lip shield separated from its fellow by a pair of scales; angular ridge of head from eye to above nostril raised to form a parapet, upraised snout projecting in young; range: Borneo; Sumatra; Java* . . . —ashy pit-viper (*T. puniceus*)
First lower lip shield in contact with its fellow behind chin shield; angular ridge of head from eye to above nostril not noticeably raised . . . 9

9. Scales around midbody 25 to 27; back dark purplish brown with or without pale green spots; range: Sumatra*. . . . . purple-spotted pit-viper (*T. purpureomaculatus*)
Scales around midbody 19 to 21 10

10. Back dark purplish brown with or without yellowish spots, but without a yellow or white side stripe; range: Philippines (Polillo and Patnanongnan Islands) . . . . Polillo pit-viper (*T. f. halieus*)
Back greenish or yellowish (occasionally brown in old or large specimens) . 11

11. Eyebrow shields large, separated across top of head by 4 to 9 scales . . 17
Eyebrow shields narrow or broken up, separated across top of head by 8 to 13 scales 12

12. Tail paler than body; belly shields 187 to 203; shields beneath tail 66 to 82; range: Philippines (Palawan Island) . Schultze's pit-viper (*T. schultzei*)
Tail colored like, or darker (rarely lighter) than body; belly shields 151 to 187; shields beneath tail 52 to 78 13

13. Color bright yellow with darker yellow streak on side (white in alcohol); end of tail spotted with reddish brown; range: Philippines (Bataan Island) —McGregor's pit-viper (*T. f. mcgregori*)
Color greenish (often bluish in alcohol) 14

14. Back spotted or barred with brown or uniform; side usually with a series of large yellow flecks on the lowest row of scales; range: Philippines (Luzon; Bohol; Mindanao; and Jolo Islands) . . . . —yellow-spotted pit-viper (*T. f. flavomaculatus*)
Back not spotted with brown; side with or without a narrow yellow or white line on the lowest row of scales 15

15. First upper lip shield partly or completely united with the nasal shield; upper lip and belly yellowish or greenish; range: Formosa; Hainan . . —white-lipped pit-viper (*T. albolabris*)
First upper lip shield completely separated from the nasal shield by a suture 16

16. Hemipenis spinose (requires dissection; females are indistinguishable from next species); range: Formosa; Hainan* . . . . —Stejneger's pit-viper (*T. s. stejnegeri*)
Hemipenis without spines; range: Borneo; Sumatra; east to Timor*. . Pope's pit-viper (*T. popeorum*)

17. Belly shields less than 175 (162 to 174) 18
Belly shields more than 175 (177 to 198) 19

18. Belly shields 162; range: Djampea Island . banded pit-viper (*T. fasciatus*)
Belly shields 168 to 174; range: Borneo Mt. Kinabalu pit-viper (*T. s. malcolmi*)

19. Head shields and scales broadly edged with black; range: Borneo; Sumatra; Nias Island* . . . . . . Sumatran pit-viper (*T. s. sumatranus*)
Head shields and scales not edged with black; range: Banka; Sumatra; Nias Island . . . . Hagen's pit-viper (*T. hageni*)

20. Range: Philippines south to Sumatra Island east to Timor* . . . —Wagler's pit-viper (*T. wagleri*)

---

*Also Asiatic mainland.

Yellow-green Pit-viper (*Trimeresurus flavoviridis*) (*Fig*. 62)

Other names. Habu.

Distribution. Known only from the northern Ryukyu Islands south of Kyushu, Japan, the habu has been reported from Okinawa, Amami-oshima, Kakeroma-jima, Uke-shima, Yoro-jima, Tokuno-shima, Tokara-shima, Kume-shima and Edateku-jima.

Description. The dorsal pattern of this boldy marked pit-viper consists of irregular, black-edged, dark green blotches, some of which unite to form a zigzag or wavy band. Each marking, with its contrasting light outer edge, contains a large central, light-colored spot, and often a number of satellite spots. The outer edges of the blotches may form vertical bars which extend down the sides nearly to the abdomen. Smaller and less distinct dark spots occupy the areas between the bars, yellowish borders outlining each dark marking. Numerous dark, elongate markings occur on top of the head and a narrow, dark stripe runs from the eye to the back of the mouth; otherwise the head is light-colored.

On the small islands of the Tokara Group, between Okinawa and Japan, a pale-colored race of the habu is found which shows a notable reduction in the color pattern. Another subspecies, with a similar reduction in color pattern, lives on Kume Shima, a small island off the southwest coast of Okinawa.

Size. This is the largest species of the genus. Adults are usually between 4 and 5 ft in length. The largest recorded specimen was taken in woods on Amami-oshima and measured 7½ ft in length, according to Koba (1958).

Habitat. On Amami-oshima and Tokuno-shime, Koba (1958) found it most plentiful in the districts supporting stands of a native palm, *Cycus revoluta.* Not restricted to this habitat, however, the habu frequents other environments and often enters buildings, huts and a variety of other man-made structures. At Kadena Air Force Base on Okinawa, for example, civilian employees discovered a 5½ ft habu in the shower room of their quarters. In another case, four specimens were taken in one day from a farmer's hut on Tokuno-shima, and on Amami-oshima a woman was struck in the face by a snake coiled on a wall case in the kitchen of a native home. These are not isolated instances, but represent fairly common occurrences that reflect the habu's predisposition for entering human habitations.

Disposition. The habu is an active, often aggressive snake which is mainly nocturnal in habits. Because of its abundance, size and hostile nature, it is greatly feared. Unlike most pit-vipers, which assume a typical, single, S-shaped striking posture, this snake, with its great length and slimness of body, gathers half its length or more into a series of close, irregular coils. From such a position, the habu can deliver a vigorous and long-range defense.

Food. A recent study of the habu's feeding habits, made by Koba (1958), shows the diet to consist of rats, hares, domestic chickens, snakes, lizards, frogs and an eel. Among these, mammals, birds and reptiles together made up 83 per cent of the food items, rats having been particularly important by number and frequency of occurrence. Young snakes had eaten small lizards.

Young. A clutch of eight eggs laid in captivity on 16 and 17 July, at Naze, Amami-oshima, is reported by Koba (1958).

Elegant Pit-viper (*Trimeresurus elegans*) (*Fig.* 66)

Other names. Sakishima habu.

Distribution. This species is known only from the islands of Yaeyama-retto in the southern Ryukyus, particularly Ishigaki, Kuroshima, Iriomote and Taketomi.

Description. The Sakishima habu is grey above with a series of dark brown, black-edged blotches down the middle of the back and a smaller row along each side. In some cases the blotches on the back unite to form a zigzag band. Indistinct, dark markings occur on top of the head, and a well-defined, black band extends along the side of the head from the eye to the back of the mouth. The markings of young snakes are more distinct than those of adults.

Keegan and Yoshina (1959) and Maki (1931) describe specimens with abnormal color and markings (Fig. 67). Some are reported to be yellowish-brown, with a row of pale spots on each side of the back, faint spots along the sides and a pale yellow belly. One specimen was reddish-brown along the middle of the back and yellowish-brown on the sides. The indistinct markings of this snake were not edged with black as is usual for the species, and the head and neck were somewhat darker than the rest of the body. There was only a trace of the band that runs backward from the eye.

Size. Adult specimens are usually between 3 and 4 ft long.

Habitat. This pit-viper inhabits lowlands as well as mountainous areas, where it is most often seen among boulders and in stone walls, old houses, cemeteries, hollow trees and bamboo groves. It is also encountered in roads and fields.

Dr. H. J. Magens, who has collected many specimens from the southern Ryukyus, believes that these snakes do not live on islands predominately of coral formation. He was told by the natives that if the snakes were introduced to coral islands they would invariably die. While the reason for this is not clear, Dr. Magens suspects it is due to the high alkalinity of the available fresh water.

Disposition. The Sakishima habu appears not to be as aggressive as the yellow-green pit-viper (habu). Those collected by Keegan and Toshiaka on the islands of Ishigaki and Iriomote, did not coil to strike when approached, but tried instead to escape. If touched, they swung around to strike momentarily, but failed to hold their ground in definite coils.

Food. Keegan and Yoshino (1959) report that it feeds on mice, frogs and small birds and their eggs.

Young. The only information concerning the breeding habits of this snake is supplied by Keegan and Yoshino (1959), who describe one nest containing several white, oblong eggs.

Pointed-scaled Pit-viper (*Trimeresurus mucrosquamatus*) (*Fig.* 68)

Other names. *Taiwan habu* (of the Japanese).

Distribution. This species is found on mainland China (Fukien, Kwangtung, Kwangsi, Szechwan), northern Burma and adjacent India, Viet Nam and Taiwan.

Description. This long, slender pit-viper resembles the elegant pit-viper (Sakishima habu), but the two are geographically separated and so should not be confused in the field. Like the yellow-green pit-viper (habu), it has a large and elongate head. The greyish or greyish-black body is marked with a row of large, irregularly-shaped, dark brown spots down the middle of the back, each one circled by black and edged with yellow. Consisting of two halves, one on each side of the back, the spots are sometimes unevenly joined; where this happens, a zigzag band is often the result. Similar but smaller markings occur low on the sides. The head is brown above and paler below, with a pattern of dark brown lines on top and a narrow, dark band along each side, from the eye to the back of the mouth. The young are colored much like the adult but show more contrast between the markings and the general body color. In addition, a number of indistinct, brownish-grey vertical bars appear between the lateral spots. In the juveniles the side of the head is darker, the band from the eye to the mouth is bordered below by a whitish line and the lips bear white markings.

Size. According to Smith (1943), the greatest length so far reported for this snake is approximately 46 in., but most specimens are less than 3 ft long.

Habitat. This species is not restricted to any particular altitude. It has been found in lowland hills not more than a few hundred feet above sea level, to mountain elevations of at least 4300 ft. On Formosa, where it is fairly common, Stejneger (1907) states that specimens are most frequently collected in the lowlands, while in northern Kwangtung, China, Mell (1922) gives its vertical range as 2300 to 3500 ft. Pope (1935) observed two specimens in a high, mountain village near Yenping, China, one well above ground just under the roof of an inhabited farm house, the other in a nearby rock wall. This species inhabits open areas as well as forested regions.

Disposition. Available information suggests that the pointed-scaled pit-viper (Taiwan habu) is sluggish and reluctant to bite. Maslin (1950) observed that no amount of teasing caused the specimens collected by him near Kiangsi, China to show any hostile signs. However, a captive specimen at the Houston Zoo demonstrated an unusual alertness to movement, only slight activity being necessary to bring it into a defensive posture. Repeated movement generally caused the snake to strike.

Food. Several specimens examined by Pope (1935) contained birds and rats.

Young. Three females from Yenping, China contained, respectively, five, nine and thirteen well-developed eggs.

Okinawa Pit-viper (*Trimeresurus okinavensis*) (*Fig.* 69)

Other names. *Himehabu*; *kufah.*

Distribution. This snake is an inhabitant of the northern Ryukyu Islands, being known from Okinawa, Amami-oshima and Tokuno-shima.

Description. The color of the Okinawa pit-viper is dull brown above. Large, irregular, dark-brown blotches occur along the middle of the back, the markings longer than wide, often with some dark edges. Occasionally the blotches fuse into a wavy or zigzag band. Another row of large spots is present along the sides, each of these markings located directly below the corresponding dorsal blotch. A prominent, broad, dark-brown band, bordered above by white, extends from the eye to the back of the mouth.

Size. The maximum known length of this species is less than 3 ft.

Food. The only information available concerning its diet is Koba's (1961) remarks that specimens from Amami-oshima had eaten birds.

Mountain Pit-viper (*Trimeresurus monticola*) (*Fig.* 70)

Distribution. The far-ranging mountain pit-viper is distributed from India (eastern Himalayas, as far west as Nepal) and southeast Tibet; eastward through China (Yunnan, Szechwan, Chekiang, Fukien), Assam, Burma, peninsular Thailand, Viet Nam to Formosa; then south into the Malay Peninsula and Sumatra.

Description. The body is light or dark olive above, with a row of large, squarish, dark brown or blackish markings on the back; occasionally there are two rows, and these may alternate with one another. A row of smaller spots occurs on the sides, each one, or a pair, directly below the corresponding larger marking. The head is dark brown on top, pale brown or yellowish on the sides, with a dark brown band from the eye to the back of the mouth. A Y-shaped marking often occurs on the neck.

Habitat. Although reported as living at low altitudes in Szechwan, China, this snake is essentially a mountain species. Stolicza (1871) claims that specimens have been found in the Himalayas at elevations up to 8000 ft, and on Mt. Omei, China at a height of 7000 ft. According to Leigh (1910), it prefers the vicinity of dwellings.

Size. Adult specimens are stout-bodied and grow to a length of between 3 and 4 ft.

Disposition. Its disposition is reported by Wall (1928) as irritable, but Pope (1935) observes that Fukien specimens proved sluggish and disinclined to strike, except when guarding eggs.

Food. The diet of this snake is mostly mammals, especially rats and mice. One specimen contained a shrew.

Young. The mountain pit-viper is one of the few species in the subfamily Crotalinae that lays eggs instead of bearing live young. It generally deposits five to eighteen eggs in a hollow in the ground or in vegetable debris, and guards them until they hatch. One such nest was discovered by Pope (1935) within a low pile of bamboo fiber waste, and another was found in a grassy, open tea field, the eggs having been laid a few inches below the surface of the ground. When hatched, the young snakes measure from $7\frac{1}{4}$ to $7\frac{1}{2}$ in.

Chasen's Pit-viper (*Trimeresurus chaseni*)

Distribution. This species is found only on Borneo.

Description. Related to the mountain pit-viper, it has a similar brownish color, and is marked with a series of irregular, blackish, light-edged blotches which change to crossbands towards the back of the body. Below, it is yellowish and heavily powdered with grey. An oblique, black stripe, bordered below with white, extends behind the eye. The tail is not prehensile. Immature specimens are like the adults, but with more clearly-defined markings.

Size. M. A. Smith (1931), who first discovered Chasen's pit-viper, gives its length as 25 in.

Flat-nosed Pit-viper (*Trimeresurus puniceus*)

Other names. Ashy pit-viper.

Distribution. It is known from peninsular Thailand, Malaya and western Indonesia. In the Pacific it has been found on Borneo, Sumatra, Java, Natuna Islands, Simalur and the Mentawi Islands (North Pagit Island).

Description. The most unique feature of the flat-nosed pit-viper is the spatulate-like snout which overhangs the nostrils. In some specimens the scales over the eyes are separated from one another and extend into an eyebrow-like tuft. The body is light brown, sometimes greyish, above, with darker markings that may be edged in black or bordered with black spots. The tail is darker than the body and mottled with brown; sometimes the end is reddish. A light, dark-edged streak runs backward from the eye.

Habits. The peculiar coiled position described by Schmidt and Inger (1957) evidently is a protective attitude assumed by the snake to simulate the leafy habitat in which it lives, just above the jungle floor.

Purple-spotted Pit-viper (*Trimeresurus purpureomaculatus*)

Other names. Shore pit-viper.

Distribution. Its range includes India (the eastern Himalayas, Bengal, Assam), Burma, the Malay Peninsula and adjacent small islands, Andaman Islands, Nicobar Islands and Sumatra. In the Pacific it is found only on Sumatra.

Description. The coloration of the shore, or purple-spotted, pit-viper is variable and without distinct markings. It may be uniformly dark purple-brown above, with or without a whitish line low on the sides near the belly. Some individuals, olive or grey-brown above, are spotted or irregularly marked with brown; occasionally pale green spots occur along the sides.

Size. This snake reaches a length of slightly more than 3 ft, Boulenger (1912) having described one of 38½ in.

Habitat. Boulenger (1912) and Tweedie (1953) both comment that this snake is partial to a sea shore environment, generally living in mangrove or other coastal vegetation. Here it may be found hiding under rocks, when they are available, or basking in the sun. Tweedie (1953) says it is common on small, offshore islands but rare on the mainland. Away from the coast it may frequently be found in bamboo jungle at elevations of from 200 to 3000 ft.

Schultze's Pit-viper (*Trimeresurus schultzei*)

Distribution. Known only from the islands of Palawan and Balabac in the Philippines.

Description. This species resembles the yellow-spotted pit-viper, also of the Philippine Islands. It is dark green or blackish brown above, marked with numerous black crossbars which are connected by zigzag lines. Along the sides near the abdomen, a distinct, canary-yellow line extends the length of the body. The top of the head is marked with a reticulate pattern of black lines, and there may be a yellow streak from behind the eye to the back of the mouth. The tail is bright red. Young snakes are bright yellow-green to blue-green; otherwise they are similar to the adults.

Size. The largest known specimen is about 48 in. long.

Yellow-spotted Pit-viper (*Trimeresurus flavomaculatus*)

Other names. Manda-dalag (on Polillo Island, for the race *halieus*).

Distribution. The known range of this pit-viper includes the following islands, all in the Philippines: Camiguin, Jolo, Luzon, Mindanao, Batan, Polillo and Patnanongan.

Description. There is considerable variation in the color and markings of the yellow-spotted pit-viper, but most individuals are bright- or olive-green, with or without a row of irregular brown blotches or crossbands on the back. The skin between the scales is brownish or blackish. A broken, sometimes continuous, line of yellow dots along the sides near the belly is characteristic of this species. Another important feature of identification is the color of the tail which, in this snake, is the same as that of the body.

The Polillo and McGregor's pit-vipers, long considered as distinct species, have recently been listed by Leviton (1961) as geographic races of the yellow-spotted pit-viper.

In color and markings, the Polillo pit-viper is similar to *flavomaculatus*, but may be marked with bright yellow spots, more prominent toward the tail. However, the characteristic narrow line of greenish spots found along the lower sides of the yellow-spotted pit-viper, is lacking in adults of this race, but is often present in the young. A specimen from Patnanongan Island, east of Polillo, has black and flesh colored skin showing between the scales, the colors alternating on the back and the black areas widening on the sides.

The bright yellow coloration of the race known as McGregor's pit-viper, *Trimeresurus f. mcgregori*, is found in no other snake of the genus. Only the darker yellow streak along the sides and a few small, reddish-brown spots near the end of the tail mark its otherwise immaculate appearance. Even the eyes are very pale.

Juvenile yellow-spotted pit-vipers from Mindanao are boldy marked, particularly along the sides of the head, where a white or yellow streak runs from just below the eye to the back of the mouth. In addition, a short, vertical bar extends down from in front of the eye and another behind it. Young specimens from Luzon are somewhat lighter in color, usually green or greenish-brown, and they lack the bold head markings of the Mindanao juveniles.

Size. These snakes seldom grow over 3 ft long.

Habitat. One specimen of the subspecies *mcgregori* was found about 6 ft above ground, coiled on some leaves that had lodged among the thick stems of a large grass, according to Taylor (1919). The Polillo pit-viper on the other hand, lives along the banks of streams or in damp localities and rarely leaves the ground. Griffin (1910) states that when the natives of Polillo are night fishing by torchlight, the snakes are commonly seen near the edge of the water. One specimen was observed to have buried most of its body in the sand close to the water's edge. Since many small fish were swimming in deeper water a few inches away, the snake may have been lying in wait to feed upon them. The native belief that the snakes are at the streams feeding on fish has given rise to the local name, *manda-dalag*. Literally translated, it means, " the fisher of the dalag (or mudfish)".

Food. Tadpoles, adult frogs and the remains of geckos have been found in the stomachs of several individuals. The diet of the Polillo pit-viper apparently consists of frogs, fish and, to a lesser extent, mammals.

Young. Two females, collected on April 28 from Kaling subprovince, Luzon Island, contained, respectively, fourteen and twenty large eggs in the oviducts. Aside from this information, nothing is known of the snake's breeding habits.

Medical importance. Taylor (1922) reports one case of poisoning by a snake of the subspecies *mcgregori* that involved Mr. Richard C. McGregor, discoverer of this form. According to Mr. McGregor, " The snake was struck with an alpen stick and fell to the ground. In attempting to put a string on its neck, I was scratched by the fangs, between the last two joints of my thumb. Mr. H. G. Ferguson immediately made several cuts across the wound with a pocket knife and tied a string around the thumb. My hand and forearm were swollen by evening. The swelling subsided within a couple of days. There was very little pain, and no further trouble was experienced ".

White-lipped Pit-viper (*Trimeresurus albolabris*) (*Fig.* 71)

Other names. Bamboo viper (Hong Kong).

Distribution. This snake is found in northeastern India, southeastern China, Formosa, Hainan, Laos, Viet Nam and the Sunda Archipelago from southeastern Sumatra to Wetar and Timor.

Description. The color of this attractive little snake is bright green above and pale green, yellowish or white lower on the sides. Indistinct, light crossbars may occur on the back, and a narrow, white stripe, low on the sides, extends the length of the body in males but is indistinct or absent in females. The end of the tail is reddish-brown above. The entire side of the head, below the eye, is white, pale yellow or light green.

Size. Adults of this rather small species rarely exceed 30 in. in length. Smith (1943) mentions one that was about 34 in. long.

Habitat. Partial to more or less open country at low elevations, this snake shows a fondness for human habitations, where it is frequently discovered in gardens. In southern Kwangtung, China, Mell (1922) found it abundant at altitudes below 1200 ft, in level or sloping, grassy and bush-covered areas. It is said by Pope (1935) to occupy the same habitats on Hainan and in Fukien, China. Within the colony of Hong Kong, Romer states that it is found on an island with no streams, pools or other permanent bodies of fresh water. Observations made by Romer, and those made independently by another herpetologist, suggest that white-lipped pit-vipers do not drink water in captivity. However, at the Houston Zoo, specimens readily drank the water which was sprinkled over their heads from a spray bulb, indicating that perhaps periodic rains satisfy their water needs in the wild.

Disposition. Most observers agree that this is a relatively slow moving and inoffensive snake, except when thoroughly annoyed. However, when defending itself, it strikes and bites vigorously.

Food. It feeds chiefly upon rodents, but frogs and lizards are also eaten.

Young. The usual number of young in a litter is seven.

Stejneger's Pit-viper (Trimeresurus stejnegeri) (Fig. 72)

Distribution. The range of this snake is not at all clearly defined. It occurs, at least, in central and southeastern China (Kwangsi, Kwangtung, Hainan, Hunan, Fukien, Chekiang), Burma, Tonkin, Hainan and Taiwan.

Description. In this snake the body is uniformly dark green above, a bit lighter below. Low on the sides, a narrow, yellowish stripe extends the length of the body, generally reaching forward to the eye in males but seldom encroaching onto the head in females. The stripe, which in both sexes runs backward to the base of the tail, is usually edged beneath with red in males, with green in females. The side of the head is uniformly green, the belly is green and the end of the tail reddish.

This species is much like the white-lipped pit-viper. Both possess a similar green coloration, a narrow white or yellowish line low on the sides, and a reddish tail. However, certain marked color differences will serve to separate them. First, the green color of this species is darker than that of the white-lipped pit-viper. Second, in this species the side of the head is nearly uniformly green, while in the white-lipped pit-viper it is white, pale yellow or very light green below the eyes.

Size. This is a somewhat smaller species than the related white-lipped pit-viper, seldom reaching a length of 2 ft.

Habitat. In contrast to the terrestrial habits of the preceding species, this is an arboreal snake with a prehensile tail. It is chiefly an inhabitant of mountains. Mell (1922) gives its vertical range in northern Kwantung, China as 2000 to 3500 ft, and Maslin (1950) writes that in Lushan, China, altitude appears to be of little significance to the snake's vertical distribution. Here, he explains, its distribution is more directly correlated with the growth of bushes and low trees than it is with elevation. Specimens were found by him in bushes and low trees at heights up to 15 ft.

The best account of the habits of this pit-viper comes from Pope (1935), who described it as abundant along the cascading streams of high mountains. On three occasions he observed them at night, prowling among boulders lying in stream beds, apparently searching for frogs. On Formosa, where the species is common, it probably lives in similar situations.

Disposition. Pope's field experience with this snake indicates that it tolerates little annoyance. When surprised, it struck viciously, often throwing the back end of its body about in a surprising manner.

Food. Frogs appear to be the main item of food in the snake's diet, but stomach examination of preserved specimens shows that it also eats small mammals.

Young. The number of snakes born in a litter varies from three to seven.

Pope's Pit-viper (*Trimeresurus popeorum*) (*Fig.* 73)

Other names. *Oelar idjo* (of the Malays); *ular bisa* (Sumatra); *oraj hedjo* (of the Sundanese); *oraj boengka laoet* (south coast of west Java); *esau* (Timor).

Distribution. The range of this snake includes, at least, Thailand, upper Burma, Cambodia, the Malay Peninsula, Borneo, Sumatra and other Indonesian islands as far east as Timor.

Description. Pope's pit-viper is green above, lighter green or yellow below, generally with an indistinct white or yellow stripe on each side near the abdomen. The color of the head is much like that of the body, and the tail is usually reddish-brown near the end. Young examples possess a white stripe on each side which is margined below with red.

Size. Large specimens of this species measure about 3 ft in length.

Habitat. This exclusively arboreal species is most abundant in hilly and mountainous country from an elevation of 3000 ft to more than 5000 ft. In common with the other green-colored pit-vipers which live in trees and bushes, it is extremely difficult to detect in dense foliage. As a result, accidents from this snake among the tea-leaf pickers of Java are not uncommon, according to Kopstein (1928).

Disposition. Not normally aggressive, Pope's pit-viper often permits a human intruder to approach it closely without striking. When aroused, it threatens with open mouth and, in the next instant, delivers a vigorous strike.

Food. The variable diet of Pope's pit-viper includes small mammals, lizards, birds, frogs and toads.

Young. The progeny, born alive, number seven to twelve in a litter.

Banded Pit-viper (*Trimeresurus fasciatus*)

Distribution. It is known only from Djampea Island.

Description. The snout of the banded pit-viper is turned up slightly. Its body color is grey-brown above, with numerous dark-olive, transverse bands, some of them broken up on the middle of the back and alternating on either side. The head is uniformly dark olive.

Size. The total length of this species is about 18 in.

Sumatran Pit-viper (*Trimeresurus sumatranus*)

Other names. *Ular bisa* (eastern Sumatra).

Distribution. Malaya, Sumatra, Borneo and Nias are included in the known range of this snake.

Description. The largest of the green pit-vipers in the Pacific, this species is bright green above, usually with very distinct, black crossbars down the back. Sometimes the dark bars are replaced by white or pinkish spots. A white stripe, frequently bordered with black below, extends along each side of the body near the abdomen. The underside is light yellowish-green. In adults, the scales on the head are broadly edged with black; young specimens have a white streak behind the eye. The green, prehensile tail, which may be banded with red on the forward part, is entirely red at the end.

Apparently the Sumatran pit-viper is most like Pope's pit-viper, with which it coexists throughout part of its range, but from which it differs in the presence of black-margined head scales and (not always) the two rows of light-colored spots along the middle of the back.

Size. This, the largest of the green pit-vipers in the Pacific, may grow to a length of 4 ft.

Habitat. In Malaya, Boulenger (1912) reports this snake as common at elevations of 2000 to 3000 ft, particularly where there is much bamboo jungle. It is also fairly abundant in the lowland jungle of that country and in the foothills.

The Mt. Kinabalu pit-viper, a race of the Sumatran pit-viper, is found on Borneo's Mt. Kinabalu.

Hagen's Pit-viper (*Trimeresurus hageni*)

Distribution. The known range of this snake includes Sumatra, Simalur, the Batu Islands, the Mentawi Islands and Nias.

Description. Hagen's pit-viper is very similar in appearance to the Sumatran pit-viper, but lacks the black-edged head scales and the black crossbars of that snake. It is light to dark green on the back, somewhat lighter on the sides, the body scales narrowly edged with black or displaying black tips. A light line, bordered beneath by a dark line or by a series of dark spots, is present along each side. Often there is a dark or light streak on the side of the head, from the eye to the back of the mouth. The tail is sometimes marked by red and green spots, or crossbands.

Size. It is reported to reach a length of 3 ft.

Wagler's Pit-viper (*Trimeresurus wagleri*) (*Figs.* 74–78)

Other names. Speckled pit-viper; bamboo snake; temple snake; *ular bakaw* (mangrove snake, of the Malays); *djalimoo* (Toradja name); *ular puckuk* (Sumatra); *papala* (in Misamis Province, Philippine Islands).

Distribution. This species occurs on the Malay Peninsula and adjoining small islands, and through Indonesia. In the Pacific it is known from the following islands: Banka, Biliton, Borneo, Celebes, Mentawi Islands, Nias, Penang, Philippine Islands (Balabac, Basilan, Jolo, Leyte, Luzon, Mindanao, Negros, Palawan, Samar), Sangire Islands, Singapore, Sumatra and Wetar.

Description. The adult color is generally green or blue-green, all of the scales black edged, with yellow-green centers. Distinct greenish or bright yellow crossbars, bordered in black, occur on the back. In most areas, the older snakes are predominately black with scattered green spots above, the scales on the sides green in color and edged in black. These have greenish bands crossing the back, which change to yellow along the sides. The head, which is broadly triangular and distinct from the neck, has a greenish-yellow streak, edged with black, running backward from the eye. Below the eye, the head is yellow and greenish-white, the top black. The end of the tail is black. Young snakes are differently colored than adults. They are green with one or two rows of distinct, transverse spots or short crossbars on the back, each marking partly white and partly red. A narrow streak, white above and red below, runs from the snout back through the eye. The end of the tail is red or reddish-brown. According to Guenther (1864), specimens from Borneo, Sumatra, Celebes and the Philippines often show the juvenile coloration long after they are mature.

Individual variation in color pattern is considerable, particularly among snakes from the islands of the Philippines. For example, among specimens of Wagler's viper from Mindanao alone, the color pattern differences are greater than they are throughout all of the other Philippine Islands combined, with one exception—on Jolo. Here, they were found by Leviton (1959) to be significantly different from Wagler's pit-viper in other parts of the range, with little evidence of individual variation. Some Mindanao specimens were uniformly blue-green without markings, some had irregular crossbands, and others were marked with clearly-defined narrow crossbands. On Negros Island, one specimen lacked barred markings, and on Jolo and Basilan, the crossbars were broad, black and about as wide as the spaces between them.

Size. Wagler's pit-viper grows to a length of about 3 ft.

Habitat. This colorful snake is the most common species of the genus. It occurs abundantly in lowland jungles, including mangrove swamps, where it lives in bushes and low trees. In some areas it inhabits hills and low mountains. DeRooij (1917) records it at 2500 to 4000 ft in the Battak Highlands of Sumatra and at 2500 to 3900 ft elevation near Bone Valley on Celebes, while Taylor (1922), without giving any specific altitude, reports it from low mountains of central Negros in the Philippines.

Disposition. Wagler's pit-vipers are slow moving, relatively docile snakes that seldom bite, even if handled roughly. For this reason they are not much feared by the natives, who handle them with disregard, and who sometimes place them near their homes as an omen of good luck. On the island of Penang, off the west coast of Malaya, numbers of these vipers are kept in the Snake Temple—further evidence of their tranquil nature.

Food. It is not discriminating in its feeding habits, taking mammals, birds, lizards and snakes. Leviton (1959) found skunks and some snake scales in the stomachs of Philippine examples.

ACKNOWLEDGEMENTS

We wish to thank Alan E. Leviton, Hobart M. Smith, and Kenneth L. Williams for the loan of published material not readily available to us. Richard Zweifel placed at our disposal the herpetological library of the American Musuem of Natural History, and Robert F. Inger and Arthur Loveridge helped in other ways. Preserved specimens were loaned through the kindness of Doris M. Cochran (for the United States National Museum) and Lawrence Curtis. Live specimens were provided by Dr. H. J. Magens, and by Theodore Reed and J. Lear Grimmer of the National Zoological Park. The following persons made certain photographs available and granted permission for their use: Commander Robert E. Kuntz, U.S.N., Herndon Dowling, Kazuo Koba, Eric Worrell, Charles Shaw, M. W. F. Tweedie, Howard K. Gloyd, Isabelle and Roger Conant. Figures 31–34 and 67 are published through courtesy of the *American Journal of Tropical Medicine and Hygiene.* All line drawings, with the exceptions of Fig. 6, Figs. 18–19, and 29–34 were prepared by Mr. Takaji Matsui of the Dept. of Entomology, 406th Medical General Laboratory, U.S. Army Medical Command, Camp Zama, Japan. The authors are greatly indebted to Mr. Matsui and to Major Gordon Field, M.S.C., U.S.A., under whose supervision this work was accomplished. Donald M. Darling prepared the line drawing (Fig. 6) of the krait body section. Several otherwise unavailable references were supplied on very short notice by Dr. Bei-Loo Chen of the Academia Sinica, Taipei, and Colonel Hinton Baker, M.C., U.S.A., Medical Research Unit, Kuala Lumpur, Malaya.

REFERENCES

ACTON, H. W. and KNOWLES, R. 1914. Studies on the treatment of snakebite. *Indian J. Med. Research* **2**, 146–148.

ANNANDALE, N. 1911. Contributions to the fauna of Yunnan based on collections made by J. Coggin Brown, B.Sc., 1909–1910. Part IV—Batrachia and reptiles. *Rec. Indian Mus.* **6**, 211.

BARBOUR, T. 1912. A contribution to the zoogeography of the East Indian Islands. *Mem. Mus. Comp. Zool.* **44**, 1.

BARME, M., HUARD, M. and NGUYEN XUAN MAI. 1962. Préparation d'un serum anti-venin d'hydrophiides. Premiers essais therapeutiques. *Ann. Inst. Pasteur* **102**, 2.

BARRETT, C. 1950. *Reptiles of Australia.* Melbourne: Cassell.

BOGERT, C. 1943. Dentitional phenomena in cobras and other elapids with notes on adaptive modifications of fangs. *Bull. Amer. Mus. Nat. Hist.* **81** (3), 285.

BOGERT, C. M. and MATALAS, B. L. 1945. Results of the Archbold expeditions No. 35. A review of the elapid genus *Ultrocalamus* of New Guinea. *Amer. Mus. Novitates* No. 1284, 1.

P. 1959. Sur l'uniformisation des méthodes de mesure de l'action anti-toxique des serums therapeutiques antivenimeux. *Proc. Fifth Internat. Mtg. Biol. Stand.* Israel. 477.

BOULENGER, G. A. 1912. *A Vertebrate Fauna of the Malay Peninsula from the Isthmus of Kra to Singapore including adjacent islands. Reptilia and Batrachia.* London: Taylor & Francis.

BOULENGER, G. A. 1913. *The Snakes of Europe.* London: Methuen.
BRONGERSMA, L. D. 1934. *Contributions to Indo-Australian herpetology.* Leyden, Holland: E. J. Brill.
BRONGERSMA, L. D. 1958. Note on *Vipera russelii* (Shaw). *Zool. Meded. Leiden* **36** (4), 55.
BRYAN, W. A. 1915. *Natural History of Hawaii.* Honolulu: Hawaiian Gazette Co.
CAREY, J. E. and WRIGHT, E. A. 1960. The toxicity and immunological properties of some sea-snake venoms with particular reference to that of *Enhydrina schistosa. Trans. Roy. Soc. Trop. Med. Hyg.* **54**, 50.
DASCH, D. 1952. *Snakes on Taiwan.* Mimeographed booklet.
DESPAX, R. 1913. Sur une collection de reptiles et de batraciens rassemblée par M. le Dr. Legendre dans les Marches Thibetaines. *Bull. Mus. Hist. Nat. Paris* **19**, 179.
EFRATI, P. and REIF, L. 1953. Clinical and pathological observations on sixty-five cases of viper bite in Israel. *Am. J. Trop. Med. Hyg.* **2**, 1085.
EVANS, G. M. 1921. An encounter with a hamadryad (*Naia bungarus*). *J. Bombay Nat. Hist. Soc.* **27**, 955.
GLOYD, H. K. 1955. A new Crotalid snake from Kume Sima, Riu Kiu Islands. *Bull. Chicago Acad. Sci.* **10** (8), 123.
GRIFFIN, E. 1909. A list of snakes found in Palawan. *Philippine J. Sci.* **A4**, 595.
GRIFFIN, E. 1910. A list of snakes from the island of Polillo, Philippine Islands, with descriptions of a new genus and two new species. *Philippine J. Sci.* **D5**, 211.
GUENTHER, A. 1864. *The Reptiles of British India.* London.
HALSTEAD, B. 1959. *Dangerous Marine Animals.* Cambridge, Maryland: Cornell Maritime Press.
HERRE, A. 1942. Notes on Philippine sea snakes. *Copeia* (1), 7.
KAUFFELD, C. F. 1946. Snakes that spit. *Animaland* **13** (3), 2.
KEEGAN, H. L. 1960. *Some Venomous and Noxious Animals of the Far East.* U.S. Army Medical Command, Camp Zama, Japan.
KEEGAN, H. L. and YOSHINO, K. 1959. *Trimeresurus elegans* (Gray), the Sakishima habu, a venomous pit-viper from the Ryukyu Islands. *Am. J. Trop. Med. and Hyg.* **8** (2), 124.
KEEGAN, H. L., WHITTEMORE, F. W. and MAXWELL, G. R. 1962. Neutralization of ten snake venoms by homologous and heterologous antivenins. *Copeia.* 313.
KINGHORN, J. R. 1956. *The Snakes of Australia.* Second edition. Wellington: Angus and Robert.
KOBA, K. 1958. Herpetofauna of the Amami group of the Loo Choo Islands (II). *Mem. Faculty of Education*, Kumamoto Univ. **6**, 173.
KOBA, K. 1959. Herpetofauna of the Amami group of the Loo Choo Islands (III). *Mem. Faculty of Education*, Kumamoto Univ. **7**, 187.
KOBA, K. 1960. Herpetofauna of the Amami group of the Loo Choo Islands (IV). *Mem. Faculty of Education*, Kumamoto Univ. **8**, 181.
KOBA, K. 1961. Food of *Trimeresurus flavoviridis flavoviridis* and *T. okinavensis* in the Amami group of the Loo Choo Islands. *Mem. Faculty of Education*, Kumamoto Univ. **9**, 220.
KOCHWA, S., GITTER, S., STRAUSS, A., PERMUTTER-MOROZ, CH. and DE VRIES, A. 1959. Production of antibodies against *Vipera xanthina palestinae* venom and venom fractions. *Proc. Fifth Internat. Mfg. for Biol. Stand.* Israel. 483.
KOCHWA, S., IZARD, Y., BOQUET, P. and GITTER, S. 1959. Sur la préparation d'un immunserum equin anti-venimeux au moyen des fractions neurotoxiques isolées du venin. *Ann. Inst. Pasteur.* **97**, 370.
KOPSTEIN, F. 1928. Observations on the effect of the venom of the Javanese " green snake ", *Lachesis gramineus. Meded. Dienst Volksgezondeheid Ned. Ind.* **68** (7), 1035.
KOPSTEIN, F. 1930. Die Giftschlangen Javas und ihre Bedeutung für den Menschen. *Zeitschr. Morph. Okol. Tiere.* **19** (213), 339.
KOPSTEIN, F. 1932. Herpetologica notitzen. *Treubia* **14** (1), 73.

LEIGH, C. 1910. An oviparous Indian viper. *Field* (3).
LEVITON, A. E. 1959. *Systematics and zoogeography of Philippine snakes.* Stanford University. Thesis.
LEVITON, A. E. 1961. Key to the dangerously venomous terrestrial snakes of the Philippine Islands. *Silliman J.* **8** (2), 98.
LOVERIDGE, A. 1945. *Reptiles of the Pacific World.* New York: Macmillan.
MAKI, M. 1931. A monograph of the snakes of Japan. *Dai-Ichi Shobo. Tokyo.*
MASLIN, T. P. 1950. Snakes of the Kiukiang-Lushan area, Kiangsi, China. *Proc. Cal. Acad. Sci.* **26** (12), 419.
MELL, R. 1922. Beitrage zur fauna sinica. I Die vertebraten Sudchinas: Feldlisten und Feldnoten der Sauger, Vogel, Reptilien, Batrachier. *Arch. Naturg.* **88** (10), 1.
MELL, R. 1929. *Beitrage zur Okologie der Chinesischen Reptilien und einer herpetologischen tiergeographie Chinas.* Berlin.
MORGAN, F. G. 1956. The Australian taipan *Oxyuranus scutellatus* scutellatus (Peters). in *Venoms*, Publication 44, Amer. Assoc. Advancement of Sci. 359.
NEUHAUS, H. 1935. Neunachweis von *Vipera russellii* auf Java. *Treubia* **15**, 49–50.
OLIVER, J. 1958. The taipan, Australia's deadliest snake. *Animal Kingdom* **61** (1), 23.
OLIVER, J. and SHAW, E. 1953. The amphibians and reptiles of the Hawaiian Islands. *Zoologica* **38** (2), 65.
POPE, C. H. 1929. Notes on reptiles from Fukien and other Chinese provinces. *Bull. Amer. Mus. Nat. Hist.* **58** (8), 335.
POPE, C. H. 1935. The reptiles of China. *Amer. Mus. Nat. Hist.*
REID, H. A. 1956. Sea-snake bites. *British Med. J.* **2**, 73.
REID, H. A. 1956. Sea-snake bite research. *Trans. Royal Soc. Trop. Med. and Hyg.* **50** (6), 517.
REID, H. A. 1962. Sea snake antivenins: successful trial. In Press. *Brit. Med. J.*
ROMER, J. D. 1952. White-lipped pit viper. *Zoo Life* **7** (4), 2.
ROMER, J. D. 1954. Notes on sea snakes (Hydrophiidae) occurring in or near Hong Kong territorial waters. *Hong Kong Univ. Fisheries J.* (1), 35.
ROOIJ, NELLIE DE. 1917. *The reptiles of the Indo-Australian Archipelago. II. Ophidia* Leiden: E. J. Brill.
SCHMIDT, KARL P. and INGER, R. F. 1957. *Living reptiles of the world.* New York: Hanover House, Garden City.
SHANNON, F. A. 1956. The reptiles and amphibians of Korea. *Herpetologica* **12**, 22.
SHAW, C. E. 1961. Snakes of the sea. *Zoonooz* **34** (7), 3.
SLEVIN, J. R. 1934. The Templeton Crocker expedition to western Polynesian and Melanesian Islands, 1933. No. 15. Notes on the reptiles and amphibians, with the description of a new species of sea snake. *Proc. Acad. Sci.* **21** (15), 183.
SMITH, M. A. 1926. *Monograph of the sea snakes* (*Hydrophiidae*). London: Taylor & Francis.
SMITH, M. A. 1930. The reptiles and amphibians of the Malay Peninsula. *Bull. Raffles Mus., Singapore* No. 3.
SMITH, M. A. 1943. *The fauna of British India, Ceylon and Burma including the whole of the Indo-Chinese subregion. Reptilia and amphibia.* Vol. 3, Serpentes. London: Taylor and Francis.
STEJNEGER, L. 1907. Herpetology of Japan and adjacent territory. *U.S. Nat. Mus. Bull.* **58**.
STOLICZA, F. 1871. Notes on some Indian and Burmese ophidians. *J. Asiatic Soc. Bengal* **40** (2), 421.
SWINHOE, R. 1870. Note on reptiles and batrachians collected in various parts of China. *Proc. Zool. Soc. London.* p. 409.
TAYLOR, E. H. 1922. *The Snakes of the Philippine Islands.* Publication 16, Bureau of Science, Manila. pp. 1–312.
TWEEDIE, M. W. F. 1941. *Poisonous Animals of Malaya.* Malaya: Malaya Publishing House.
TWEEDIE, M. W. F. 1953. *The Snakes of Malaya.* Government Printing Office, Singapore.

VAN DENBURGH, J. and THOMSON, J. C. 1908. Description of a new species of sea snake from the Philippine Islands, with a note on the palatine teeth in the proteroglypha. *Proc. Cal. Acad. Sci.* **3**, 41–48.

WALL, F. 1818. A popular treatise on the common Indian snakes, part XXV. *Jour. Bombay Nat. Hist. Soc.* pp. 625.

WALL, F. 1921. *Ophidia taprobanica or the snakes of Ceylon.* Colombo: H. R. Cottle.

WALL, F. 1924. The hamadryad or king cobra, Naia hannah (Cantor). *Jour. Bombay Nat. Hist. Soc.* **30**, 189.

WALL, F. 1928. *The Poisonous Terrestrial Snakes of our British Indian Dominions (including Ceylon) and how to recognize them.* Bombay: Diocesan Press.

WERNER, F. 1920. *Die Lurche und Kriechtiere.* Vol. 2 *in Brehm's Tierleben.* Leipzig and Vienna.

WORRELL, E. 1952. *Dangerous Snakes of Australia.* Sydney: Angus and Robertson.

VAN HOESEL, J. K. P. VAN. 1958. Note on *Vipera russelii* (Shaw). *Zool. Meded. Leiden.* **36** (4), 55–76.

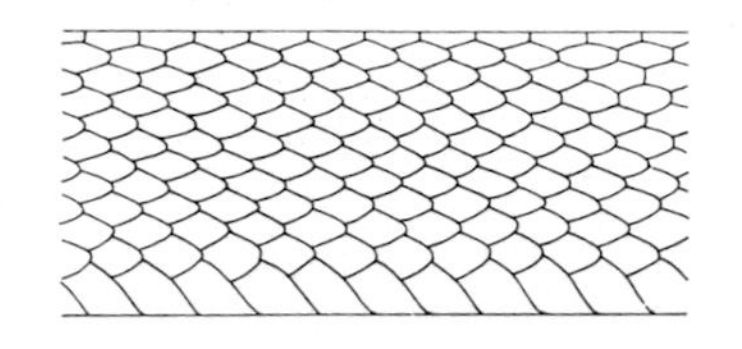

FIG. 1. Body section showing smooth scales.

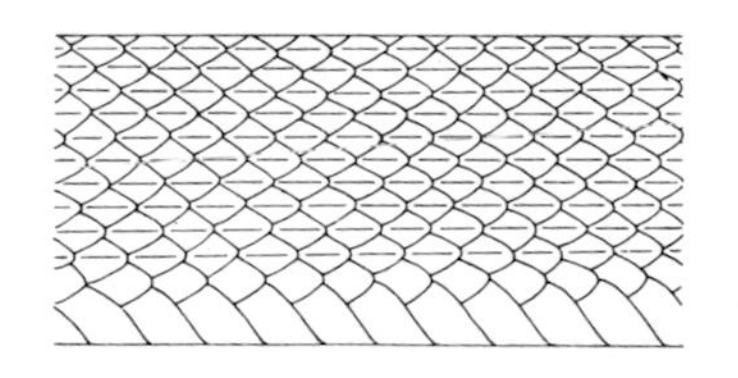

FIG. 2. Body section showing keeled scales.

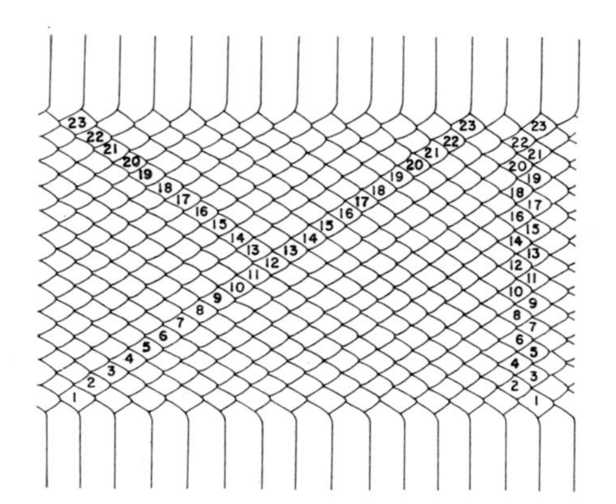

FIG. 3. Expanded body section of snake illustrating methods of making dorsal scale counts.

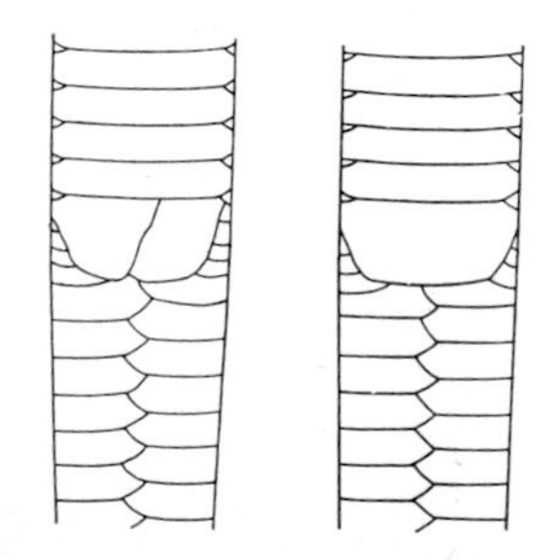

FIG. 4. Underside of tail showing divided (on left) and single (on right) anal plates.

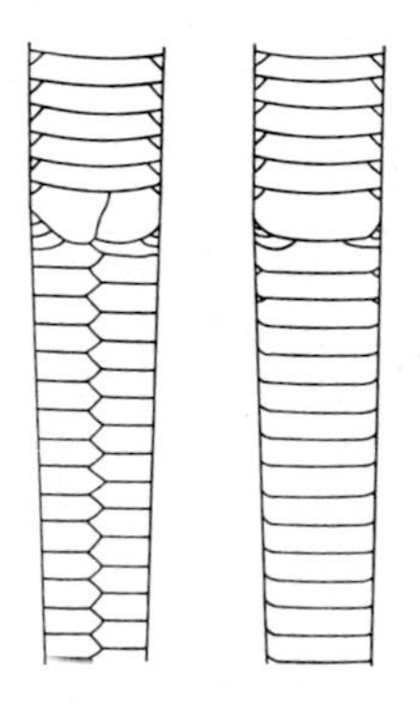

FIG. 5. Underside of snake showing double (on left) and single (on right) scale rows under the tail.

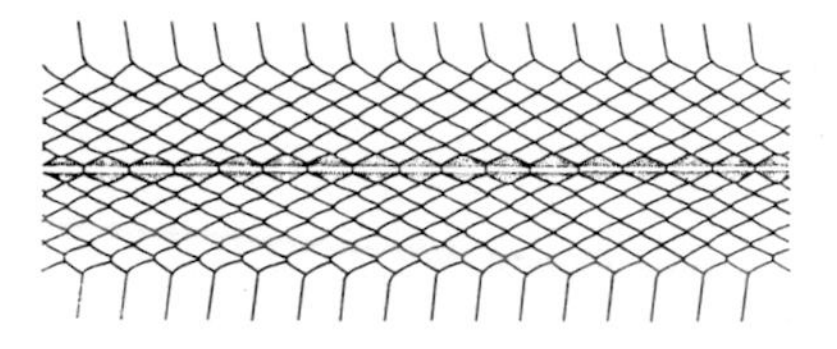

FIG. 6. Expanded body section illustrating enlarged vertebral scales (those down the middle of the back).

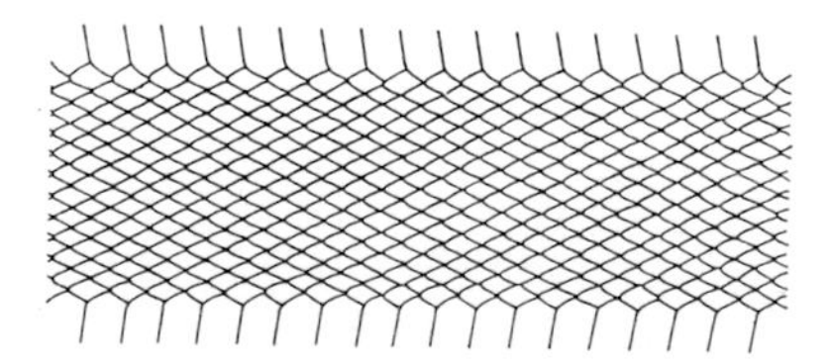

FIG. 7. Expanded body section showing normal (not enlarged) vertebral scales.

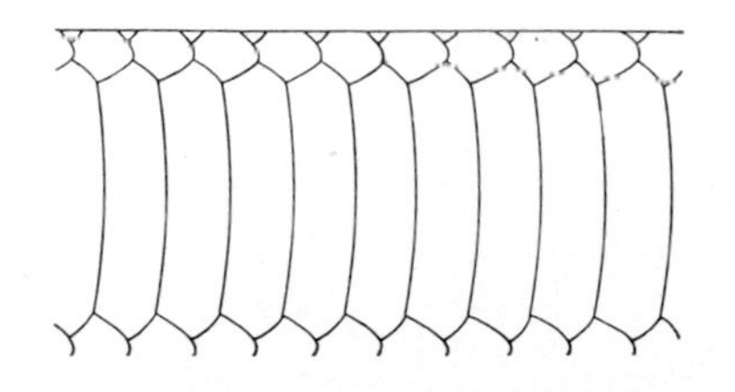

FIG. 8. Underside of snake showing normal ventrals (belly shields).

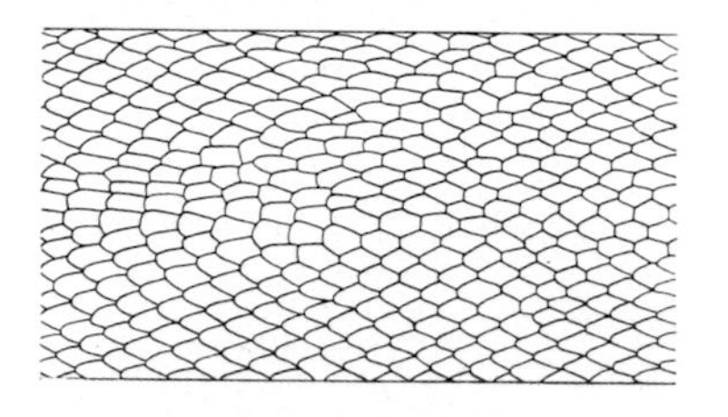

FIG. 9. Underside of snake illustrating ventrals separated into two halves (genus *Astroitia*).

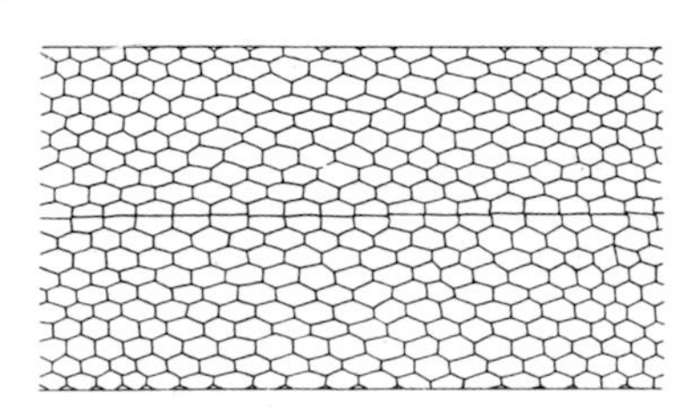

FIG. 10. Underside of snake showing ventral plates small and with a median groove (genus *Pelamis*).

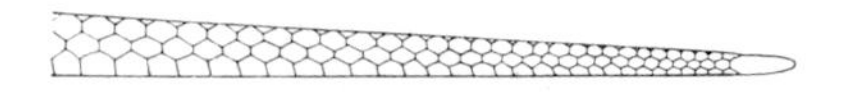

FIG. 11. Normally pointed tail.

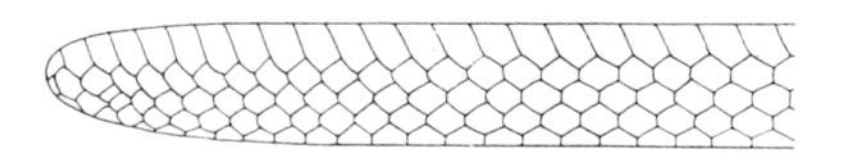

FIG. 12. Blunt tail.

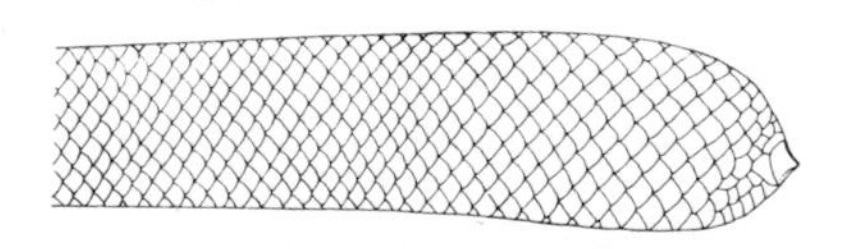

FIG. 13. Vertically compressed (paddle-like) tail of the sea snakes.

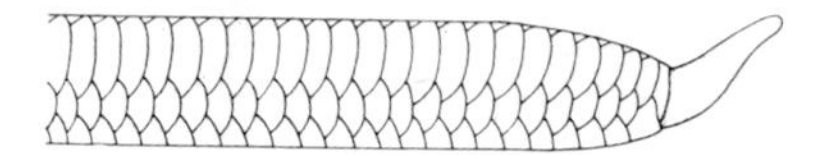

FIG. 14. Tail compressed toward tip and ending in a spine (*Acanthophis*).

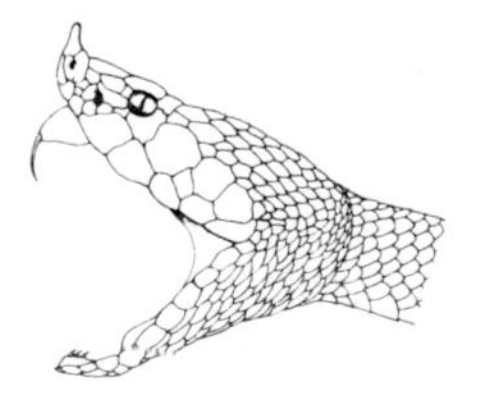

FIG. 15. Side view of the long-nosed pit-viper showing the upturned nasal appendage.

FIG. 16. Palato-maxillary arch showing maxillary bone not reaching forward as far as palatine.

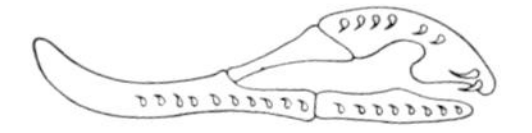

FIG. 17. Palato-maxillary arch showing maxillary bone extending forward as far as palatine.

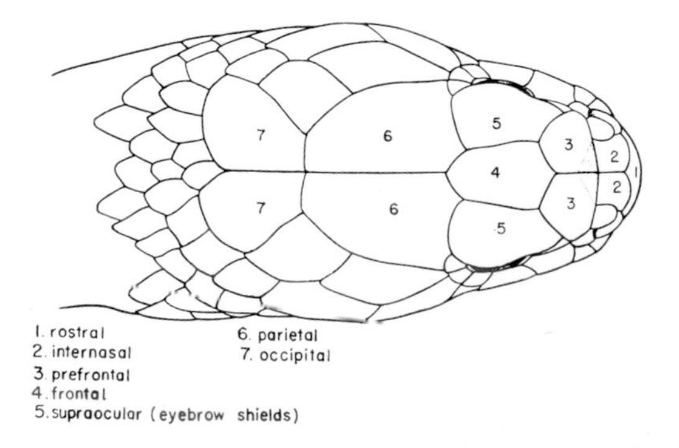

FIG. 18. Top view of a king cobra's head with the scales identified: 1, rostral; 2, internasal; 3, prefrontal; 4, frontal; 5, supraocular (eyebrow shields); 6, parietal; 7, occipital.

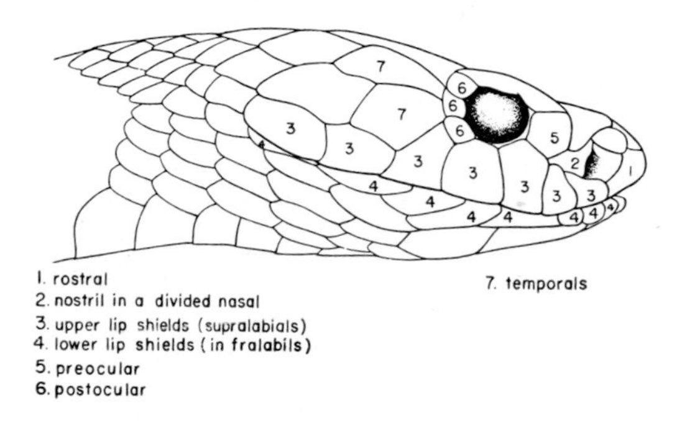

FIG. 19. Side view of a king cobra's head with the scales identified: 1, rostral; 2, nostril in a divided nasal; 3, supralabials (upper lip shields); 4, infralabials (lower lip shields); 5, preocular; 6, postocular; 7, temporals.

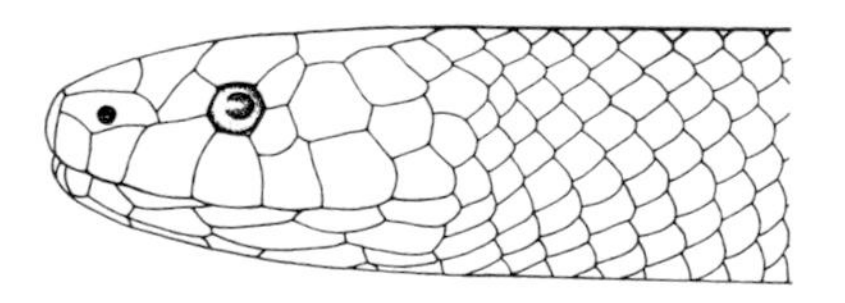

FIG. 20. *Laticauda laticaudata*, side of head.

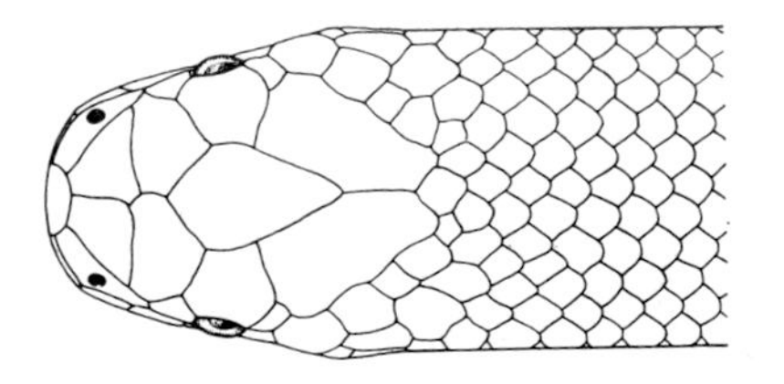

FIG. 21. *Laticauda laticaudata*, top of head.

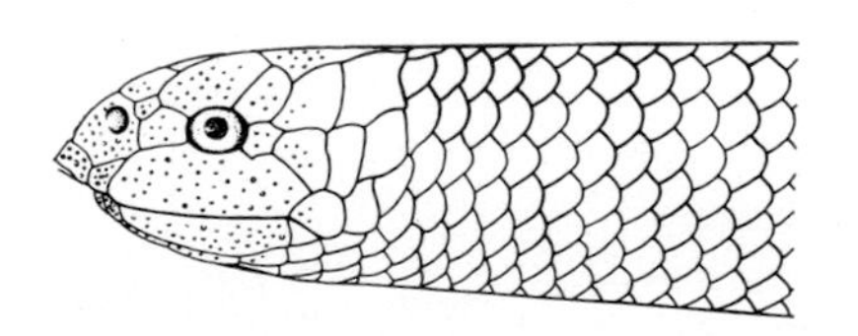

FIG. 22. *Emydocephalus ijimae*, side of head.

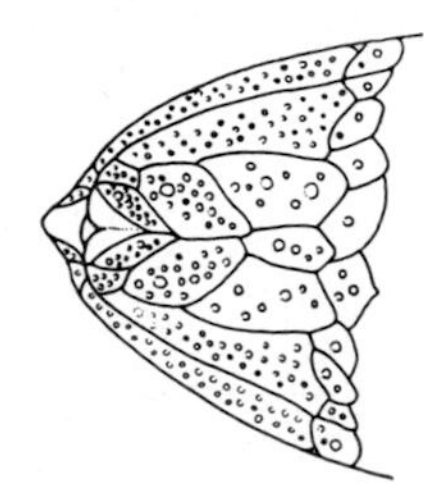

FIG. 23. *Emydocephalus ijimae*, chin.

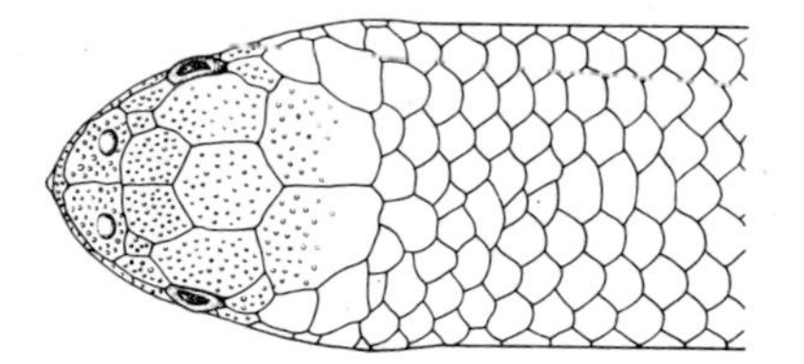

FIG. 24. *Emydocephalus ijimae*, top of head.

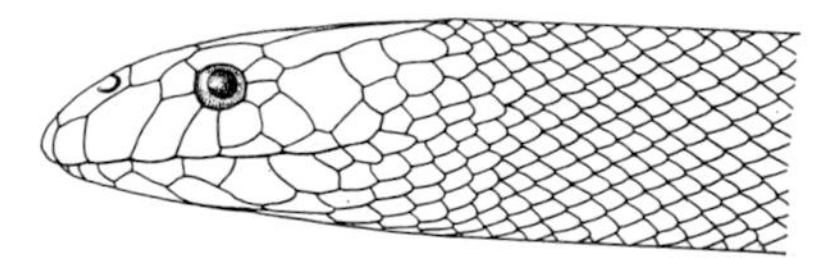

FIG. 25. *Hydrophis melanocephala*, side of head.

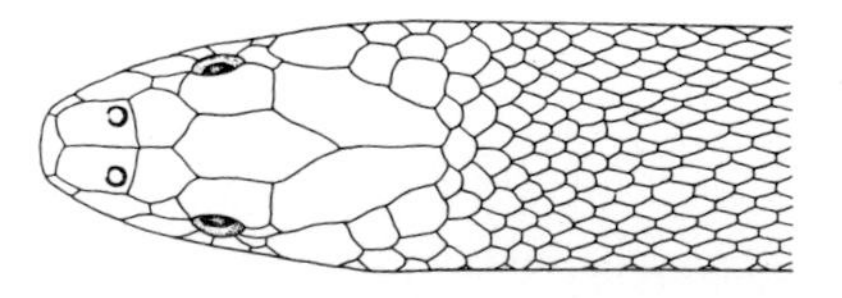

FIG. 26. *Hydrophis melanocephala*, top of head.

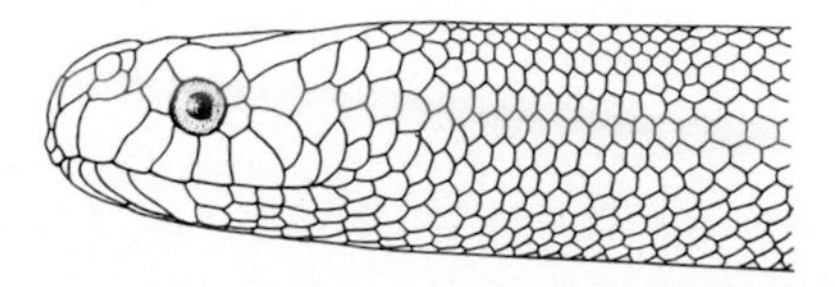

FIG. 27. *Thalassophis anomalus*, side of head.

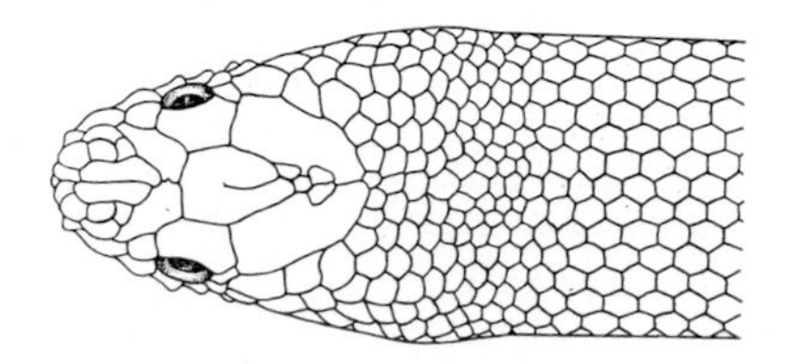

FIG. 28. *Thalassophis anomalus*, top of head.

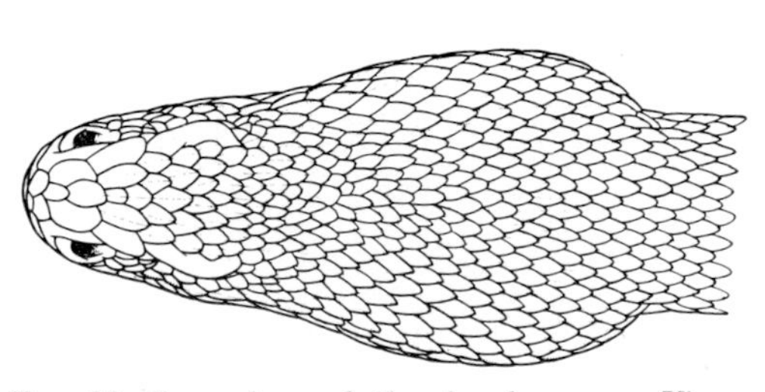

FIG. 29. Top view of the head, genus *Vipera*.

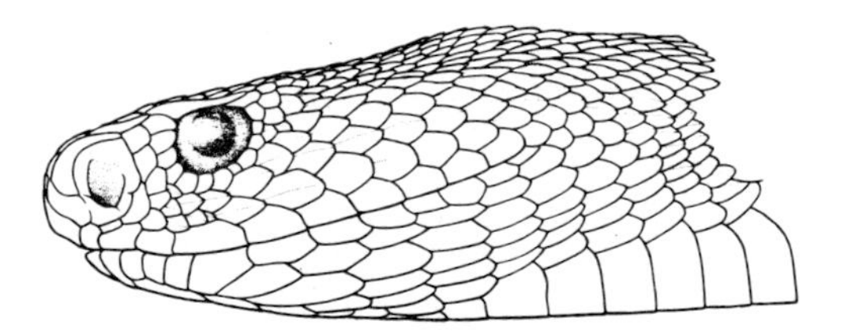

FIG. 30. Side view of the head, genus *Vipera*.

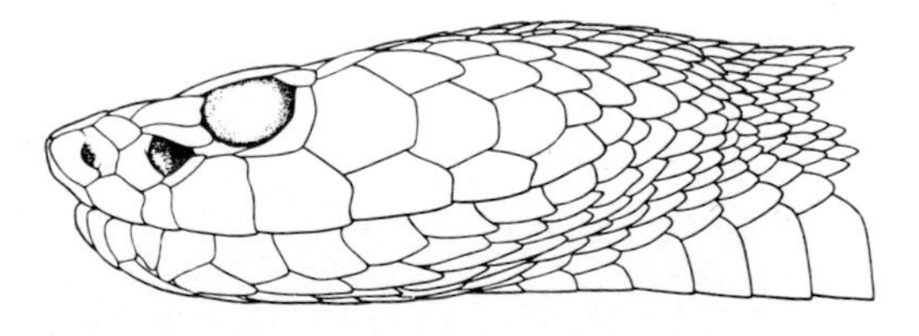

FIG. 31. Side view of the head, genus *Agkistrodon*.

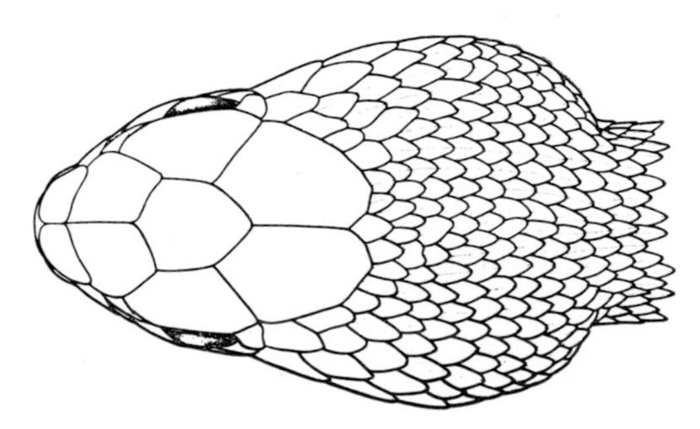

FIG. 32. Top view of the head, genus *Agkistrodon*.

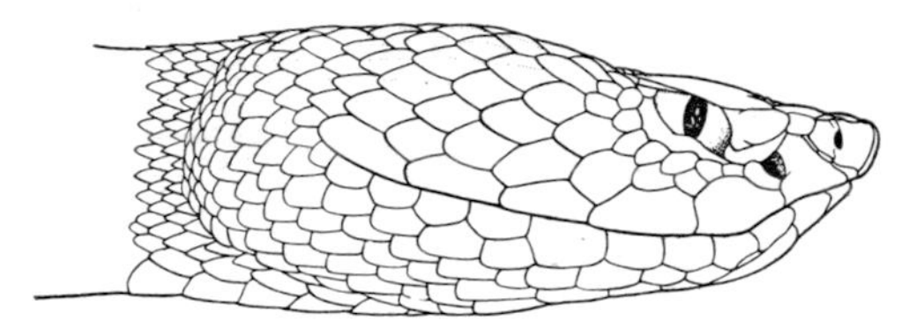

FIG. 33. Side view of the head, genus *Trimeresurus*.

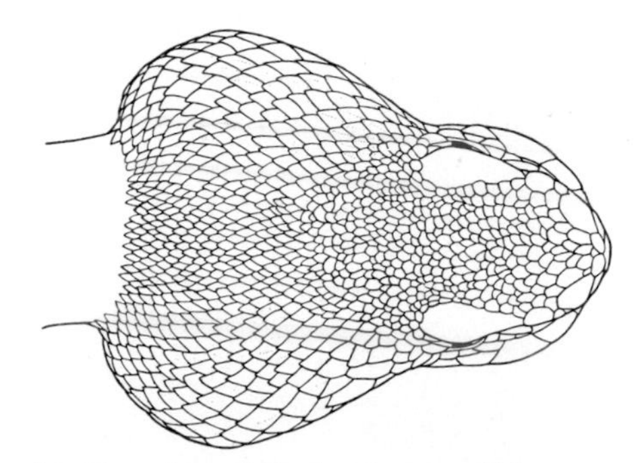

FIG. 34. Top view of the head, genus *Trimeresurus*.

FIG. 35. Skull of common cobra, *Naja naja*, with the relatively short and immovable fangs (Houston Zoo Photo).

FIG. 36. Skull of a pit-viper, showing the movable and relatively long fangs (Houston Zoo Photo).

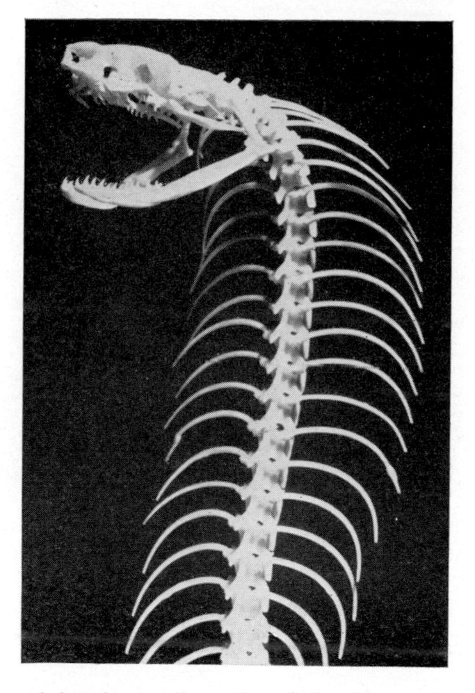

FIG. 37. Skull and hood-spreading ribs of the king cobra (Houston Zoo Photo).

FIG. 38. Red-headed krait, *Bungarus flaviceps* (U.S. Army Photo).

FIG. 39. Banded krait, *Bungarus fasciatus* (Houston Zoo Photo).

FIG. 40. Many-banded krait, *Bungarus multicinctus* (Photo Commander R. E. Kuntz, U.S.N.)

FIG. 41. Adult king cobra, *Ophiophagus hannah* (New York Zoological Society Photo).

FIG. 42. King cobra hooded (New York Zoological Society Photo).

FIG. 43. Juvenile king cobra emerging from egg (New York Zoological Society Photo).

FIG. 44. Common cobra from Formosa, *Naja naja atra* (Houston Zoo Photo).

FIG. 44A. Common cobra from Formosa, *Naja naja atra* (Houston Zoo Photo).

FIG. 45. Striped coral snake, *Calliophis j. japonicus* (Photo by Kazuo Koba).

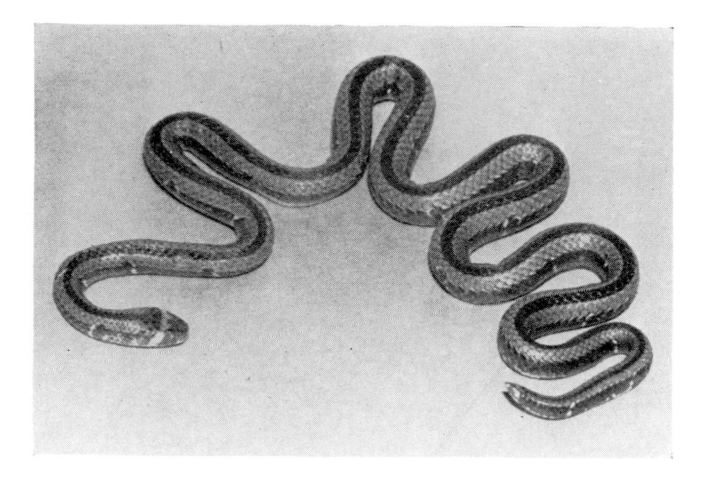

FIG. 46. Sauter's striped coral snake, *Calliophis j. sauteri* (Photo by Commander R. E. Kuntz, U.S.N.).

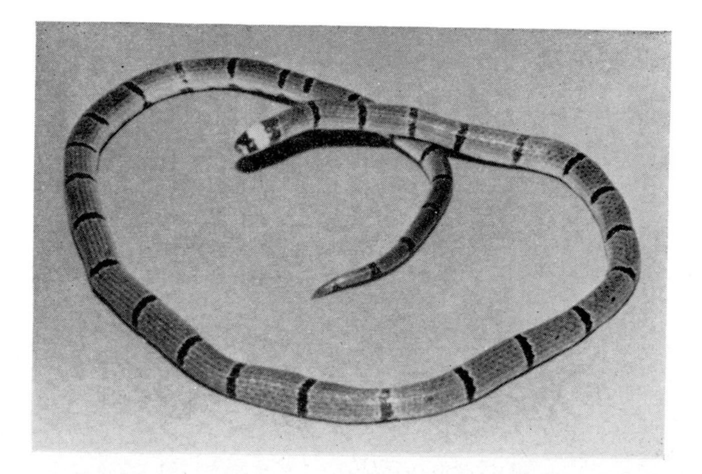

FIG. 47. Banded coral snake, *Calliophis macclellandi* (Photo by Commander R. E. Kuntz, U.S.N.).

FIG. 48. Death adder, *Acanthophis antarcticus* (Houston Zoo Photo).

FIG. 49. Taipan, *Oxyuranus scutellatus* (Photo by Eric Worrell).

FIG. 50. Head of taipan (Photo by Eric Worrell).

FIG. 51. Spotted-headed snake, *Demansia psammophis* (Photo by Eric Worrell)

FIG. 52. Common mulga snake, *Pseudechis australis* (Photo by Eric Worrell).

FIG. 53. Banded sea snake, *Laticauda colubrina* (San Diego Zoo Photo).

FIG. 54. Erabu-unagi, *Laticauda semifasciata* (Photo by Commander R. E. Kuntz, U.S.N.).

FIG. 55. *Hydrophis cyanocinctus* (Photo by Commander R. E. Kuntz, U.S.N.).

FIG. 56. Common adder, *Vipera berus* (Houston Zoo Photo).

FIG. 57. Russell's viper, *Vipera russelii*, from mainland Asia (Houston Zoo Photo).

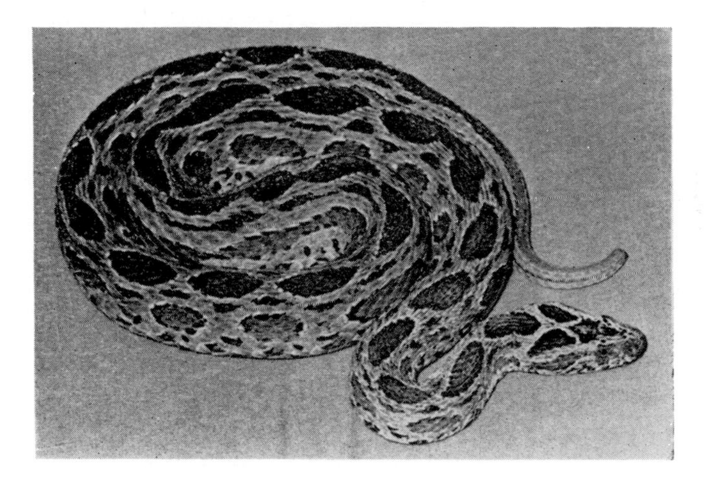

FIG. 58. Russell's viper from Formosa (Photo by Commander R. E. Kuntz, U.S.N.).

FIG. 59. Malayan pit-viper, *Agkistrodon rhodostoma* (Photo by M. W. F. Tweedie).

FIG. 60. Long-nosed pit-viper, *Agkistrodon acutus* (Houston Zoo Photo).

FIG. 61. Pallas' pit-viper (mamushi), *Agkistrodon halys* (Houston Zoo Photo).

FIG. 62. Yellow-green pit-viper (habu), *Trimeresurus flavoviridis* (Houston Zoo Photo).

FIG. 63. Yellow-green pit-viper (habu), Kume-shima race, *Trimeresurus f. tinkhami* (Photo by Howard K. Gloyd).

FIG. 64. Typical habitat of the yellow-green pit-viper (habu) on Amami-oshima, Ryukyu Islands (Photo by Kazuo Koba).

FIG. 65. The yellow-green pit-viper (habu) is often found in and about human habitations. This farmer's hut in a sugar-cane field on Tokuna-shima, Ryukyu Islands, was found to harbor four specimens (Photo by Kazuo Koba).

FIG. 66. Elegant pit-viper (Sakishima habu), *Trimeresurus elegans* (Houston Zoo Photo).

FIG. 67. An unusual color phase of the elegant pit-viper (Sakishima habu) from Ishigaki Island, Ryukyu Islands (Photo by Hugh Keegan).

FIG. 68. Pointed-scaled pit-viper (Taiwan habu), *Trimeresurus mucrosquamatus* (Photo by Commander R. E. Kuntz, U.S.N.).

FIG. 69. Okinawa pit-viper, *Trimeresurus okinavensis* (Photo by Kazuo Koba).

FIG. 70. Mountain pit-viper, *Trimeresurus monticola* (Photo by Isabelle Hunt Conant).

FIG. 71. White-lipped pit-viper, *Trimeresurus albolabris* (Houston Zoo Photo).

FIG. 72. Stejneger's pit-viper, *Trimeresurus s. stejnegeri* (Houston Zoo Photo).

FIG. 73. Pope's pit-viper, *Trimeresurus popeorum* (Houston Zoo Photo).

FIG. 74. Adult Wagler's pit-viper, *Trimeresurus wagleri* (Houston Zoo Photo).

FIG. 75. Head of adult Wagler's pit-viper (Houston Zoo Photo).

FIG. 76. Juvenile Wagler's pit-viper (Photo by M. W F. Tweedie).

FIG. 77. Head of juvenile Wagler's pit-viper (Photo by M. W. F. Tweedie).

FIG. 78. Unmarked Bornean race of Wagler's pit-viper (Photo by M. W. F. Tweedie).

STUDIES ON THE ANTITOXIC ACTION OF DIHYDROLYPOIC ACID (DIHYDROTHIOCTIC ACID) AND TETRACYCLINE AGAINST HABU SNAKE (*TRIMERESURUS FLAVOVIRIDIS* HALLOWELL) VENOM

YOSHIO SAWAI, MASAAKI MAKINO, and YOSHIHARU KAWAMURA*

FOLLOWING a survey of habu snake bite on the Amami Islands of Japan in 1957, the authors have carried out studies on the improvement of the treatment. Although mortality rate was reduced by antivenin, local necrosis was not infrequently a problem. In previous papers, preparation, purification and freeze-drying of the antivenin, and the effect of $CaNa_2EDTA$ against habu venom were reported by Sawai *et al.* (1961a, b). The present paper deals with the antitoxic action of dihydrolipoic acid (DLA) or dihydrothioctic acid and tetracycline (TC) upon the venom.

MATERIALS AND METHODS

The DLA and lipoic acid (LA) were supplied by the Fujisawa Pharmaceutical Co., Osaka, Japan, and TC by the Lederle (Japan) Ltd.

Habu venom was harvested from the specimens of habu (*Trimeresurus flavoviridis* Hallowell) captured on Amami Oshima Islands, and was freeze-dried. Habu antivenin was prepared in horses in our laboratory.

The antitoxic actions of DLA and TC were measured as follows: Serial dilutions of DLA or TC were mixed with various concentrations of the venom *in vitro*, and were incubated at 37 °C for 1 hr, and then injected intramuscularly into the legs of mice, guinea pigs or rabbits. The antilethal and antinecrotic effects were observed after 24 hr. Their effects, combined with the antivenin, were also tested in mice by the injection of serial dilutions of antivenin, either intramuscularly after mixing with venom and each of the agents, or intraperitoneally immediately after intramuscular injection of venom, which was previously treated with the agents. Curative effects were tested by injecting DLA or TC locally with or without antivenin 5 or 30 min after the injection of venom in mice.

*Laboratory of Biological Products, Institute for Infectious Disease, University of Tokyo, Shiba-shirokane-dai-machi, Minato-ku, Tokyo, Japan.

RESULTS

Antitoxic Effects of Lipoic Acid (LA), Dihydrolipoic Acid (DLA) and Tetracycline (TC) on Habu Snake Venom in Mice

0.1 ml of habu venom ranging from 75 to 300γ was mixed with DLA, LA or TC 0.31 to 2.5, or 5.0 mg and incubated. Then, 0.1 ml of each mixture was injected intramuscularly into the left hind leg of 3 or 5 mice. For control purposes, the same amount of venoms mixed with or without 0.1 ml of antivenin were injected into mice. These mice were killed after 24 hr, and inspected to determine cause of death and the grade of local lesions.

The results, summarized in Table 1, show that 1.25, or 5 mg, of DLA or TC

TABLE 1*. ANTITOXIC EFFECTS OF LIPOIC ACID (LA), DIHYDROLYPOIC ACID (DLA) AND TETRACYCLINE (TC) UPON HABU SNAKE VENOM IN MICE

Venom Dosage (γ)

	75		150		300	
LA (mg)						
0.31	0/3	1.5	0/3	2.5	3/3	3.0
0.62	0/3	1.3	0/3	2.0	3/3	2.3
1.25	0/3	1.0	0/3	1.1	0/3	1.8
2.5	0/3	0.6	0/3	1.3	1/3	2.1
DLA (mg)						
0.31	0/3	1.0	0/3	1.5	0/3	2.6
0.62	0/3	0.3	0/3	0.3	0/3	0.6
1.25	0/3	0	0/3	0	0/3	0.3
2.5	0/3	0	0/3	0	0/3	0
TC (mg)						
0.31	0/4	0	0/4	0	2/4	0.4
0.62	0/4	0	0/4	0	0/4	0.2
1.25	0/4	0	0/4	0	0/4	0
2.5	0/4	0	0/4	0	0/4	0
5.0	0/4	0	0/4	0	0/4	0
Antivenin						
0.1 ml	0/5	0	0/5	0	0/5	0
none	0/4	2.3	3/4	2.5	5/5	3.0

**Symbols*

Numerators of fractions indicate the number of mice which died. Denominators of fractions indicate number of mice used.

The figures in column to right of fractions listed under each venom dosage represent average extent of lesions of mice tested. Degree of lesion formation is symbolized as follows:

0—No lesions or only slight hemorrhage at point of injection.
1—Hemorrhage and myolysis of one-third of thigh.
2—Hemorrhage and myolysis in two-thirds of thigh.
3—Hemorrhage and myolysis extending to trunk.

completely prevented the lethal effects or local lesions caused by 150 or 300γ of venom, whereas LA prevented only the lethal action of 150γ of venom and incompletely blocked local lesion formation.

In the next experiments, antitoxic effects of DLA and TC against increasing doses of venom were further observed in guinea pigs and rabbits. 2.5 mg or 20 mg of DLA dissolved in 0.2 ml were mixed with 0.1 ml of varying doses of habu venom and incubated. These were injected intramuscularly in a volume of 0.3 ml, into the left hind leg of guinea pigs. In rabbits, DLA or TC of varying amounts, ranging from 20 mg to 100 mg, were dissolved in 1.0 ml of saline and mixed with 0.1 ml of venom dilutions. After the incubation, 1.1 ml of the mixture was injected intramuscularly into the left thigh of rabbits. After 24 hr, the animals were sacrificed and local lesions were inspected.

The results, given in Table 2, show that 10 mg of DLA completely neutralized 9.6 mg of venom in guinea pig, and 100 mg of DLA neutralized 38.4 mg of venom in rabbits. On the other hand, 20 mg of TC neutralized 9.6 mg of venom in rabbits. In control animals, 1.2 or 9.6 mg of venom caused considerable lesions at the locus of injection.

TABLE 2*. ANTITOXIC EFFECTS OF DIHYDROLIPOIC ACID AND TETRACYCLINE AGAINST HABU SNAKE VENOM IN GUINEA PIGS AND RABBITS

Venom Dosage (mg)

Guinea pigs:

DLA(mg)	1.2		2.4		4.8		9.6	
	H	M	H	M	H	M	H	M
2.5	+	−	++	+	+++	+++	++++	++++
5.0	−	−	−	−	−	−	×	+
10.0	−	−	−	−	−	−	−	−
20.0	−	−	−	−	−	−	±	−
none	+++	++++	++++	++++				

EFFECTS OF DLA OR TC COMBINED WITH ANTIVENIN IN MICE

Neutralizing Effects of Antivenin upon Habu Snake Venom which was previously treated with DLA or TC

Three or four mice received injections intramuscularly in the left hind leg with 0.1 ml of a mixture of 150 to 2400γ of venom and 2.5 mg of DLA or TC which had been incubated at 37°C for 1 hr. Immediately after the injection, 0.1 ml of antivenin diluted serially from 1 : 2 to 1 : 64 was

Venom Dosage (mg)

Rabbits:

DLA(mg)	9.6		19.2		38.4	
	H	M	H	M	H	M
20	–	–	–	–	–	+
50	–	–	–	+	–	+
100	–	–	–	–	–	–
none	++++	++++				

Rabbits:

TC (mg)	2.4		4.8		9.6	
	H	M	H	M	H	M
20	–	–	–	–	–	–
50	–	–	–	–	+	–
100	–	–	–	–	–	–
none	+++	+++				

**Symbols*

H—Hemorrhage: – none; + extending over one-third of the thigh; ++ extending over two-thirds of the thigh; +++ extending over entire thigh; ++++ extending to the trunk.

M—Myolysis: – none; + 2 × 2 cm; ++ 5 × 5 cm; +++ 10 × 10 cm; ++++ over 10 × 10 cm.

injected intraperitoneally into the same mice. Four control mice were injected with untreated venom, with or without antivenin.

Results are summarized in Table 3. Neutralization of antivenins was accelerated when the venoms were treated with DLA or TC. Local lesions and death were prevented in animals which had received injections of 1200γ of venom which had been treated with DLA, or 600γ of venom which had been treated with TC. In controls, complete neutralization occurred only after injections with antivenin diluted in a 1 : 2 ratio against 150γ of venom.

Neutralizing Effects of Antivenin Injected Intramuscularly in Mice Combined with DLA or TC and the Venom

In this experiment, antivenin and venom diluted serially were mixed and incubated either with or without 2.5 mg of DLA or TC, and then injected in 0.2 ml amounts intramuscularly into a leg of each of four or five mice. The results, as summarized in Table 4 indicated that neutralization with antivenin-DLA or TC mixture occurred to a greater degree than with control animals. Thus, 600γ of venom was almost completely neutralized by antivenin-TC mixture. In controls, 150γ of venom alone was completely neutralized by 1 : 2 diluted antivenin.

TABLE 3*. EFFECTS OF ANTIVENIN INJECTED INTRAPERITONEALLY UPON HABU SNAKE VENOM TREATED BY DIHYDROLYPOIC ACID OR TETRACYCLINE IN MICE

Venom Dosage (γ)

Antivenin	150		300		600		1200		2400	
DLA:										
1 : 2	0/3	0	0/3	0	0/3	0	0/3	0	2/3	0.3
1 : 4	0/3	0	0/3	0	0/3	0	0/3	0	2/3	0.6
1 : 8	0/3	0	0/3	0	0/3	0	0/3	0	2/3	0.6
1 : 16	0/3	0	0/3	0	0/3	0	0/3	0	2/3	0.6
1 : 32	0/3	0	0/3	0	0/3	0	0/3	0	1/3	0.8
1 : 64	0/3	0	0/3	0	0/3	0	0/3	0	0/3	1.1
TC:										
1 : 2	0/4	0	0/4	0	0/4	0	0/4	0.5	2/4	1.0
1 : 4	0/4	0	0/4	0	1/4	0	3/4	2.0	4/4	2.5
1 : 8	0/4	0	0/4	0	0/4	0	2/4	1.3	4/4	1.8
1 : 16	0/4	0	0/4	0	0/4	0	0/4	0.5	4/4	1.0
1 : 32	0/4	0	0/4	0	0/4	0	1/4	0.8	3/4	0.8
1 : 64	0/4	0	0/4	0.5	0/4	0	0/4	0.3	3/4	0.8
Control:										
1 : 2	0/4	0	1/4	1.0						
1 : 4	0/4	1.0	4/4	2.0						
1 : 8	1/4	2.0	4/4	3.0						
1 : 16	3/4	3.0	4/4	3.0						
none	4/4	3.0								

**Symbols*

Numerators of fractions indicate the number of mice which died. Denominators of fractions indicate number of mice used.

The figures in column to right of fractions listed under each venom dosage represent average extent of lesions of mice tested. Degree of lesion formation is symbolized as follows:

0—No lesions or only slight hemorrhage at point of injection.
1—Hemmorhage and myolysis of one-third of thigh.
2—Hemorrhage and myolysis in two-thirds of thigh.
3—Hemorrhage and myolysis extending to trunk.

TREATMENT OF EXPERIMENTAL ENVENOMATION WITH DLA OR TC AND ANTIVENIN

Experiments described above showed that *in vitro* neutralization of venom mixed with DLA or TC occurred, and that these substances accelerated neutralization of venom with antivenin. Therefore, combined effects of DLA or TC and antivenin on experimental envenomation was investigated. In these studies venom was injected into animals before treatment was given.

As shown in Table 5, mice were given intramuscular injection in the leg with 0.1 ml of saline solutions containing varying amount of venom. Five or 30 min after the injection of venoms, each of three or five mice received

TABLE 4*. EFFECTS OF THE ANTIVENIN INJECTED INTRAMUSCULARLY IN MICE COMBINED WITH DIHYDROLYPOIC ACID OR TETRACYCLINE UPON THE VENOM

Venom Dosage (γ)

Antivenin	150		300		600		1200		2400	
DLA:										
1 : 2	0/4	0	0/4	0	0/4	0	0/4	0	2/4	1.0
1 : 4	0/4	0	0/4	0	0/4	0	2/4	0.2	3/4	0.7
1 : 8	0/4	0	0/4	0	0/4	0	0/4	0	2/4	0.7
1 : 16	0/4	0	0/4	0	0/4	0	2/4	0.2	2/4	1.0
1 : 32	0/4	0	0/4	0	0/4	0	0/4	0.2	4/4	1.2
1 : 64	0/4	0	0/4	0	0/4	0	1/4	0.5	2/4	1.2
TC:										
1 : 2	0/5	0	0/5	0	0/5	0.5	2/4	1.5	2/4	2.2
1 : 4	0/5	0	0/5	0	0/5	0.7	0/4	1.2	4/4	2.5
1 : 8	0/5	0	0/5	0	0/5	0.5	1/4	1.1	4/4	2.5
1 : 16	0/5	0	0/5	0	0/5	1.0	1/4	1.3	4/4	2.5
1 : 32	0/5	0	0/5	0.4	0/5	0.5	1/4	1.7	4/4	2.5
1 : 64	0/5	0	0/5	0.4	0/5	0.4	1/4	1.2	4/4	2.5
Control:										
1 : 2	0/5	0	1/5	0.4	5/5	1.4				
1 : 4	0/5	0.4	2/5	1.5	5/5	1.5				
1 : 8	4/5	1.7	4/5	1.9	5/5	1.8				
1 : 16	5/5	2.0	5/5	2.6	5/5	2.7				
1 : 32	5/5	2.6	5/5	2.7	5/5	2.7				
1 : 64	5/5	2.8	5/5	3.0	5/5	3.0				
none	5/5	3.0								

**Symbols*

Numerators of fractions indicate the number of mice which died. Denominators of fractions indicate number of mice used.

The figures in column to right of fractions listed under each venom dosage represent average extent of lesions of mice tested. Degree of lesion formation is symbolized as follows:

0—No lesions or only slight hemorrhage at point of injection.
1—Hemorrhage and myolysis of one-third of thigh.
2—Hemorrhage and myolysis in two-thirds of thigh.
3—Hemorrhage and myolysis extending to trunk.

0.1 ml of antivenin, or 2.5 mg of DLA or 0.625 mg of TC intramuscularly into the needle mark of envenomation.

Thirty min after evenomation, mice which had been treated with DLA or TC within 5 min after the envomation, were further given intraperitoneal injections of 0.1 ml of antivenin. Death and/or local lesions were recorded 24 hr following the injection of venom.

Results showed that treatment with DLA was equal to that with antivenin, and prevented lethal effects and local lesions in mice which received 75 or 300γ of venom. In the case of TC, the curative effects were less pronounced than with antivenin, but decreased local lesion formation in the group of mice receiving TC 5 min after the injection of 75 or 150γ of venom.

TABLE 5*. TREATMENT OF EXPERIMENTAL ENVENOMATION IN MICE BY ANTIVENIN AND DLA AND TC

Treatment Status

Venom Dosage (γ)

	Untreated		DLA (5)		A (5)		DLA (5) + A (30)		DLA (30)		A (30)	
75	1/4	2.5	0/4	1.0	0/4	1.0	1/4	0.7	0/4	1.2	0/4	1.5
150	3/4	3.0	0/4	1.5	1/4	1.5	2/4	0.7	1/4	2.0	1/4	1.5
300	4/4	3.0	2/4	1.5	3/4	2.0	2/4	1.2	2/4	2.2	3/4	2.0
600			4/4	2.7	4/4	2.5	4/4	2.2	4/4	2.7	4/4	3.0

Venom Dosage (γ)

	Untreated		TC (5)		A (5)		TC (5) + A (30)		TC (30)		A (30)	
37.5	0/3	2.2	0/3	1.0			0/5	0.8	0/5	1.8	0/3	0.6
75	1/3	2.5	1/3	1.0	0/3	0.3	1/5	1.0	1/5	2.2	0/3	0.8
150	2/3	3.0	2/3	1.7	0/3	1.0	1/5	1.2	5/5	2.4	0/3	1.4
			0/5	1.6†					0/5	3.0†		
300							3/5	1.8				

**Symbols*

DLA (5) Animals treated with 2.5 mg DLA 5 min intramuscularly after envenomation
DLA (30) Animals treated with 2.5 mg DLA 30 min intraperitoneally after envenomation.
A (5) Treatment with 0.1 ml intramuscularly 5 min after envenomation.
A (30) Treatment with 0.1 ml intraperitoneally 30 min after envenomation.
†Untreated control animals.

DISCUSSION

Experimental results described here indicate inhibitory effects of DLA or TC upon activity of habu snake venom. 1.25 mg of DLA or TC was equal to 0.1 ml antivenin in prevention of death and local lesion formation.

Since DLA was more effective than LA in preventing the toxic effects the venom, free SH radicals of DLA appeared important in antitoxic action, although these mechanisms have not yet been elucidated. In a study on mercury poisoning, Ohashi (1950) showed that mercury combined with DLA is fixed and gradually excreted into urine and probably in feces. Among the

SH compounds, BAL or Cystein was also shown to be effective in neutralizing venom, although they were more toxic, or less stable, than DLA.

The antitoxic action of TC seems to be a sort of chelation as demonstrated by Maeno *et al.* (1959a, b) with EDTA. However, as shown in this paper, the antihemorrhagic, antinecrotic and antilethal actions of TC are more complete than that of EDTA as previously demonstrated by Sawai *et al.* (1961). Therefore, another mechanism of inactivation *besides TC inhibition of proteinase action of the venom* should also be considered.

It was proven that DLA or TC accelerated the neutralizing effect of diluted antivenin. The combined effects of these were more marked when the venom was previously treated with the agents and injected separately with the antivenin, as shown in Tables 3 and 4. These facts suggested that DLA or TC combined not only with the venom, but also with the antivenin *in vitro*. Therefore, it may be assumed that the agents might combine with various substances before they reach venom *in vivo*. Mashita (1958) reported that TC could be combined with serum albumin or metal ion. The tendency, as mentioned above, was more conspicuous when these were administered after the injection of venom, as shown in Table 6. Antitoxic effects of DLA or TC, as expected from the experiments *in vitro*, were not observed *in vivo*. Antivenin showed favorable effects *in vivo* as well as *in vitro*.

The antibiotic effect of TC is also expected to be of value in clinical use, since the wounds of habu snake envenomation are often exposed to contamination. Clinical use of the agents were carried out in 1961 on Amami and Okinawa Islands.

SUMMARY

Antitoxic effects of dihydrolypoic acid (DLA) and tetracycline (TC) on habu snake (*Trimeresurus flavoviridis*) venom were investigated in experimental animals.

2.5 mg of DLA or 1.25 mg of TC neutralized both necrotic and lethal action of 300γ or more of venom in mice. Such effects were equal to that of 0.1 ml antivenin. 10 mg of DLA neutralized 9.6 mg venom in guinea pigs, and 38.4 mg of venom was neutralized by 100 mg of DLA in rabbits. 20 mg of TC neutralized 9.6 mg venom in rabbits.

2.5 mg of DLA or TC accelerated neutralizing effects of serially diluted antivenin in a volume of 0.1 ml of 300γ to 1200γ of venom in mice.

DLA injected locally 5 or 30 min after envenomation with 75γ to 300γ of venom exerted the same effects as 0.1 ml of antivenin.

0.625 mg of TC also prevented local myolytic effects of 150γ venom injected 5 min before administration of this antibiotic. It was ineffective if administered 30 min after venom injections had been given.

These results suggested that DLA and TC were useful remedies in addition to antivenin, for treatment of habu envenomation.

ACKNOWLEDGMENT

The authors are deeply indebted to the Ministry of Education and the Deliberation Committee on the Reconstruction of Amami Islands for the financial aid to carry out these investigations.

REFERENCES

MAENO, H., MITSUHASHI, S., SAWAI, Y. and OKONOGI, T. 1959. Studies on habu snake venom. 2a. Enzymatic studies on the proteinase of habu snake venom. *Japan J. Microbiol.* **3**, 131.

MAENO, H., MITSUHASHI, S., SAWAI, Y. and OKONOGI, T. 1959. Studies on habu snake venom. 2b. Further purification and enzymatic and biological activities of H-proteinase. *Japan J. Microbiol.* **3**, 227.

MASHITA, K. 1958. Achromycin and Achromycin V. *Achromycin Therapy.* (Japanese)

OHASHI, A. 1960. Studies on mercury poisoning. Detoxidating effect of dithiol agents specially of thioctic acid. *Sangyo Igaku.* **2**, 1.

SAWAI, Y., MAKINO, M., MIYASAKI, S., KAWAMURA, Y., MITSUHASHI, S. and OKONOGI, T. 1961. Studies on the improvement of treatment of habu snake (*Trimeresurus flavoviridis*) bite. 2. Antitoxic action of monocalcium disodium ethylene diamine tetraacetate on Habu venom. *Japan J. Exp. Med.* **31**, 267.

SAWAI, Y., MAKINO, M., MIYASAKI, S., KATO, K., ADACHI, H., MITSUHASHI, S. and OKONOGI, T. 1961. Studies on the improvement of treatment of habu snake bite. 1. Studies on the improvement of habu snake antivenin. *Jap. J. Exp. Med.* **31**, 37.

STUDIES ON BOMBAY SNAKES
SNAKE FARM VENOM YIELD RECORDS AND THEIR PROBABLE SIGNIFICANCE

P. J. DEORAS*

KLAUBER (1956) mentioned that quantity of venom injected, as well as venom toxicity, was an important factor in determination of danger from snakebite. He also made some observations on snake venom yield records, and of the need for further work on this subject. Among points discussed by Klauber, was the lack of influence of sex upon venom yield, and that the quantity of venom obtained by milking snakes was greater than that delivered during a natural bite. However, Harris (1932) stated that captive snakes yielded less venom than wild specimens, and Lamb (1904) believed that snakes give more venom in a natural bite, than during a laboratory milking. These differing opinions indicated that there was a need for further investigation in this field; and that effects of captivity in the laboratory, and in natural surroundings might give information which would be of value in the study of the epidemiology of snakebite.

Except for the paper by Lamb (1904), there has been very little work done on venom output of Indian snakes. The only other paper on the subject is that of Acton and Knowles (1914), who found that total venom yield of a specimen of *Echis carinatus*, 13.6 in. in length, was 18.8 mg. These workers also found that a captive cobra, 4 ft 2 in. in length, yielded 105 mg of venom during a bite.

For some time now, a polyvalent snake antivenin has been produced at the Haffkine Institute. At first, venom was obtained from snakes kept in small cages. As the snakes did not long survive under these conditions, it was decided to establish a snake farm where specimens could be kept in natural surroundings. In addition to increasing longevity of the snakes, this arrangement would offer an opportunity for various studies on the biology of medically important snakes of India. This snake farm was completed in 1952, and since that time it has housed cobras, kraits, and Russell's viper. These snakes have served as sources of supply of venom for horse immunization, and as study material for results reported in this paper.

*Assistant Director, Haffkine Institute, Bombay, India.

MATERIALS AND METHODS

The general arrangement of the snake farm is similar to that at the Queen Saovabha Institute at Bangkok, except that it is larger, is covered with an iron trellis, and in part with a roof. The snake farm is divided into compartments for each of the species of snakes under study. In each of these compartments an effort has been made to duplicate the environments in which the snakes are most frequently seen. A general view of the snake farm is shown in Fig. 1.

FIG. 1. General view of a snake farm at the Haffkine Institute, Bombay.

Each compartment measures 35½ ft by 26 ft, and is, essentially, an island surrounded by a moat 2 ft in width and 16 in. deep which is bounded by an outer smooth surfaced retaining wall 5 ft in height. The water supply in the moat is kept fresh by a constant inflow and discharge system. Many aquatic insects are found in the moat, and small fishes have been introduced to prevent mosquito breeding.

Several species of plants have been used to give shade and cover to the snakes in each of the compartments. It was found that *Argyreia speciosa* was particularly well suited for this purpose, as it spreads quickly and gives excellent shade.

Snakes on each of the islands hide in pits which are protected from light and rain by removable covers and by roofed structures which are modified to suit the habits of the snakes housed in them. Once a week the snakes are fed with live mice. The mice are placed in the compartments at night. In addition to mice, small snakes are supplied as food for kraits, and frogs as food for the cobras. It was noticed that large frogs, which were first supplied as cobra food, eluded the snakes and themselves ate many of the mice. Subsequently only small frogs were supplied.

The moat and ground area of each compartment are cleaned daily. The snakes are not disturbed during the process, and are rarely seen in the open. Russell's vipers sometimes rest among the vegetation or on ledges, but the cobras and kraits are in hiding during the daytime.

There have been no snakebite accidents in the snake farm since it has been established. Maximum numbers of snakes on hand at one time were 64 kraits, 34 cobras, and 35 specimens of Russell's viper. Size, sex, and longevity data arc maintained on the specimens in the colony, and comparative data are kept on examples of the same species living in small cages in the laboratory.

DESCRIPTION OF COMPARTMENTS OF THE SNAKE FARM

Cobra Compartment

Figure 2 is a drawing of the structures in the cobra compartment. The cobras prefer to hide in clay pots in the pit, which is covered by a removable wooden platform provided with access holes. During the winter paper cuttings are placed in the pit to give protection against cold.

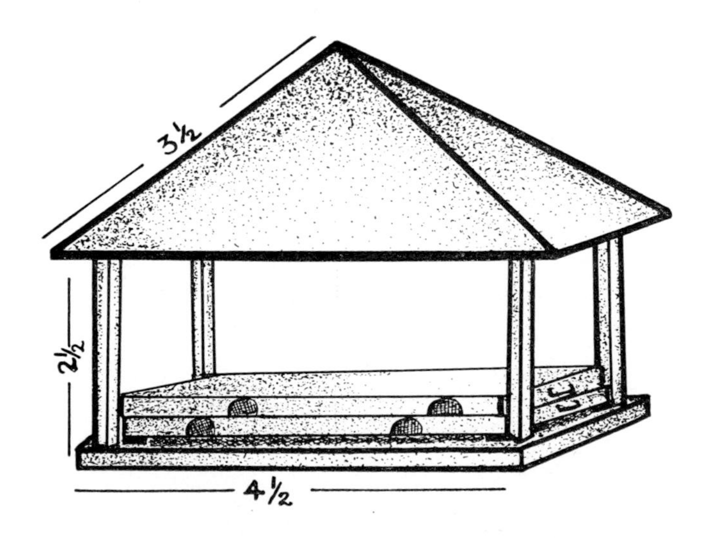

FIG. 2. Drawing of structure in cobra compartment. A wooden canopy stands on a cement platform. Two wooden covers at the base of the canopy cover the pit.

Russell's Viper Compartment

Arrangement of facilities for housing Russell's vipers is shown in Fig. 3. Inside the structure are wooden shelves on which the snakes rest. Dense xerophytic vegetation grows on this island. Iron access pipes are present at the base of the enclosure.

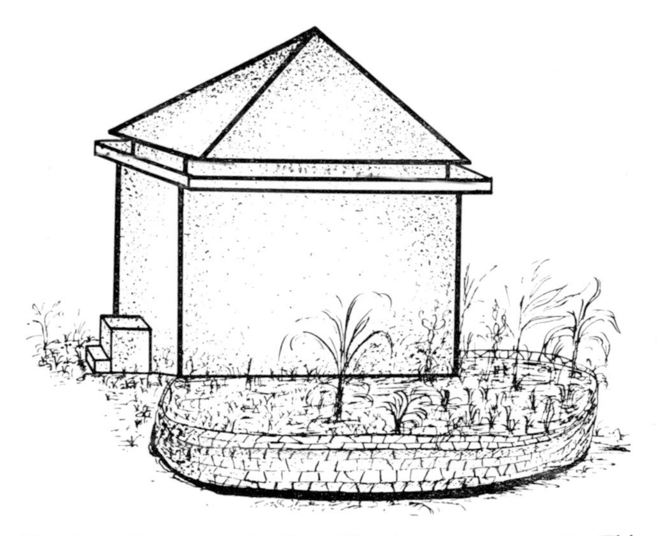

Fig. 3. Drawing of structure in Russell's viper compartment. This small room has a tin canopy.

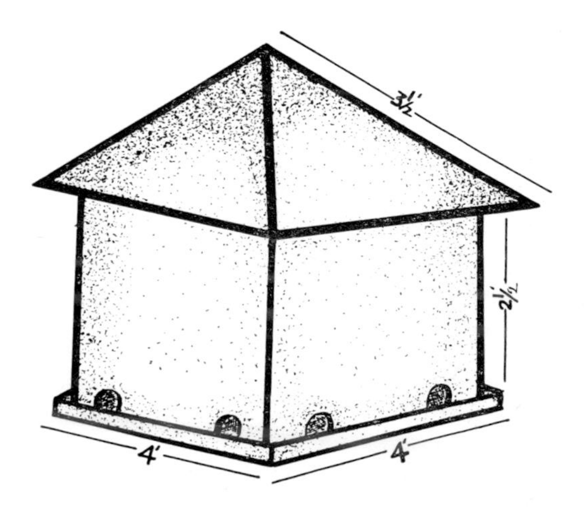

Fig. 4. Drawing of structure in krait compartment. This is a small concrete room containing rocks under which the snakes may hide.

Krait Compartment

The krait compartment is similar to that provided for the cobras, except that the structure is walled. Small access holes are present at the base of each wall. As in the Russell's viper compartment, the roof is removable. The room is provided with stone slabs which serve as hiding places for the snakes. This structure is shown in Fig. 4.

During the past three years, a total of 353 snakes have died at the Institute. Of these, 145 had been kept in the snake farm and the remainder in the laboratory. Greatest mortality occurred during June, July, and August (the rainy season). Greatest longevity for a cobra (female) in the snake farm was 4 years, 1 month, 24 days; for a Russell's viper (female) 3 years, 5 months, 26 days; and for a krait (male) 2 years, 8 months, 24 days. In the laboratory a cobra has lived for 27 months, and a Russell's viper has lived for 26 months.

Average maximum temperature at the snake farm was 29.92°C; average minimum was 25.23°C. Average maximum relative humidity was 84.12 per cent; average minimum was 64.55 per cent. Average monthly temperature and humidity records in the snake farm are shown in Tables 1 and 2.

TABLE 1. AVERAGE MONTHLY TEMPERATURES AT A SNAKE FARM IN BOMBAY

Place	Jan.	Feb.	Mar.	Apr.	May	June	July	Aug.	Sep.	Oct.	Nov.	Dec.
Room	27	29	30	30.7	31	30	27	26.8	27.7	29	26.5	25.8
Farm	25	28	28.5	29	31	29.5	27.5	28	29.5	30	28	24.9

TABLE 2. AVERAGE RELATIVE HUMIDITY AT A SNAKE FARM IN BOMBAY

Place	Jan.	Feb.	Mar.	Apr.	May	June	July	Aug.	Sep.	Oct.	Nov.	Dec.
Room	70.6	73.4	73	72.6	73.5	74	77	81	76	70	64	68
Farm	75.2	78.5	79	76.5	73	81	82	82	71	75	79	67

VENOM COLLECTION STUDIES

Under ordinary circumstances, each snake is milked once a month, and after this process is force-fed with a mixture of milk, egg flip, and shark liver oil. The cobras and kraits are captured for this purpose by seizing the tail of the reptile and pinning down its head with a round stick. Russell's vipers are handled by pinning down the head with a forked stick. Venom may be collected in a petri dish or a small glass, but in this laboratory the method of choice is to collect the venom in a funnel which leads directly to an ampoule. The ampoule is then processed, the venom is freeze-dried and stored at 4°C. If desired, venom from each fang of a snake may be collected separately. Various techniques for venom collection are illustrated in Fig. 5, 6 and 7.

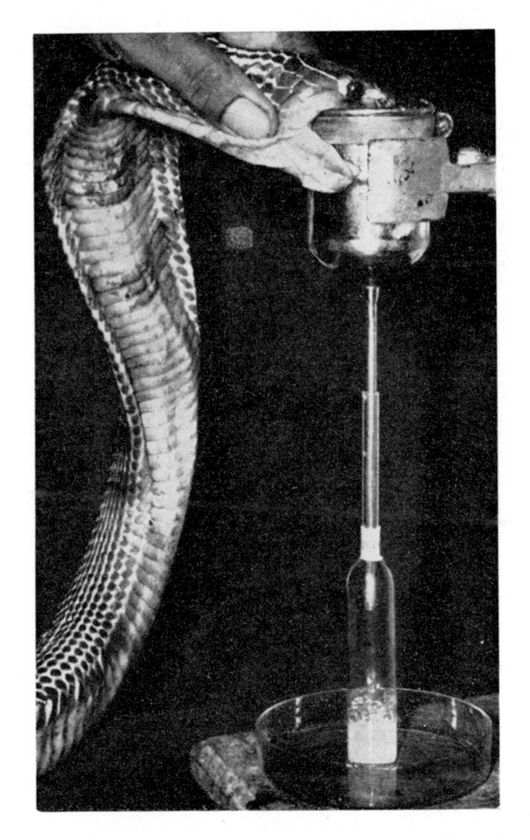

FIG. 5. Collection of venom from a cobra. The snake bites through a plastic cover on the glass funnel which leads into an ampule.

Venom Collection Speed

Allen and Murrayday (1940) and Allen and Maier (1941) described their technique of milking snakes and stated that they had been able to milk as many as 150 specimens in 1 hr. Although we have been able to milk a snake which has already been caught in 30 sec, the total time required for the process, including capture of the specimens, is considerably greater.

Venom Yield from Color Varieties of Cobras

It is a common belief in India that black cobras are more dangerous than those of lighter color. In order to determine whether venom yield records might, in part, give the answers to this question, five black and five brown cobras of the same sex were milked once each month for one year. The average venom yield for black cobras was greater than that for brown cobras. These results are shown in detail in Table 3.

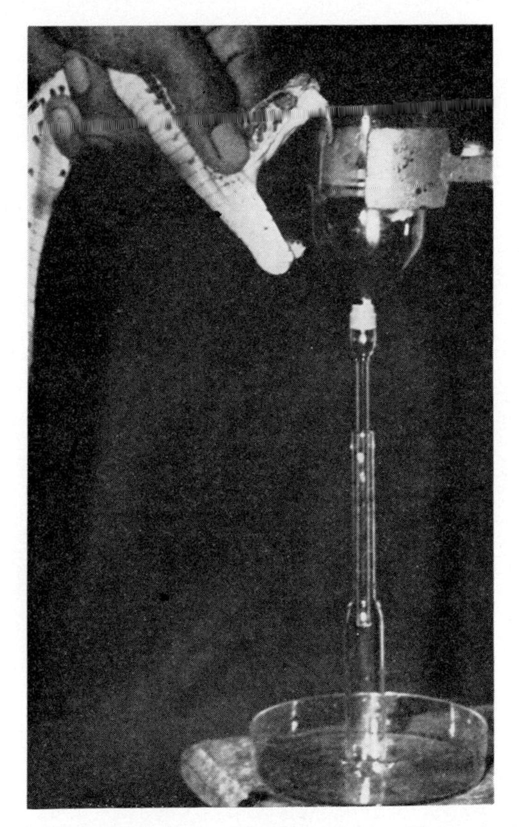

FIG. 6. Collection of venom from a Russell's viper. The snake bites over the edge of a glass funnel which leads into an ampule.

Effects of Milking Frequency on Venom Yield

In order to determine effect of milking frequency on venom yield, snakes in one group were milked at 15-day intervals throughout a 12-month period. During the same period, snakes of another group were milked once each month. In light of known variations in venom yield, differences in average venom yields of specimens of the two groups do not seem particularly significant. These data are shown in Table 4.

Effects of Environment on Venom Yield

From 1953 to 1957 a comparison was made of venom yields of snakes kept in cages in the laboratory and those maintained under natural conditions in the snake farm. Venom yield records shown in Table 5 represent average yields from specimens of equal size. Equal numbers of specimens were included in each test group. During each year, the average yield from cobras and kraits kept in the snake farm was greater than from specimens of those snakes maintained in the laboratory. Such consistent differences in yield did not occur between the two groups of Russel's vipers.

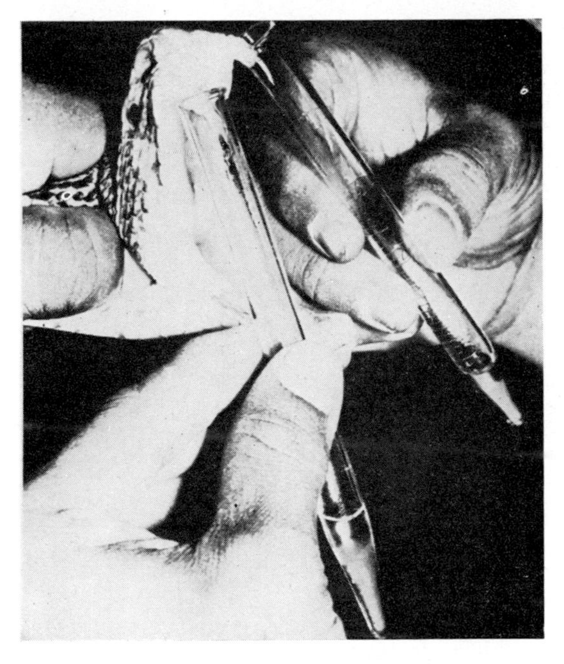

FIG. 7. Illustration of technique used in separate collection of venom from each fang of a snake.

Venom Yield Differences in Male and Female Snakes

Data showing average venom yields by male and female cobras, kraits kept at the Haffkine Institute, and Russell's vipers during 1954 and 1955 are presented in Table 6a. Average yields from specimens kept in the laboratory and those kept in the snake farm are presented separately in Table 6b. In each case, yields recorded are from snakes of equal size.

Venom yields from male cobras and kraits are greater than from females of these species. Male Russell's vipers kept in the laboratory gave slightly more venom than females. The reverse was true of specimens kept in the snake farm.

Venom Yields from Individual Fangs

Further studies of venom yields from male and female snakes involved separate collection of venom from each fang of an individual snake. Data obtained by use of this technique, in which both cobras and Russell's vipers were milked, are presented in Table 7. In this experiment, venom was collected from individual fangs of five male and five female cobras; and of equal numbers of male and female Russell's vipers. Even though the female cobras were larger than the males, the total venom yield from these females was less than that from the males. Russell's viper females yielded slightly more venom than males of equal size. There was a distinct difference in venom yields from individual fangs of female Russell's vipers. Weight of dry venom in proportion to volume of liquid venom collected was distinctly greater in cobras than in Russell's vipers.

TABLE 3. VENOM YIELDS OF BROWN AND BLACK COBRAS*

Month	Black	Brown	Remarks
January	0.151	0.152	
February	0.150	0.149	
March	0.177	0.133	
April	0.213	0.121	
May	0.215	0.136	Black variety seems to give more venom.
June	0.283	0.137	
July	0.249	0.154	
August	0.210	0.0889	
September	0.198	0.0908	
October	0.185	0.089	
November	0.166	0.0832	
December	0.146	0.0794	
Average	0.1909	0.1182	

*Figures indicate average venom yields (in g). Five black and five brown cobras milked once each month. Weight given is that of dry venom.

TABLE 4. VENOM YIELDS IN GRAMS FROM SNAKES MILKED AT 15-DAY AND 30-DAY INTERVALS

Periodicity in milking	Cobra	Krait	Russell's viper
30 days	0.1305	0.0282	0.1016
15 days	0.1274	0.00985	0.0881

Experiment to Determine Effect of Season on Venom Yield

In an attempt to determine possible effects of season on venom yield, three cobras were milked 17 times from October 1952 to July 1953. On each occasion, venom from all three snakes was collected in the same ampoule. Total venom yield data from each of these milkings is presented in Table 8. There was a considerable amount of variation, but smallest amounts of venom were collected during the cooler months.

TABLE 5. VENOM YIELDS IN GRAMS FROM SNAKES KEPT ON A SNAKE FARM AND FROM SPECIMENS CAGED IN A LABORATORY

Year	Farm	Laboratory	Statistical significance
Cobra			
1953	0.2118	0.1314	
1954	0.1522	0.1160	
1955	0.1501	0.1190	Farm output significantly more than room at 5 per cent level of significance.
1956	0.1670	0.0996	
1957	0.1530	0.1434	
Krait			
1953	0.0221	0.0107	
1954	0.0260	0.0216	
1955	0.0184	0.0164	Farm output significantly more than room at 5 per cent level of significance.
1956	0.0154	0.0144	
1957	0.0171	0.0042	
Russell's Viper			
1953	0.1519	0.1015	
1954	0.1376	0.1010	
1955	0.0834	0.1269	Room more significant.
1956	0.0666	0.0789	Not significant.
1957	0.1029	0.0905	Not significant.

TABLE 6a. VENOM YIELDS IN GRAMS FROM MALE AND FEMALE SNAKES

Year	Male	Female	Statistical significance
Cobra			
1954	0.1542	0.1148	The venom yield of a male snake is significantly more than the female.
1955	0.1731	0.1245	
Krait			
1954	0.0242	0.0106	The venom yield of a male snake is significantly more than the female.
1955	0.0191	0.0095	
Russell's Viper			
1954	0.1013	0.1090	The difference in the venom output is not significant.
1955	0.0985	0.0982	

DISCUSSION

The cause of higher venom yields by snakes kept in natural surroundings in the snake farm, as compared with those kept in cages in the laboratory is not known. It may be that this is due to the fact that snakes on the farm are less frequently disturbed than caged animals kept in a laboratory where passers-by may disturb the specimens.

Venom yield is not always proportional to size. At the Haffkine Institute, it has been found that a cobra less than 4 ft in length may give more venom than a specimen over 5 ft long. Another example is afforded by a color variation of the common cobra from central India. Although these specimens are never more than 2½ ft in length, they may give as much venom as the larger common cobra from other areas.

Weight loss of venom by drying is much greater in Russell's viper venom than in cobra venom. This loss was also greater than the 12.6 per cent weight loss reported for viper venom by Kellaway (1937). Reynolds (1960) noted that neurotoxic venoms are more toxic, weight for weight, than haemotoxic venoms. This is borne out by the much lower CLD for mice of cobra or krait venoms, as compared with Russell's viper venom.

TABLE 6b. VENOM YIELDS IN GRAMS FROM MALE AND FEMALE SNAKES KEPT IN THE LABORATORY AND ON A SNAKE FARM

Room		Farm	
Male	Female	Male	Female
Cobra			
0.1789	0.1342	0.2027	0.1772
Krait			
0.0228	0.0099	0.0255	0.0112
Russell's Viper			
0.1687	0.1565	0.0975	0.1251

TABLE 7. VENOM YIELDS FROM INDIVIDUAL FANGS OF COBRAS AND RUSSELL'S VIPERS

		Male		Female	
		Right fang	Left fang	Right fang	Left fang
*Cobra**					
Liquid weight	(g)	1.419	1.412	0.9046	1.0245
Liquid volume	(ml)	1.5	1.5	1	1
Dry weight	(g)	0.5191	0.5039	0.3404	0.3655
Russell's Viper†					
Liquid weight	(g)	2.6605	2.5235	3.1532	2.3426
Liquid volume	(ml)	2.6	2.45	3	3
Dry weight	(g)	0.2325	0.3150	0.4852	0.333

*Cobra male specimens 4 ft 3 in. to 4 ft 9 in. in length; female specimens 4 ft 9 in. to 4 ft 11 in. in length.

†Russell's viper specimens all between 4 ft and 4 ft 2 in. in length.

TABLE 8. MONTHLY VARIATION IN AVERAGE POOLED VENOM YIELD OF THREE COBRAS

Date of milking	Average amount of venom given in g
29 Oct. 52	0.516
17 Nov. 52	0.622
2 Dec. 52	0.380
12 Dec. 52	0.453
31 Dec. 52	0.488
15 Jan. 53	0.438
30 Jan. 53	0.468
24 Feb. 53	0.450
24 Mar. 53	0.469
30 Mar. 53	0.552
17 Apr. 53	0.595
23 Apr. 53	0.684
4 May 53	0.549
28 May 53	0.743
9 June 53	0.849
14 July 53	0.880
28 July 53	0.613

The variations in amounts and color of venom obtained from individual fangs of snakes are interesting in light of published comments on color variation. Amaral (1929) thought that the color of venom might be associated with presence of lipoid fractions. Minton (1953) discussed variations in toxicity of venom samples, and Klauber (1956), in discussing *Crotalus ruber ruber*, mentioned variation in color of venom among young and adult snakes. At the Haffkine Institute it has been found that this color variation is not as marked in venom from snakes which are milked frequently. It has also been noticed that venom from one fang of a specimen of Russell's viper may be yellow, while the venom from the other fang is white.

SUMMARY

A description has been given of the construction and operation of a snake farm at the Haffkine Institute in Bombay, India. This farm provides natural surroundings for captive snakes of three species: the cobra, *Naja naja*; the krait, *Bungarus caeruleus*; and Russell's viper, *Vipera russelli*. Techniques for extraction and processing of venom are discussed, and a method for collection of venom samples from individual fangs is described. It was found that venom yields from snakes kept in natural surroundings on the snake farm were greater than those from snakes kept in the laboratory. Male cobras and kraits yielded larger amounts of venom than females. Average pooled venom yields from three cobras milked 17 times over a period of 10 months showed considerable variation. The smallest venom yields were obtained during the cooler months of the year. Weight loss of venom during drying was considerably greater with Russell's viper venom than with cobra venom. Variations in venom color are common. Yellowish venom is most frequently encountered in snakes which have not been milked for long periods of time. Differences in venom color may be observed in venom collected separately from each of the fangs of a snake.

ACKNOWLEDGEMENTS

I am extremely thankful to the Indian Council of Medical Research for sponsoring this entire project. I owe a deep debt of gratitude to Dr. V. R. Khanolkar, Dr. K. C. K. E. Raja and Dr. P. M. Wagle for their help and encouragement in this work. My heartfelt thanks are due to Mr. N. E. Vad for his loyal and untiring cooperation and to Mr. H. M. Pandit for help in the initial stages. Lastly, I am thankful to the Director, Haffkine Institute for the facilities that were made available for this work, and to Mr. Naik for typing.

REFERENCES

Acton, H. W. and Knowles, R. 1914. The dose of venom given in nature by a cobra in a single bite. *Indian J. Med. Res.* **1** (3), 388.

Acton, H. W. and Knowles, R. 1914. The dose of venom given in nature by the *Echis carinatus* at a single bite. *Indian J. Med. Res.* **1** (3), 414.

Allen, E. R. and Maier, E. 1941. The extraction and processing of snake venom. *Copeia.* (4), 251.

Allen, E. R. and Murryday, M. R. 1940. A snake in the hand. *Nat. Hist.* **46** (4), 234.

Amaral, A. Do. 1926. Collectanea Ophiologica. 6 Da Occorrencia de Allinismo em Cascavel, *Crotalus terrificus* (Laur.) *Rev. Mus. Paul.* **15**, 53.

Amaral, A. Do. 1929. Phylogency of the rattlesnakes. *Bull. Antivenin Inst. Am.* **3** (1), 6.

Harris, H. 1932. *California's Medical Story, San Francisco*, pp. xviii–421.

Kellaway, C. H. 1937. Snake venoms. I. Their constitution and therapeutic application. II. Their periperal action. III. Immunity. *Bull. Johns Hopkins Hosp.* **60** (1), 1.

Klauber, L. M. 1956. *Rattlesnakes: Their habits, life histories and influence on mankind.* 2. Berkley and Los Angeles: University of California Press.

Lamb, G. 1904. On the serum therapeutic of cases of snakebite. *Lancet* **2** (4236), 1273.

Minton, S. A. 1953. Variation in venom samples from copper heads (*Agkistrodon contortrix mokeson*) and timber rattlesnakes (*Crotalus horridus horridus*). *Copeia.* (4), 213.

Reynolds, A. H. 1960. Venomous snakes and their bites. *Boston Med. Quarterly* **11** (4), 105.

THE EVOLUTION OF TREATMENT OF SNAKEBITE IN THAILAND

CHANYO BENYAJATI* and CHALOEM PURANANANDA†

SNAKEBITE is one of the most important public health problems in Thailand. This paper includes a discussion of the nature of the problem, and a review of the evolution of methods for treatment of snakebite.

Thailand occupies most of the Malay Peninsula from 6 to 20 degrees north of the Equator. Its area is about 200,000 square miles (about the size of France). The topography of the country may be divided into four regions: the hilly northern region; the eastern plateau; the mountainous, sandy, south; and the densely populated central plain. Agriculture is the most important profession. Main crops are rice, teak, and rubber. Mining and fishing are next in importance as means of earning a living. The climate is tropical. There are three seasons: a long, rainy season; a hot, dry summer; and a very short winter.

The nature of the land, climate, and vegetation is favorable for reptile life. Most important of these animals are the snakes, which are found throughout the country. These reptiles constitute a hazard particularly to agricultural workers, who are exposed to snakebite when working barefooted in the fields. The Government is greatly concerned with proper treatment of snakebite, and has always taken an active part in instruction of the people in first-aid measures, and development of effective antivenins.

Over the years there have been several changes in measures for snakebite treatment.

The treatment of snakebite cases in the old days depended mainly on local medicinal herbs, with or without alcohol; these were applied either locally or taken by mouth. Results were uncertain. There were, of course, many successfully treated cases. This was probably due to the sub-lethal doses of venom introduced by the bite. Most of the prescriptions were kept in secret. The only two known were pieces of antler in velvet of the stag or deer (*Cervus equinus*) and a certain species of dark green mold (*Chlorosplenium aerutinosus*), which grows on dead heartwood. The application of the antler in velvet is done by rubbing one flat surface on lime juice, then applying it to the wound.

*Department of Medicine, Chulalongkorn Hospital Medical School, Bangkok, Thailand.

†Queen Saovabha Institute, Bangkok, Thailand.

The antler in velvet will adhere to the wound. This has an effect of suction and retards the distribution of venom in the body. The authors noticed that an attempt to separate a piece of antler in velvet from a snakebite or wound by slight force was not successful. As soon as the person received specific antivenin serum, the pieces of antler dropped off.

It was not until 1917 that the use of antivenin was introduced into Thailand. At first there were only two sera, one against cobra venom and another against Russell's viper venom. In 1925, the Pasteur Institute of Bangkok established a snake farm to keep deadly poisonous snakes of the country for extracting venoms for the production of antivenin. Since then, the treatment of snakebite cases has been more successful. There are still people who believe in using the old methods of treatment. The Institute had often treated serious cases which had been first treated by the old methods and arrived at the Institute in a very serious condition. Many of these patients were snake charmers.

Even after snake antivenins had been introduced into Thailand, the Institute instructed the public in first-aid treatment. This consisted of incisions over the fang marks to allow free bleeding and rubbing of the area with potassium permanganate. It was then advised that suction be applied to the wound and that a tourniquet be applied. Later it was discovered that the incision and suction method is apparently of no value and that only the tourniquet was useful as a first-aid measure.

Some patients seen by the authors have arrived with tourniquets already in place, and these have apparently recovered after administration of antivenin. However, when the tourniquet was released, symptoms often returned and more antivenin was needed.

When antivenin first came into use, many physicians were not acquainted with symptoms of snakebite, and it was necessary to use polyvalent antivenin. As more information became available, it became possible to determine the identity of the species of snake causing the bite by the symptoms of the patient. Since then, it has been possible to use more potent, specific antivenins, and treatment has been more successful. Use of smaller amounts of antivenin has also resulted in less serum sickness.

When large amounts of antivenin are used, serum sickness is a problem. Cortisone and its derivatives were first used to prevent serum sickness in snakebite patients. However, it was found that patients given these drugs recovered more quickly than those treated by serum alone. For this reason, cortisone alone was used in treatment of mild cases of snakebite. This was successful, more so in treatment of Russell's viper bite, than in cobra bite.

Experiments with laboratory animals to determine effects of glucocorticoids in snake envenomation treatment have given equivocal results. *In vitro* tests have not demonstrated neutralization of any snake venoms by cortisone and its derivatives.

Although there are many species of snakes in Thailand, relatively few of these are venomous. Species of medical importance include the king cobra, *Ophiophagus hannah*; the common cobra, *Naja naja*; the banded krait, *Bungarus fasciatus*; the Malayan pit viper, *Agkistrodon rhodostoma*; Russell's viper, *Vipera russelli siamensis*; and the green tree vipers of genus *Trimeresurus*. Specific antivenins against venoms of all but the last of these are produced at the Queen Saovabha Institute. At present these antivenins are in liquid form, but soon all antivenins produced by the Institute will be lyophilized.

In order to give maximum protection to the people, these antivenins are stocked in about 2000 health centers and 100 hospitals throughout the country.

A survey is under way to more accurately determine the distribution of each of the species of venomous snakes in Thailand. When this information is available it should aid in diagnosis of snakebites (in respect to identity of species inflicting the bites) and should be of practical value in planning storage of antivenins in the various regions of Thailand.

After needs of the people of Thailand have been met, excess antivenins are distributed in neighboring countries where the same species of snakes occur.

In summary, it may be said that treatment of snakebite in Thailand, as in other countries, started with folk remedies, using local medicinal plants and other materials, which did not neutralize venom and were effective only from a psychological basis. Antivenin, introduced in the country in 1925, proved highly effective in treatment of snakebite, and was adopted throughout the country. Although cortisone and its derivatives were introduced originally to prevent serum sickness in patients treated with antivenin, it was found that these drugs also quickened recovery of the patients. Used alone, they often proved effective in treatment of mild cases of viper bite. Mechanism of action of cortisone and similar drugs is not known, as laboratory tests have shown no true neutralization of any of the snake venoms by these materials. Nevertheless, they are highly recommended by the authors for use in treatment of snakebite.

SNAKEBITE IN MALAYA

H. A. Reid*

In Malaya, about 1200 snakebite patients are treated each year in Government hospitals. Seventy per cent of these bites occur in the two northwest States, Perlis and Kedah, which contain only 13 per cent of the population in Malaya. During the last three years, prospective epidemiological and clinical studies of 1159 patients bitten in northwest Malaya have been carried out. The pit viper *Ancistrodon rhodostoma* (Boie) caused 85 per cent of these bites. This pit viper is confined to the north in Malaya, accounting for the high snakebite rate in this region. It is not found on Penang Island, although it occurs in Sumatra, Thailand, Burma and Vietnam. Snakebite is a serious medical problem in north Malaya. Opportunities for research on bites by *A. rhodostoma* are probably unique in that a large number of victims are available (over 270 patients in a year in Sungei Patani Hospital, one of the Government hospitals in Kedah State) and the snake can nearly always be reliably identified, since it does not move away after biting human victims. It has often been recovered at the site of the accident several hours later. Other snakes of medical importance in Malaya (see Fig. 1) are sea snakes, common cobras and the two *Trimeresurus* pit vipers *T. wagleri* (Boie) and *T. purpureomaculatus* (Gray).

Venom yields and toxicity to animals in laboratory experiments suggest that cobras and sea snakes are the most dangerous of these types, whilst *A. rhodostoma* is the least dangerous, but this is misleading. Specimens of *A. rhodostoma* caused half the 32 snakebite fatalities in northwest Malaya during 1957–1959. Sea snakes and cobras were responsible for one-quarter each. The prospective epidemiological study by Reid, Thean and Martin (1962) confirmed that snakebite in Malaya is mainly an occupational hazard and rural health problem. Most victims are fishermen, farmers or rubber estate workers. Weeders on rubber estates are particularly prone to bites by *A. rhodostoma.* Young men are the main victims, males being bitten more than twice as often as females, although the sexes are approximately equal in numbers in this region. There is a higher incidence amongst Indians than amongst Malays or Chinese, because most rubber estate workers are Indians, whereas Malays work as farmers, and Chinese are more commonly occupied

*Director, Snake and Venom Research Institute, Consultant Physician, General Hospital, Penang, Malaya.

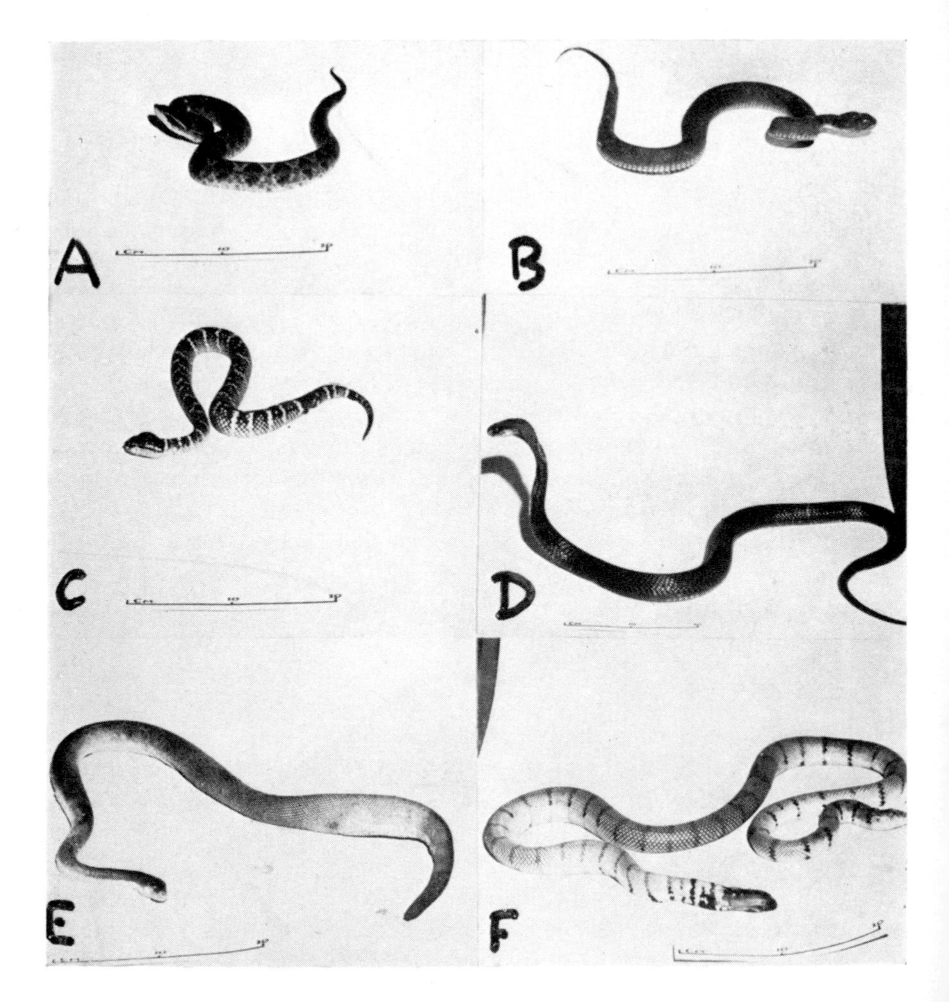

FIG. 1A, *Ancistrodon rhodostoma*, the Malayan pit viper: the most common cause of snakebite in Malaya where it is confined to northern parts.

B, *Trimeresurus purpureomaculatus*, the shore pit viper: common in swamps around Malaya.

C, *Trimeresurus wagleri*: a common tree viper in Malaya.

D, *Naja naja*, the common cobra: usually uniform black in Malaya, although yellow-brown specimens are also found.

E, *Enhydrina schistosa*, the common sea-snake. This is the main cause of sea-snake-bite amongst fishing folk in Asia.

F, *Hydrophis spiralis*, another common sea-snake species. It is the longest of all sea-snakes growing up to 10 ft in length.

in towns. Over 82 per cent of land snakebites are on the foot, toe or lower leg because, of course, the victim is bitten through treading on the snake.

Sea snake bites are quite often in the fingers, since sorting nets is a common sea snake hazard. Two-thirds of all snakebite vitims are bitten in the daylight, and only one-third in the dark. Severity of poisoning shows no significant variation according to the day, the month, or with bites in the light or dark. Nearly half the patients come to hospital within 2 hr of the bite, 75 per cent within 4 hr of the bite. There is little difference in poisoning severity amongst patients coming within 4 hr of the bite, but with longer intervals severe poisoning results in an increasing percentage. This emphasizes how hospital patients are a selected group; as time elapses after the bite an increasing number without evident poisoning do not bother to seek medical advice.

An outstanding feature of these Malayan studies has been the low morbidity in bites by poisonous snakes. Thus in 824 cases in which the snake was reliably identified as a viper, cobra or sea snake, all potentially lethal to humans, 441—over one-half—of the victims escaped with slight or no poisoning. Severe envenoming resulted in only 10 per cent, death in 1.3 per cent of these 824 cases. Allowing for the number of victims bitten without coming to hospital, it is estimated that there are 233 cases of snakebite per 100,000 population each year in Central Kedah State and 20 cases per 100,000 population on Penang Island. Yearly deaths per 100,000 population are similarly calculated as 2.3 for Central Kedah, 0.39 for Penang Island and 0.54 for Malaya generally. Of 733 *A. rhodostoma* victims, 576 (79 per cent) applied a tourniquet after the bite. There was no significant difference in the poisoning between 79 per cent with and 21 per cent without a tourniquet; 49 per cent showed slight or no poisoning, 41 per cent moderate, and 10 per cent severe in those with tourniquets, compared with 56, 33 and 11 per cent in those without tourniquets. Local necrosis was less common in the tourniquet group (8.5 per cent) than in those not applying ligatures (9.1 per cent), but the difference is not statistically significant.

SEA SNAKEBITES

Fishing folk in Asian coastal waters are the main human victims of sea snakes. The danger to bathers has been greatly exaggerated. From Penang Island beaches there have only been two fatal sea snakebites during the seven years 1955–1961 compared with over 30 deaths from accidental drowning in bathers using the same beaches. The clinical features of sea snakebite poisoning in human victims differ markedly from those recorded in animal experiments. In the latter, predominantly neurotoxic effects are described. In humans, however, sea snake venom is primarily myotoxic as reported by Reid (1961a). Generalized muscle-movement pains and myoglobinuria are the outstanding symptoms of poisoning. There is a close similarity to other syndromes with myoglobinuria, particularly Haff disease. Death may result from respiratory failure (through skeletal muscle damage, inhalation of vomit and secretions, and respiratory infection), hyperkalaemia, or acute renal failure. In severe cases recovery may take up to six months. Marsden and Reid (1961) found that the principal pathological lesion is necrosis of skeletal muscle. As with other types of myonecrosis, renal damage often results. Histological changes in the nervous system and in smooth and cardiac muscle are notably absent. Reid (1961b) discussed diagnosis, prognosis and treatment.

Land snake antivenins do not neutralize sea snake venom. Carey and Wright (1960) showed that experimental antiserum made with venom of the common sea snake *Enhydrina schistosa* (Daudin) was also effective against venoms of other sea snake species. Specific sea snake antivenene, the first refined therapeutic sea snake antivenene to be made, is now prepared at the Commonwealth Serum Laboratories, Melbourne, Australia, by immunizing horses with *E. schistosa* venom supplied from the Snake and Venom Research Institute, Penang. Reid (1962a) reported use of this antivenene in treatment of two patients with severe sea snakebite poisoning. Prognosis for one of these patients, in light of previous experience, was very poor. Recovery of both patients was dramatic. A third patient, not given antivenene, since he had only slight poisoning, took two weeks to recover. One of the most gratifying aspects of these trial cases is the fact that antivenene was successful although not given until 7 and 8 hr after the bite. It is therefore not only safe, but very desirable, to wait until there is clear evidence of poisoning before giving the sea snake antivenene. Reid (1961b) has suggested that if a victim is seen within one hour of being bitten before symptoms of poisoning may have developed, or if the patient arrives with an effective tourniquet applied one should give a placebo injection and observe the patient, having removed the tourniquet in the latter case. If significant poisoning symptoms do not ensue during the next hour, antivenene is *not* indicated. The clinical signs confirming envenoming and the need for antivenene may be summarized as follows:

1. Generalized muscle aches, pains and stiffness on movement coming on $\frac{1}{2}$ to 1 hr after the bite.
2. Examination 1 to 2 hr after the bite reveals moderate or severe pain on passive movement of arm, thigh, neck or trunk muscles.
3. Myoglobinuria becomes evident on inspecting the urine 3–6 hr after the bite. Dusky yellowness with positive protein and occult blood tests precedes by an hour or so the red-brown colour of myoglobinuria. The most reliable confirmatory laboratory test of myoglobinuria is by electrophoresis. This technique was described by Whisant, Owings, Cantrell and Cooper (1959).

If antivenene is indicated by clinical findings, a serum sensitivity test should be performed by subcutaneous injection of 0.2 ml (0.02 ml with positive allergic history). If there is no general reaction to this test dose, the antivenene should be administered by intravenous drip over a period of 30 min to 1 hr. If reactions occur during administration, they can usually be controlled by adrenaline subcutaneously, with or without intravenous antihistamine drugs. The minimum effective dosage is one ampoule (neutralizing 10 mg *E. schistosa* venom). In severe poisoning, as shown by ptosis, weakness of external eye muscles, dilatation of pupils with sluggish light reaction and leucocytosis exceeding 20,000, two or more ampoules would be advisable. Children respond well to smaller doses of antivenene than those required by adults (contrary to previous textbook statements).

COBRA BITES

Cobra bites in Malaya are not so common as sea snake or viper bites. In a series of 33 cases in which *Naja naja* was personally identified, no poisoning followed in 20 cases; it was trivial or moderate in five, severe in three, and fatal in one. Although cobra venom is neurotoxic in laboratory experiments, this effect is highly exceptional in human victims in Malaya. The main effect in humans is local and necrotising. Necrosis principally affects the subcutaneous tissues and can be very extensive. Neurotoxic effects were only seen in four of these 33 cases. A flaccid paresis developed quickly after the bite, but unlike sea-snake envenoming in which the paresis due to direct muscle damage continues for weeks or months, the paresis of cobra poisoning is shortlived, lasting only a few days. Reid (in press) found that specific cobra antivenene does not prevent local necrosis.

VIPER BITES: *ANCISTRODON RHODOSTOMA* (BOIE)

The viper, *Ancistrodon rhodostoma*, is much the most common cause of human snakebite in Malaya. In a recent series of 250 cases, one-half of the patients had slight or no poisoning, one-third moderate poisoning and only one-sixth had severe poisoning. Reid (in press) found that swelling is the paramount clinical feature of local poisoning. It comes on rapidly within a few minutes of the bite and in all cases at least 75 per cent of the final swelling occurs within 12 hr of the bite. This swelling, which is one of the most accurate clinical guides to venom dose, is due to rapid diffusion of the venom up subcutaneous tissues affecting vascular endothelium externally rather than from within the lumen and resulting in exudation of plasma. Sometimes large numbers of erythrocytes also migrate. Extensive limb discoloration and anaemia result in these cases. Blisters, serous or sanguineous, are not uncommon at the site of the bite, but more extensive ones beyond the bite indicate a high venom dose. Local necrosis occurred in 10·8 per cent of

250 patients. It was much more common in toe and finger bites (27 per cent) compared with an incidence of 5·6 per cent in foot bites, 7·0 per cent in leg bites and nil with six hand bites. The necrosis is usually confined to cubcutaneous tissues (eventually involving the skin), and often leads to prolonged morbidity although permanent ill-effects are rare. Except as a complication of necrosis *local bacterial infection did not occur in any case.*

Systemic poisoning in human victims mainly involves the blood clotting mechanism. The *in vitro* effects of *A. rhodostoma* venom on normal human plasma without calcium, or on fibrinogen solutions, vary according to the concentration of venom used. With high concentration a clot quickly forms, but quite shortly dissolves. Lowering the concentration of venom results in clots, which do not completely dissolve, but become more and more flimsy. Agitation will now render the clot invisible, yet the supernatant " plasma " no longer clots after addition of thrombin. Still lower concentrations, but higher than those likely to be encountered in human victims, have no observable effect. The venom dissolves gelatin.

Systemic poisoning followed in 39 per cent of the 250 patients. It was slight in 11 per cent (poor-clotting blood), moderate in 13 per cent (non-clotting blood) and severe in 15 per cent. The latter all had clinical signs of a haemorrhagic syndrome consisting of haemoptysis in 78 per cent, positive Hess test in 74 per cent, discoid skin petechiae in 58 per cent, bleeding gums in 46 per cent, oozing from the bite in 30 per cent, haematemesis in 8 per cent, haematuria and oozing from sores both in 3 per cent. Haemoptysis is by far the most important and the earliest sign of severe systemic poisoning. It is important to ask the patient to cough hard in order to produce the blood-stained spit, as otherwise this valuable sign may be overlooked. Haemoptysis has been observed as early as 20 min after the bite. It is *not* due to bleeding from the gums, which is less common, and follows later in the clinical course of the patient. The Hess test is often positive, but is of no value if the skin is dark. Embolic discoid petechiae are another distinctive feature of *A. rhodostoma* systemic poisoning. They are perfectly circular, slightly raised and vary in diameter from 3 to 15 mm. Characteristically they are sparsely scattered over limbs, trunk and face regardless of the bite site. In very severe cases they may be profuse, but usually they are only up to a dozen in all. Shock is one of the lethal mechanisms in *A. rhodostoma* bites, and is partly hypovolaemic due to loss of circulating fluid into the bitten limb. Tensely swollen lower limb can accommodate half or more of the total blood volume. Another factor may cause shock of earlier onset in certain cases. This is probably intravascular coagulation in pulmonary and hepatic capillaries, which decreases the venous return to the heart, and causes a drastic fall of cardiac output in a somewhat similar manner to endotoxin shock as reported by Hardaway, Husni, Greever, Noyes, and Burns (1961). Detailed investigation of the coagulation defect in systemic poisoning following *A. rhodostoma* viper bites will be reported elsewhere by Reid, Chan, and Thean (to be published). The long persistence of this coagulation defect, if specific antivenin is not given (the defect can last for over three weeks), is a matter of outstanding and possibly, far-reaching interest.

Controlled therapeutic trials using double-blind technique with random allocation of patients have been carried out to assess the value of both specific antivenin and prednisone in *A. rhodostoma* poisoning. The results will be published shortly by Reid, Thean, and Martin (to be published). Specific antivenin is dramatically successful in rectifying systemic poisoning, but of little or no help as regards local poisoning.

SUMMARY

A prospective epidemiological study of 1159 personally observed patients bitten by snakes during a three-year period in northwest Malaya indicated that snakebite is a rural and occupational hazard.

The pit viper *Ancistrodon rhodostoma* (Boie) caused 85 per cent of the bites in northwest Malaya where snakebite is a serious medical problem. Other snakes of medical importance were sea snakes, common cobras, and the two pit vipers, *Trimeresurus wagleri* (Boie) and *T. purpureomaculatus* (Gray).

The clinical features of snakebite poisoning in human victims differed significantly from those recorded in animal experiments. Thus sea snake venom was myotoxic rather than neurotoxic in humans. Cobra bites in Malaya caused local necrosis which in some cases was very extensive. Neurotoxic symptoms were most exceptional. In systemic poisoning following bites by *A. rhodostoma*, the main feature was a coagulation defect, which, in the absence of specific antivenene, was unusually prolonged and persistent.

In 824 of 1159 personally observed patients, the snake was reliably identified as a potentially lethal viper, cobra or sea snake. Yet 53 per cent of these 824 victims escaped with slight or no poisoning. This has very important implications in the treatment of snakebite. A refined specific sea snake antivenene has been developed. The indications and recommendations for using it were summarized.

REFERENCES

Carey, J. E. and Wright, E. A. 1960. The toxicity and immunological properties of some sea snake venoms with particular reference to that of *Enhydrina schistosa*. *Trans. Roy. Soc. Trop. Med. Hyg.* **54**, 50.

Hardaway, R. M., Hashni, E. A., Greever, E. F., Noyes, H. E. and Burns, J. W. 1961. Endotoxin shock: A manifestation of intravascular coagulation. *Ann. Surg.* **154**, 791.

Marsden, A. T. H. and Reid, H. A. 1961. Pathology of sea snake poisoning. *Brit. Med. J.* **1**, 1290.

REID, H. A. 1961a. Myoglobinuria and sea snakebite poisoning. *Brit. Med. J.* **1**, 1284.

REID, H. A. 1961b. Diagnosis, prognosis, and treatment of sea snakebite. *Lancet* **1**. 399.

REID, H. A. 1962. Sea snake antivenene: Successful trial. In press, *Brit. Med. J.* **2**, 576.

REID, H. A., THEAN, P. C. and MARTIN, J. W. 1962. Epidemiology of snakebite in North Malaya. In press, *Brit. Med. J.*

WHISNANT, C. L., OWINGS, R. H., CANTRELL, C. G. and COOPER, G. R. 1959. Primary idiopathic myoglobinuria in a Negro female: Its complications and a new method of laboratory diagnosis. *Ann. Intern. Med.* **51**, 140.

VENOMOUS ARGENTINE SERPENTS OPHIDISM AND SNAKE ANTIVENIN

J. W. ABALOS* and I. PIROSKY†

THE Republic of Argentina encompasses most of the southern part of South America. Its area in the American Continent extends from the 22nd parallel to the 55th and comprises torrid, moderate, and cold climatic zones. Its snake fauna numbers a hundred species, which are most widely dispersed in the central and northern regions of the country.

SNAKE FAUNA OF ARGENTINA

Family Typhlopidae: represented by two species.

Family Leptotyphlopidae: represented by three species.

Family Boidae: represented by three species

Family Colubridae: represented by 70 species.

Family Elapidae: represented by three species; all of genus *Micrurus*. These snakes, commonly known as coral snakes, are not abundant, although in the Province of Santiago del Estero we have collected more than a hundred specimens each year. Coral snakes feed on other snakes, including venomous species, but usually do not accept food in captivity. In spite of the potency of their neurotoxic venom, coral snakes are not a great hazard to man due to their subterranean habits and lack of aggressiveness. Cases of coral snake bite in man are rare, but are always very serious, and may end fatally. Because of the scanty venom secretion by these snakes, and the rarity of accidents caused by them, it has not been considered necessary to produce coral snake antivenin in Argentina.

Family Crotalidae: represented by eight species of *Bothrops*, and one of *Crotalus*. Information concerning each of these is presented in this paper.

Bothrops atrox (Linneus, 1758)

This snake, commonly known as the fer-de-lance, is the most widely distributed species of the genus. It is found in all the South American countries with the exception of Uruguay and Chile; in all of Central America and part of Mexico. In Argentina it is found only in the Province of Misiones, in the extreme northeast.

*Herpetologist, National Institute of Microbiology, Santiago del Estero, Argentina.
†Director, National Institute of Microbiology, Buenos Aires, Argentina.

B. atrox reaches a great size; specimens are frequently 1.50 m in length. Its head, definitely triangular, is well distinguished from the neck. Its general color is reddish gray; the head has no design or noticeable spots. On the dorsal surface of the body extending laterally there are dark, narrow, angular designs accompanied by paraventral spots which always meet. The belly is light yellow. The snake presents an overall velvety appearance.

The properties of its venom, which produce liquid blisters on the bitten area, give it the popular name of " burner ".

Bothrops jararaca (Wied, 1824)

This species has a more restricted geographical distribution than the *atrox*. It is found in Southern Brazil, Paraguay, and in Argentina, in the province of Misiones. It is a species of medium size. Most adult specimens measure about one meter in length. Its general coloring is olive-yellowish or gray. The head shows irregular dark spots and from the eye a black streak runs down to the corner of the mouth. There are dark dorsal and lateral markings which are not distinct. It is very aggressive.

Bothrops jararacussu (Lacerda, 1884)

This is a snake of great size; some specimens exceed two meters in length. Its head is large and it has powerful fangs. Its general color is blackish. On the dorsal area of the body it shows, on each side, yellow zigzag lines whose angles meet in the midline, thus presenting rhomboids which vaguely resemble those of the rattlesnake. The ventral region is white with black spots. The head has a yellow line on either side. It occurs in Southern Brazil, Eastern Bolivia, Paraguay, and Argentina, in the latter it is found only in Misiones Province.

Bothrops cotiara (Gomes, 1913)

This reptile is smaller than the previously described species; its length is less than one meter. It usually lives in moutainous regions. It is found in Southern Brazil, and in Argentina it has only been found in Misiones Province.

The coloring of the body is grayish green with large black lateral triangular spots that meet or alternate in the midline; it also has small paraventral spots. The belly is dark with yellow spots. Characteristic of this species is a large dark marking in the form of a V on the head. Contained in this marking is a light greenish design in the shape of a double cross.

Bothrops alternata (Dum. & Bibr., 1854)

This snake is found in Southern Brazil, the eastern part of Paraguay, Uruguay, and the northeastern part of Argentina. It seems to prefer humid regions.

FIG. 1. Position of Argentina in South America.

FIG. 2. *Micrurus lemniscatus frontalis*.

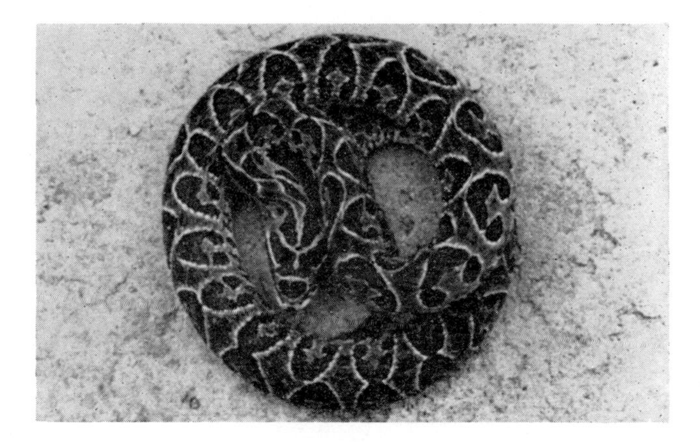

FIG. 3. *Bothrops alternata.*

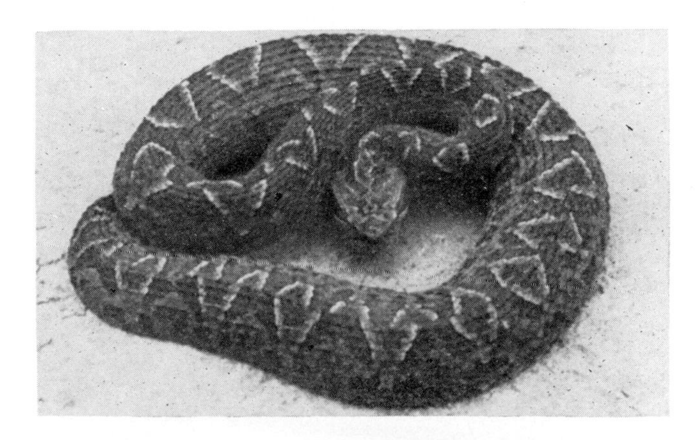

FIG. 4. *Bothrops neuwiedii meridionalis.*

This is a fairly large snake and often measures 1.50 m in length. It is popularly called the " cross-snake " because of a design on its head which is in the shape of a cross formed by light lines on a dark background. This design varies; sometimes it looks like an anchor or a spur. On the back of the body, on a gray background, it has a series of kidney-shaped designs, tangent in themselves or alternating. These are black with white margins and are very noticeable. Within each kidney-shaped spot is found a clear zone, whose shape recalls an iron spearhead. The abdomen is white with black spots.

This snake is easily enraged and is aggressive. When angry it flattens itself against the ground. It is the cause of many snakebites.

Bothrops neuwiedii (Wagler, 1824)

In Argentina is found the subspecies *B. neuwiedii meridionalis* of Amaral. This is the venomous serpent most widely distributed in the country and it is the cause of most snakebite in man. Its length surpasses a meter. Its general coloring is gray, slightly red laterally. The general color is that of dirt. On the head it has irregular dark spots. The designs of the body do not correspond to a well defined design; they unite in the center of the dorsum. The belly is white. This species is easily recognized because of small horny protuberance on the tip of its tail.

This snake and *B. alternata* vibrate the tail and shake it against the ground producing a characteristic noise, which, to a lesser degree, resembles the noise of a rattlesnake; this many times causes incidents to be credited to the latter species, when actually they were caused by species of *Bothrops*.

Bothrops ammodytoides (Leybold, 1873)

This snake belongs exclusively to the Argentine fauna. It is found in the mountainous regions of the central and southern zone of the country. It is not abundant, and rarely exceeds 50 cm in length. Its coloring is similar to that of *B. neuwiedii*, with irregular dorsal spots, which sometimes unite, forming a chain design in the midline. It is easy to recognize because of its raised snout, which has gained it the name of " ñata ". Snakebites of *ammodytoides* are not frequent.

Crotalus durissus terrificus (Laurentius, 1768)

The systematic position of the Argentine rattler is not entirely clear. The technical name most frequently used will be followed in this paper.

It is found in the northern and central parts of the country, and is particularly abundant in the Province of Santiago del Estero. This is a rocky region, with annual rainfall of less than 600 mm.

Its length does not exceed 1.50 m, its body is corpulent, and its movements heavy. Its general coloring is yellow with ring-shaped dorsal rhombs. The coloring darkens towards the caudal region and the posterior portion of the tail is black. We have found up to 13 segments on this harmonious structure.

This snake is slightly aggressive.

THE PROBLEM OF SNAKEBITE

Statistical studies have not been made in Argentina but there must be thousands of cases with some deaths annually of snakebite incidence in the northern and central regions.

Bites of species of Micrurus

Because of their subterranean habits and slight aggressiveness, the corals rarely bite man. In Brazil, most of the cases registered have been by individuals who were collecting snakes by hand.

From what is known, the poisonings produced by these serpents are always of rapid evolution, generally ending in the death of the victim. The clinical picture is characterized by numbness of the affected area; thoracic pains, especially precordial; palpebral ptosis; difficulty of vision; loss of equilibrium; abundant salivation; anguish; respiratory difficulties; even complete motor paralysis and death by mechanical asphyxia.

A special antivenin is produced at the Instituto Nacional de Microbiologia (National Institute of Microbiology) for use in event of laboratory accidents

Bite by Crotalus

Because of its lack of aggressiveness, its heavy movements, and the alert given by the sound of its rattle before attacking, a relatively small number of snakebites to man are caused by *Crotalus durissus terrificus*. These are not in proportion with the abundance of this snake in these areas. In the Province of Santiago del Estero, for example, these have been the most numerous among snakes gathered for preparation of antivenin. In four years of observation made in a hospital where hundreds of cases of snakebite have been treated, it was found that none of these had been due to *Crotalus*.

Rattlesnake bites, when they occur, are always deadly and require speedy medical attention. The symptomatology evidences the marked neurotropic action of the venom of Argentine rattlesnake. The local symptoms are slight. The marks left by the fangs can be observed, and there is sometimes a light edema. There are generalized pains, lessening of sight, palpebral ptosis, vomiting, diarrhea, loss of equilibrium, and uremia. Death is caused by lesions of the nervous system and kidneys.

Snakebite by species of Bothrops

Snakebites by serpents of genus *Bothrops* are more numerous than those caused by other snakes in Argentina. We have seen in our roster of venomous

FIG. 5. *Crotalus durissus terrificus.*

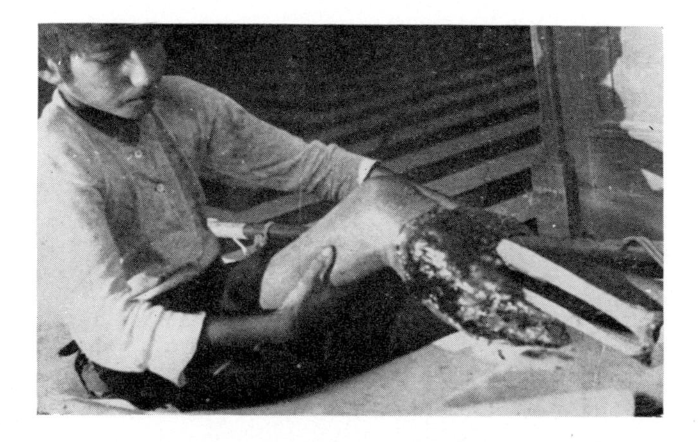

FIG. 6. After effects of a bite by *Bothrops alternata.*

species, that four of them are limited in distribution to Misiones Province of the extreme northeast. *Bothrops ammodytoides*, a relatively rare Patagonian species found in mountainous regions is of small size and does not represent a real problem. *B. alternata* and *B. neuwiedii* are the species which produce the greatest number of snakebites. *B. alternata* is particularly abundant in the so called "Argentine littoral" which comprises the extensive region between the Parana and Uruguay Rivers and the neighboring zone of the Chaco and Santa Fe Provinces. Snakes of this species are responsible for a large proportion of the snakebites of man. Its aggressiveness, and the capacity of its venom glands make it extremely dangerous. *B. neuwiedii meridionalis* is dispersed through a greater area and produces almost 100 per cent of the incidents of snakebites in the zones in which *B. alternata* is not found.

Bites by serpents of the genus *Bothrops* are characterized by intense local effects, including pain, hemorrhage, congestion of the bitten area, hemorrhagic edema which invades the surrounding tissues and spreads extensively. Gangrene with necrosis often follows. This results in the loss of tissues and even limbs. These lesions are often aggravated by the tourniquet used as a first-aid measure. It is probably that stoppage of the circulation in this manner that facilitates the proteolytic action of the venom.

The general condition is characterized by initial shock, nausea, vomiting, dizziness, hemorrhages through the nasal and buccal, mucosa and blood-stained diarrhea. Following this is a more intense toxic picture with stimulation, general clonic contractures, intense dyspnea, cyanosis without extensive involvement of the respiratory system.

Death rates following bites of these snakes vary according to species.

ANTIVENINS

In Argentina the Instituto Nacional de Microbiologia (National Institute of Microbiology) of Buenos Aires has the responsibility for developing antivenin to supply the needs of the country. Four types of snake antivenins are produced. These are: monovalent anti-*Crotalus terrificus*, bilvalent antivenin, anti-*Bothrops alternata* and *B. neuwiedii* antivenin; polivalent anti-*C. terrificus*, *B. alternata* and *B. neuwiedii* antivenin and polivalent "Misiones" anti-venin, which protects against each of the above species in addition to *B. jararaca* and *B. jararacussu.*

The immunization of equines is effected through the administration of progressive doses of dried venom, which is used in a solution of 1 per cent.

These sera are purified and concentrated by means of enzyme and differential thermocoagulation.

They are assayed for potency of neutralization tests in which mixtures of serum and venom are injected intravenously into 20 g white mice.

Required potency levels for these antivenin are:

Bivalente–neutralizes 2.7 to 4.3 mg of venom of *B. alternata.*

Polivalente—neutralizes 2.5 to 3 mg of venom of *B. alternata.*

Polivalente—neutralizes 0.4 mg of venom of *C. d. terrificus.*

Monocrotalico—neutralizes 0.4 to 0.4 mg of venom of *C. d. terrificus.*

The antivenin production program has recently been intensified with the installation of a venom collecting center in the northern part of the country (Santiago del Estero) and a chain of small collecting stations where snakes abound.

SUMMARY

A brief review of the snakebite problem in Argentina is presented. Distributions of the most important venomous species are presented, and information is given concerning their distribution and medical importance. The most widely distributed species in the country are *Bothrops neuwiedii meridionalis*, *Bothrops alternata*, and *Crotalus durissus terrificus.*

The first two of these are responsible for most snakebites reported in the country. Information is given on the four antivenins available in Argentina for treatment of snakebite. These are produced by the Instituto Nacional de Microbiologia (National Institute of Microbiology).

VENOMOUS SEA SNAKES OF VIET NAM AND THEIR VENOMS

MICHEL BARME*

VENOMOUS sea snakes belonging to the family *Hydrophiidae* are numerous along the coasts of Viet Nam. Our collecting program has resulted in capture of several thousand of these reptiles. The following species were represented among specimens taken: *Lapemis hardwickii*, *Enhydrina schistosa*, *Hydrophis cyanocinctus*, *Microcephalophis gracilis*, *Kolpophis annandalei*, *Aipysurus eydouxii*, *Thalassophina viperina*, *Pelamis platurus*, *Hydrophis fasciatus*, *Kerilia jerdoni*, and *Hydrophis ornatus*.

The distribution of these snakes along the Vietnamese coast-line is uneven. In South Viet Nam, where sea snakes are most abundant, *Lapemis hardwickii* represented about 75 per cent of the snakes captured; while in Central Viet Nam, *Hydrophis fasciatus* has been more frequently taken. These two zones are separated by the region of Nhatrang, where the Hydrophiidae seem to disappear totally. Whenever these snakes are found, they seem to be concentrated around estuaries where net fishing is intensely practiced. Seasonal variations in the number of Hydrophiidae captured have also been noted. For example, near Phan Thiet, in South Viet Nam, one haul of a net rarely brings in more than two snakes during the dry season, while during the rainy season (from July to November) their number may reach several hundred at one throw of the net. It is probable that the rivers, filled with organic wastes in the rainy season, attract the fishes on which the sea snakes feed. This increase in the number of sea snakes corresponds also to the time of the birth of the young snakes, which form a higher percentage of collections made after July.

As the Vietnamese fishermen are in daily contact with large numbers of sea snakes, snakebites are frequent among them. Bites usually occur when the fishermen enter the water to take care of their nets, or at the time of the sorting of the fish in the net. This is done with bare hands. Each year fatal cases are numerous, but actual numbers remain unknown because of superstitions which forbid the fisherman to make them known, and also because many villages where these accidents occur are isolated far from urban centers.

*Director, Laboratory Institute Pasteur of Saigon, South Viet Nam. Present address: Institute Pasteur, 28, Rue du Dr Roux, Paris 15, France.

FIG. 1. *Lapemis hardwickii*. This is the sea snake most frequently encountered along the coast of Viet Nam. The example shown is a juvenile specimen.

FIG. 2. Fishing with a net in South Viet Nam. The pocket of the net is dragged up on to the sand. The three cylindrical floats, above and slightly to the left, indicate the position of the pocket. The arrow marked the partially submerged entrance to the nets where venomous snakes are captured along with the fish. The fishermen who enter the water on such occasions, are often victims of snake-bite.

Each of these snakes gives only a small quantity of venom. This varies among individuals, and species, from 0.5 mg to 30 mg (expressed in dry weight). However, the toxicity of these venoms is particularly high, as is

FIG. 3. A view through the net showing a sea snake captured along with the fish.

shown by the results of our tests made on mice of 20 g inoculated intravenously. Results are expressed in minimum lethal doses (dry poison weight):

Lapemis hardwickii	4 μg
Enhydrina schistosa	2.5 μg
Hydrophis cyanocinctus	7 μg
Kolpophis annandalei	11 μg
Microcephalophis gracilis	2.5 μg
Hydrophis fasciatus	3.5 μg
Thalassophina viperina	7 μg
Pelamis platurus	10 μg

These levels of toxicity appear higher than those for venoms of land snakes evaluated under the same conditions. For example, *Ancistrodon piscivorius* produces a venom for which the minimum lethal dose is 150 μg. The same dosage value for venoms of *Naja Haje* and *Trimeresurus gramineus* is 20 μg.

The symptoms of experimental envenomation of laboratory animals recalled those of curarization (poisoning by use of curare) and bring death by asphyxiation. In the rabbit, sea snake venom causes a paralysis which begins with a " hypotonic " of the muscles of the nape of the neck, then reaches the forelegs, and finally, the rest of the musculature.

The power of the neurotoxic factor of these venoms seems to conceal the presence described as discernible *in vitro* by Barme and Detrait (1959), of enzymes such as a lecithinase and an anticoagulant. These venoms also contain a hyaluronidase, but not a cholinesterase, nor an acid-amino-oxidase.

FIG. 4. Another occasion for snakebite—when the fishermen using only their hands, take the fish from the pocket of the net. At such times they often come in contact with snakes hidden among the fish.

Immunochemical analysis, according to Oudin's method (1955), reveals a complex antigenic structure. The venom of *Lapemis hardwickii*, in opposition to a homologous antiserum, has caused nine distinct lines of immune-precipitate to appear. Certain of these fractions are common to the venoms of other species. When tested with *Lapemis* antivenom, four lines of immune-precipitate have appeared with the venoms of *Enhydrina schistosa*, *Kolpophis anandalei*, *Pelamis platurus*, two lines with the venom of *Hydrophis cyano-cinctus*, and one line with the venom of *Microcephalophis gracilis*.

Barme *et al.* (1962) have attempted prepared of a specific antivenin in a horse with the poison of *Lapemis*. The development of neutralizing power was measured by the method of titration which consists in inoculation of mice intravenously with a mixture consisting of a fixed volume of serum and an equal volume of venom at various concentrations. At the end of 6 months, the horse furnished a serum in which 1 ml neutralized 400 μg of homologous venom (LD_{100} in mice).

The antigenic similarity existing between the venoms of different species of *Hydrophiidae* and shown by the immunochemical method, is found again in the results of the tests of crossed sero-neutralisation in the mouse. The same serum neutralizing 400 μg of the poison of *Lapemis*, neutralized 150 μg (60 LD_{100}) of the venom of *Enhydrina*, and 250 μg of the venom of (35 LD_{100}) *Hydrophis cyanocinctus*.

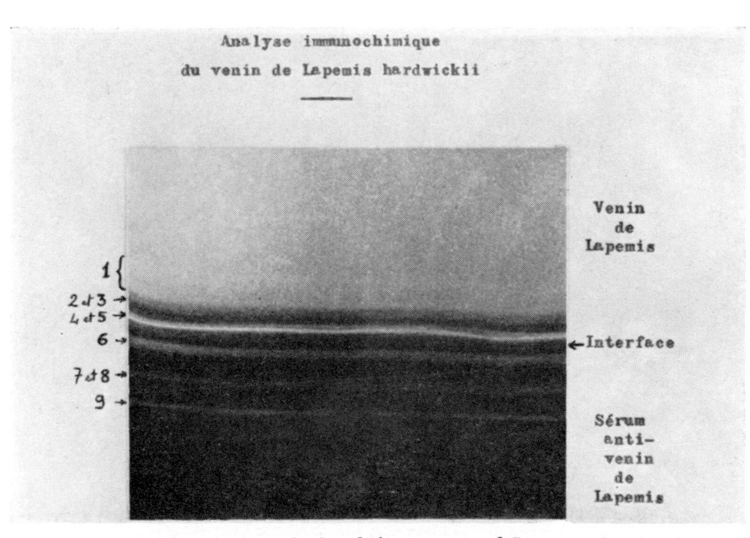

FIG. 5. Immunochemical analysis of the venom of *Lapemis hardwickii*. The nine lines of the immune precipitate are separated on one side or the other of the interface dividing the two zones of gel, that with venom at the top, that with anti-venin below. The method, utilizing parallel surfaces, is that of Oudin.

A theurapeutic experiment was tried in July 1961 on a fisherman who had been bitten by a specimen of *Lapemis hardwickii*. After the injection of 20 ml of this serum, the paralytic symptoms regressed rapidly, and the next day the recovery of movement was complete. It is evidently not possible to know if such an antivenom injection had really stopped a fatal evolution. Numerous experiments will be necessary before conclusions can be made to the efficacy of such antivenon. These experiments are now under way. The therapeutic activity of this Hydrophiidae antivenin should be increased in its neutralizing power, completed eventually by a purification. The antigenic likenesses existing between the poisons of the different kinds of Hydrophiidae are numerous. This situation may facilitate the preparation of a polyvalent antivenin. This is highly desirable because of the variety of species of sea snakes to which the fishermen of Viet Nam are susceptible.

REFERENCES

BARME, M. et DETRAIT, J. 1959. Etude de la composition des venins des Hydrophiidés. *C.R. Acad. Sciences* (Paris) **248**, 312.

BARME, M., HUARD, M. and NGUYEN XUAN MAI. 1962. Préparation d'un serum anti-venin d'Hydrophiidés-Premiers essais thérapeutiques. *Ann. J. Pasteur*, 102, 497.

OUDIN, J. 1955. L'analyse immunochimique par la méthode des gels. *Ann. I. Pasteur* **89**, 531.

NOTES ON THE WHITE-LIPPED PIT VIPER, *TRIMERESURUS ALBOLABRIS* GRAY, IN HONG KONG

J. D. ROMER*

THE crotaline snake *Trimeresurus albolabris* Gray, whilst certainly not highly venomous, is the species responsible each year for a great majority of the venomous snake-bites which occur in the Colony of Hong Kong. It is for this reason that these notes have been prepared, with the hope that they may prove of interest both to herpetologists and those concerned with the subject of snake-bite.

POPULAR NAMES

It is somewhat unfortunate that " Bamboo Snake " (or " Green Bamboo Snake " when translated from the Chinese) is the well-established name by which this snake is known in Hong Kong. At least one other distinct species occurring elsewhere, namely *T. gramineus* (Shaw) of peninsular India, is also known as " Bamboo Snake " (or as " Bamboo Pit Viper "). Moreover, with reference at least to *T. albolabris* in Hong Kong, there is no indication of any particular association with bamboo. Although the name " *White-lipped* Pit Viper " denotes a character which is neither specific nor constant, it is certainly not entirely inappropriate and conforms with the scientific name of the species.

COLORATION AND SEXUAL DIMORPHISM

In coloration this snake is usually uniformly green above (rarely with indistinct dark cross-bands); pale greenish yellow, yellow, or whitish below. The upper lip is whitish (at least after preservation), pale green, or yellow. The tip and at least part of the upper surface of the tail is reddish brown. A narrow white lateral line along each side of the body on scale-row 1 is distinct in males, indistinct or absent in females. There is also distinct sexual dimorphism in regard to size. Whilst females attain considerably

*Pest Control Officer, Urban Services Department, Hong Kong.

longer over-all lengths than males, the length of the tail in relation to total length in males is greater than it is in females in both adults and young (Table 1). The longest male (630 mm) and the longest female (915 mm) which I have encountered during periods totalling over eleven years in the Colony are included in Table 1.

TABLE 1. MEASUREMENTS (in mm) AND TAIL/TOTAL LENGTH RATIOS IN MALE AND FEMALE *T. albolabris* GRAY

Age	Sex	Total length	Tail	Ratio (%) of tail/ total length
Adult	Male	630	125	19.8
Young adult	Male	338	60	17.8
Newly-born	Male	198	37	18.7
Newly-born	Male	197	37	18.8
Newly-born	Male	191	35	18.3
Newly-born	Male	188	36	19.1
Adult	Female	915	133	14.5
Young adult	Female	411	54	13.1
Newly-born	Female	200	27	13.5
Newly-born	Female	195	30	15.4
Newly-born	Female	195	27	13.8
Newly-born	Female	194	30	15.5
Newly-born	Female	185	28	15.1

GENERAL DISTRIBUTION

The known geographical range of *T. albolabris* extends from parts of East Punjab and Madhyapradesh (Central Provinces) in India, Kathmandu in Nepal, through the whole of the Indo-Chinese subregion from the eastern Himalayas to southern China, Taiwan (Formosa), and Hong Kong in the north; Hainan; Thailand (Siam) and Burma north of latitude 13°; the Andaman and Nicobar Islands, Sumatra, Java, and Indonesia as far south as Timor (Smith, 1943). There are no records for the Malay Peninsula. In southern China according to Pope (1935) it has been found in various localities in the provinces of Kwangsi, Kwangtung, and Fukien.

LOCAL OCCURRENCE AND HABITAT

In Hong Kong the White-lipped Pit Viper occurs widely on Hong Kong Island, where it is fairly common. Within this Colony it has also been recorded from Stonecutters Island and from several parts of the New Territories (including the mainland, Cheung Chau Island, and Lantau Island). Usually inhabiting hilly wooded localities, its vertical distribution here extends roughly from sea level up to at least 1500 ft (approx. 457 m) in the hills. It is not infrequently found in the vicinity of human habitations.

GENERAL HABITS

Although sometimes encountered in day-time, resting in low vegetation or elsewhere, *T. albolabris* is predominantly nocturnal. Owing to lack of detailed information on a sufficient number of specimens, it is difficult to determine to what extent this species is terrestrial and to what extent scansorial. It seems probable, however, that during the day some specimens rest among vegetation above ground-level, descending at night in search of food. An adult female, which I kept in captivity for 6 or 7 years, habitually rested in the fork of a small branch in the day-time during warm seasons, and spent prolonged periods on the floor of the cage beneath a piece of bark only during hibernation. Whilst invariably living well in captivity, neither the specimen just mentioned nor any of several others kept for lesser periods ever lost the normal habit of this species of striking readily at intruders. This habit is pronounced and I have known the young, when interfered with, to strike within a few hours of birth.

FEEDING HABITS

The feeding habits of *T. albolabris* are now fairly well established. Pope (1935) refers to observations and dissections indicating that it feeds chiefly on rats, but also on lizards (*Calotes versicolor*) and frogs. Gressitt (1941) mentions two specimens, both of which contained the remains of frogs. Of four local specimens which I examined myself for stomach contents, three each contained a gecko and one a rat; the latter specimen was the 915 mm female already mentioned, which contained an adult rat (*Rattus rattus*) measuring 160 mm in head + body length. My own captive specimens accepted tame mice (*Mus musculus*), and very young ones bred in captivity fed readily on small frogs. The water requirements of this species do not appear to be great, but I have occasionally observed an adult captive specimen in the act of drinking while hanging almost vertically from a branch.

REPRODUCTION

My observations on reproduction in this species refer to a female which I kept in captivity for 6 or 7 years. During the hibernation period through the winter of 1953–54 this snake was kept in a cage by itself, and on 19–20 July 1954 (having remained in isolation) produced ten living young and one dead embryo. The measurements of nine of these are given in Table 1. When found, two of the living young were still enclosed within their embryonic membranes. Each one of several examined with a hand lens had a distinct egg-tooth. In subsequent years the same female produced young on two other occasions, although details are available for only one of them. This was on or about 23 June 1958, when thirteen young were produced, three of which were still within their embryonic membranes when born and failed to survive. On this occasion a male had been kept together with the female.

AETIOLOGY

Being typically sluggish by nature, and depending for protection largely on its cryptic coloration, *T. albolabris* seldom moves when approached. It is primarily for this reason, coupled with its readiness to strike when closely approached, that bites by this species occur. There is also the further consideration that many of the local Chinese villagers walk either barefooted or with footwear of a type which covers very little of the feet. As would be expected, bites are usually on the extremities, those involving the hands sometimes resulting from grass-cutting activities.

INCIDENCE OF BITES

In regard to the annual incidence of bites by this species involving humans in Hong Kong, it is impossible from the available information to make anything more than a very rough estimate. In 1953, in response to a request from the World Health Organization, an estimate was provided of the *total* number of snake-bite cases (i.e. regardless of the species involved) occurring annually within the Colony of Hong Kong. The basis of this estimate was that, during the twelve months from August 1951 to July 1952, twenty cases of snake-bite were seen at the Colony's largest Government hospital (situated on Hong Kong Island). Thus, allowing for cases seen at other hospitals or clinics, and for those treated elsewhere with Chinese medicines or possibly not treated at all, it was estimated that about 100 cases occur in the Colony each year. Whilst details of the relative numbers of each of the species involved are not available, there is little doubt that the majority are attributable to *T. albolabris*. Apart from several small opistho-glyphous species, the only other venomous snakes known from Hong Kong are *Bungarus fasciatus* (Schneider), *B. multicinctus* Blyth, *Callophis macclel-landi* (Reinhardt), *Naja naja* (Linn.), *N. hannah* (Cantor), and certain sea snakes (Romer, 1961). Although some of these undoubtedly give rise to bites, there is no indication that even the combined numbers of such bites approach the numbers caused by *T. albolabris*.

EFFECTS AND TREATMENT OF BITES

The venom of this species, like that of most vipers, is predominantly haemotoxic in its effects on man. In at least the great majority of cases its action is localized within the bitten limb. Oedema, discoloration, and pain are common. Occasional consequences include headache, slight palpitation, slow pulse, tightness of the affected extremities, trembling, and depression (the last two probably resulting from fear). Necrosis, temporary local paralysis, and secondary infection are rare. There does not appear to be any *definite* record of an adult ever having died, either in Hong Kong or elsewhere, in consequence of being bitten by *T. albolabris*. Pope (1935) states that: " Maxwell (1912, p. 244) reports the death of a 33-year-old man in southern Fukien after the bite of a ' *Lachesis gramineus* ', but it is of course impossible to say whether the snake in question was *T. albolabris* or *T. stejnegeri*." A paper by Lin (1954) contains two tables giving mortality rates for " *T. gramineus* ". One lists 14 deaths out of 2108 bites during the 10-year period 1923–1932 (0·66 per cent mortality), and the other a mortality of 0·90 per cent for the period 1904–1938. Again, however, as there are two species of green pit vipers recorded for Taiwan (*T. stejnegeri* and *T. albolabris*) and *T. gramineus* as now recognized does not occur there, it is impossible to say whether *T. albolabris* was responsible for any of these deaths. As would be expected, children are sometimes bitten by *T. albolabris* in Hong Kong, and such cases usually recover. It would appear, however, that in exceptional cases involving children death might result, since Herklots (1951) remarks that: " . . . not a single case had been recorded of an adult having been killed by a bamboo snake, though cases had occurred even in Hong Kong of children dying after being bitten ". As with bites by any species of venomous snake, various factors influence the effects produced within the possible range for the species, probably the most important in the majority of cases being the quantity of venom actually introduced into the victim's body. In general, the effects of bites by *T. albolabris* may normally be expected to vary from the mildest of consequences to extensive local swelling and considerable discomfort. No specialized line of treatment or antivenene is normally given in Hong Kong, except that at the Queen Mary Hospital antitetanus serum is administered and in some cases the patient is kept under observation, usually for not more than 24 hr.

ACKNOWLEDGMENTS

I am grateful to the several members of the medical staff, in particular to Dr. Yue Man-young, of the Medical and Health Department, Hong Kong for kindly providing information relating to bites by *T. albolabris*. Nevertheless, the responsibility for any shortcoming in presentation rests entirely with me.

REFERENCES

GRESSITT, J. L. 1941. Amphibians and reptiles of southeastern China. *Philippine J. Sci.* **75** (1), 1.

HERKLOTS, G. A. C. 1951. *The Hong Kong Countryside.* Hong Kong: The South China Morning Post.

LIN, CHAU-CHING. 1954. *Venomous Snakes in Taiwan.* Paper issued by Taiwan Serum Vaccine Laboratory, Shihlin, Taipei.

MAXWELL, J. P. 1912. Snakes and snakebite in the Fukien Province. *China Med. J.* **26** (4), 243.

POPE, C. H. 1935. *The Reptiles of China. Natural History of Central Asia,* **10**. New York: The American Museum of Natural History.

ROMER, J. D. 1961. Annotated Checklist with Keys to the Snakes of Hong Kong. *Memoirs of The Hong Kong Natural History Society* (5).

SMITH, M. A. 1943. *Serpentes. Reptilia and Amphibia,* **3**. *The Fauna of British India, Ceylon and Burma, including the Whole of the Indo-Chinese Sub-region.* London: Taylor & Francis.

EFFECT OF SEVERAL AGENTS ON THE LETHAL ACTION OF TWO COMMON VENOMS

FLAVIO MORALES, KASIAN BHANGANADA, and JOHN F. PERRY*

ALTHOUGH specific antiserum is highly effective in treatment of bites of most poisonous reptiles, it may not be readily available at the time envenomation occurs or individual hypersensitivity to horse serum may preclude its use. Other agents are utilized in the treatment of this condition but evaluation of their effectiveness has usually been based on clinical impressions. Since many factors other than treatment influence outcome in clinical cases of snake bite, it is usually desirable that the effects on lethality of those agents used in treatment be determined by more precise methods. In the investigations reported here, some of the hemodynamic changes produced by the venoms of two common snakes have been recorded and the effects of several types of treatment on the lethality and observed hemodynamic changes have been observed.

METHOD

Healthy adult mongrel dogs of either sex weighing from 7.4 to 12.5 kg were utilized. All animals were anesthetized with intravenous sodium pentobarbital (25 mg/kg). Arterial blood pressure was recorded by means of a plastic catheter in the femoral artery connected to a pressure transducer and Sanborn recorder. Portal vein and inferior vena cava pressures were recorded in like manner. Plasma volume was measured utilizing radioactive iodinated serum albumin before and 20 min following injection of venom. In a few animals it was again determined at 90 to 120 min. Venous hematocrit was measured at the same time that plasma volume was determined. Dried venom of *C. adamanteus* or *Naja naja* obtained from a commercial source was dissolved in 1 to 2 ml of normal saline and administered intravenously. In animals studied to observe hemodynamic and plasma volume changes, 0.75 mg *C. adamanteus* venom/kg or 2 mg *Naja naja*/kg were given.

*Department of Surgery, Medical School, University of Minnesota, Minneapolis 14, Minnesota.

In the second portion of the experiments wherein animals received treatment, several methods were employed. In each animal arterial pressure was monitored until the animal died, or in the case of survivors, until blood pressure had stabilized at normal levels. Animals were considered to be survivors only if they lived 10 or more days after envenomation.

Crotalus adamanteus envenomation

Untreated controls. *C. adamanteus* venom in dosage ranging from 0.75 to 8.0 mg/kg body weight was administered intravenously to 17 dogs and the animal observed until death. Duration of survival following venom injection was recorded.

Whole blood. Fresh whole blood was obtained from donor dogs and heparinized. Venom in doses of 2 mg/kg was given intravenously to each of three dogs. As soon as mean arterial pressure had fallen to 60 mm of mercury, whole blood was transfused rapidly into the femoral vein and an attempt made to maintain arterial blood pressure at normal levels.

Norepinephrine. Each of six animals received 2 mg *C. adamanteus* venom/kg intravenously. As soon as arterial blood pressure had fallen to 60 mm Hg, norepinephrine was given intravenously (8 mg norepinephrine in 500 ml saline). The sympathomimetic agent was administered by drip at a rate to maintain arterial blood pressure at normal levels.

Norepinephrine and whole blood. Each of four animals received 1.5 to 2.0 mg of venom/kg. When arterial pressure had fallen to 60 mm of Hg, norepinephrine (8 mg norepinephrine in 500 ml normal saline) was begun as a slow intravenous drip. When blood pressure had risen to 100 mm Hg or above under the influence of the agent, fresh heparinized whole blood previously obtained from donor dogs was given in volumes varying from 250 to 400 ml and the rate of norepinephrine administration gradually decreased if blood pressure remained stable. Conversely, the rate of norepinephrine administration was increased if arterial pressure began to fall.

Antivenin (pretreatment). Three dogs received commercial antivenin as pretreatment. One animal received three units and two dogs each received two units of the antiserum intravenously, 10 to 15 min prior to administration of 1.5 mg of venom/kg. No other treatment was given.

Antivenin after venom administration. Six animals received 2 mg venom/kg intravenously. One and one half to 30 min thereafter, antiserum was given intravenously and the animal observed. No other treatment was given. Two animals received three units, one four units and three animals five units of antiserum.

Norepinephrine and antivenin. Each of five animals received 1.5 to 2.0 mg venom/kg intravenously. As soon as blood pressure fell following venom injection, intravenous drip of norepinephrine (8 mg in 500 ml normal saline) was started. When blood pressure reached normal levels, antivenin was given intravenously. Two animals received three, one animal four and three animals five units of antivenin.

Hydrocortisone (pretreatment). Eleven animals received 15–30 mg hydrocortizone/kg intravenously. One half to one hour later 0.85 to 1.5 mg venom/kg was given. No other treatment was administered.

Hydrocortisone after venom administration. Each of seven animals received 0.75 to 1.0 mg of venom/kg and within 2–3 min 30–50 mg of hydrocortisone/kg intravenously. Repeat doses of hydrocortisone of 12.5 to 25 mg were given every 8 hr as long as the animal lived.

Naja naja envenomation

Untreated controls. Sixteen adult mongrel dogs received intravenous doses of *N. naja* venom ranging from 1 to 3 mg/kg. Each animal was artificially ventilated by mechanical respirators and endotracheal tube and all were observed until death.

Hydrocortisone (pretreatment). Five animals received hydrocortisone in doses varying from 15 to 30 mg/kg 30 to 60 min prior to injection of 2 mg venom/kg. Three of the animals received additional hydrocortisone following venom administration.

Hydrocortisone after venom administration. Eleven animals were given 2 to 2.5 mg venom/kg. and beginning 20 min to 1 hr thereafter received repeated doses of hydrocortisone intravenously; a total of 40 to 150 mg hydrocortisone/kg was given.

RESULTS

Hemodynamic changes following intravenous administration of a lethal dose of rattlesnake venom are shown in Fig. 1. There is a precipitous fall in peripheral arterial pressure immediately followed after a time by recovery to normal or nearly normal levels. This is not sustained however and the animal passes into a stage of progressive hypotension until death. An abrupt rise in portal pressure coincides with the initial fall in arterial pressure. Portal pressure then falls somewhat but rises secondarily. This second peak gradually disappears as arterial pressure falls. A small increase in inferior vena cava pressure occurs just prior to death.

Changes in hematocrit and plasma volume observed following intravenous administration of venom of *C. adamanteus* are shown in Tables 1 and 2. As expected there was a fall in plasma volume and a rise in hematocrit in most animals studied. It was not possible to correlate duration of survival with the extent of plasma loss or hematocrit increase however.

Characteristic changes in arterial and portal vein pressure observed in dogs following intravenous administration of 2 mg venom of *Naja naja*/kg

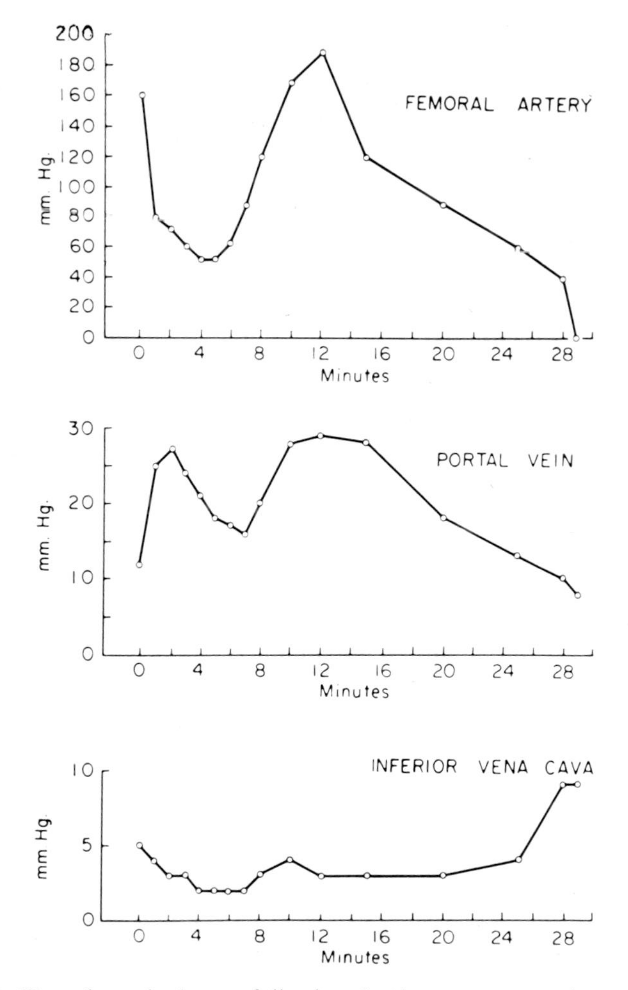

FIG. 1. Hemodynamic changes following *C. adamanteus* venom intravenously.

are shown in Fig. 2. A precipitous fall in arterial blood pressure follows venom administration. This usually rises again to near normal levels where it is maintained until a preterminal phase, where a rapid fall occurs terminating

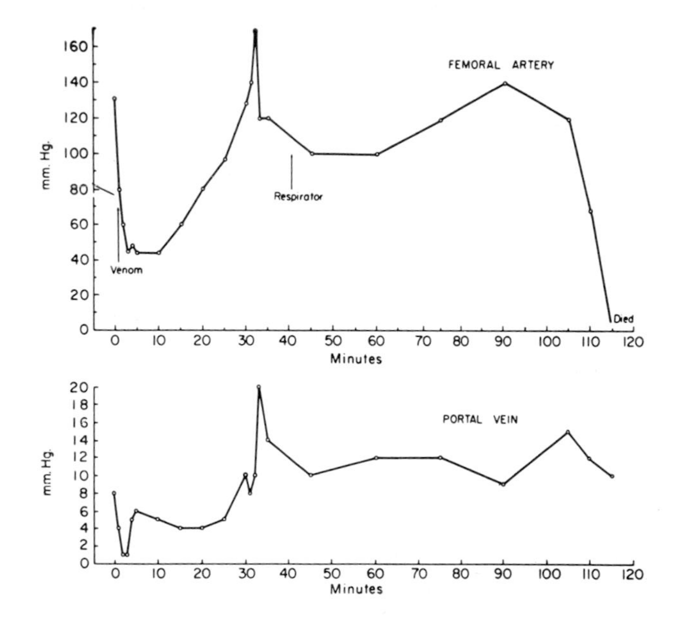

FIG. 2. Hemodynamic changes following *N. Naja* venom intravenously

TABLE 1. CHANGES IN HEMATOCRIT FOLLOWING INTRAVENOUS INJECTION OF *C. adamanteus* VENOM

Animal number	Control per cent	Time	Inter-mediate hemato-crit	Per cent change	Time	Final hemato-crit	Per cent change	Time of death, min
1	51	18	46	− 9.8	110	37	−27.5	142
2	49	19	87	+73.5				29
3	49	18	63	+28.6				22
4	47	20	64	+36.1	110	65	+27.8	120
5	32	22	40	+25				66
6	52	25	88	+69	60	80	+53.8	6 hr
7	42	20	59	+40.5	60	69	+64.2	125
8	41	20	46	+12.2				115
9	42	20	53	+26.3				6 hr

in death of the animal. In the experiment shown in Fig. 2 artificial respiration was not provided until respiratory failure occurred and arterial pressure had begun to fall. Restoration of respiratory function resulted in some improvement in arterial blood pressure but the rapid terminal fall is still observed. Portal venous pressure falls initially and then rises to above normal levels at about the time arterial blood pressure recovers. It is thereafter maintained at levels slightly above normal until a preterminal phase when it may again rise. Inferior vena cava pressure showed no change except a slight rise terminally.

TABLE 2. CHANGES IN PLASMA VOLUME FOLLOWING INTRAVENOUS INJECTION OF *C. adamanteus* VENOM

Animal number	Control, ml	Time, min	Intermediate volume, ml	Per cent change	Time, min	Final volume, ml	Per cent change	Time of death, min
1	520	18	510	− 1.9	110	495	− 4.8	142
2	640	19	444	−30.6				29
3	460	20	403	−14.0				22
4	682	20	452	−28.8				120
5	1145	22	1020	−10.9				66
6	457	25	469	+ 2.6	60	400	−12.5	6 hr
7	700	20	740	+ 5.6	60	435	−37.8	125
8	760	20	640	−15.8				115
9	625	20	560	−10.4				6 hr

Changes of hematocrit and plasma volume following intravenous administration of venom of *N. naja* are shown in Tables 3 and 4. These changes are of about the same magnitude as those observed with *C. adamanteus* venom. Again there is no correlation between duration of survival and change in hematocrit or plasma volume.

TABLE 3. CHANGES IN VENOUS HEMATOCRIT FOLLOWING INTRAVENOUS INJECTION OF *Naja naja* VENOM

Animal number	Control per cent	Time	Intermediate hematocrit	Per cent change	Time	Final hematocrit	Per cent change	Time of death, min
1	47	20	63	+34				6 hr
2	40	20	48	+20				47
3	49	20	67	+36.8	120	61	+24.5	12 hr
4	43	20	58	+34.8				99
5	39	25	45	+15.4	90	58	+48.8	6 hr
6	44	20	60	+36.3				160
7	39	25	60	+35				51
8	32	20	54	+68.8				71

Results of treatment of experimental *C. adamanteus* envenomation are as follows:

Untreated controls. Following intravenous administration of *C. adamanteus* venom, the precipitous fall in arterial pressure occurred in all animals, followed after a few minutes by a rise to nearly normal levels in some animals. In others arterial pressure rose somewhat less, but in all there was a distinct increase in arterial blood pressure above the lowest level observed immediately following venom injection. Thereafter arterial pressure again fell and all animals passed into a state of progressive hypotension to death.

TABLE 4. CHANGES IN PLASMA VOLUME FOLLOWING INTRAVENOUS INJECTION OF *Naja naja* VENOM

Animal number	Control ml	Time, min	Intermediate volume, ml	Per cent change	Time, min	Final volume, ml	Per cent change	Time of death, min
1	590	20	560	− 5.1				6 hr
2	610	20	535	−12.3				47
3	305	20	263	−13.7	120	270	−11.4	12 hr
4	311	20	316	+ 1.6				99
5	695	25	638	− 8.2	90	625	−10.0	6 hr
6	985	20	517	−47.8				160
7	475	25	211	−55.5				51
8	815	20	630	−22.7				71

TABLE 5. LENGTH OF SURVIVAL OF UNTREATED DOGS FOLLOWING INTRAVENOUS INJECTION OF *Crotalus adamanteus* VENOM

Number of animals	Dosage of venom injected, mg/kg	Survival time, min
11	0.75–0.85	Range 10–125 Mean 74
3	1–2	Range 10–20 Mean 15
3	4–8	Range 10–10 Mean 10

Eleven animals receiving 0.75 to 0.85 mg of venom/kg survived an average of 74 min (10–125 min). When doses of venom 1 mg/kg or larger were given, the animal died very quickly usually surviving only a few minutes (maximum 20 min). It appeared, therefore, that a dose of venom 0.75 mg/kg or greater would cause a uniform, rapidly lethal outcome against which the effect of experimental treatment could be judged. The above data are summarized in Table 5.

Table 6 shows the results of treatment of envenomated dogs by several methods.

Whole blood. Following the administration of 2 mg venom/kg, rapid transfusion of whole blood in amount of 250 to 400 ml to each of three animals led to no demonstrable beneficial effect. No animal lived longer than 15 min. Attempts to maintain circulating blood volume and arterial blood pressure by this means was of no avail and survival time was no different from that of untreated animals.

TABLE 6. EFFECTS OF SEVERAL AGENTS USED IN TREATMENT OF LETHAL *C. adamanteus* ENVENOMATION IN DOGS

			Survival	
Number dogs	Dose of venom, mg/kg	Treatment	Number animals	Duration
3	2	†Whole blood	3	<15 min
6	2	†Norepinephrine	6	Range 27–75 min (mean 50 min)
4	1.5–2.0	†Norepinephrine Blood	4	Range 28–40 min (mean 31 min)
3	1.5	*Antivenin	1 2	95 min survived
6	2.0	†Antivenin	2 4	12 + 16 min survived
5	1.5–2.0	†Antivenin Norepinephrine	2 3	Survived 106–271 min (mean 162 min)
11	0.85–1.5	*Hydrocortisone 15–30 mg/kg	2 9	6 hr 7–182 min (mean 54 min)
7	0.75–1.0	†Hydrocortisone 30–100 mg/kg	1 6	1.5 hr 12–24 hr (mean 18 hr)

*Before venom. †After venom.

Norepinephrine. Although survival time was slightly prolonged when animals were injected with 2 mg venom/kg and subsequently treated with norepinephrine by intravenous drip, all died. Duration of life after venom injection ranged from 26 to 75 min with average value of 50 min. Infusion of the drug caused a rapid rise in arterial blood pressure almost immediately to normal levels. This was more prompt and higher than the secondary rise in arterial pressure seen in untreated animals. However, pressure again fell and was progressively refractory to the agent, and gradually increasing amounts of it were necessary to maintain the arterial blood pressure at even lower levels.

Norepinephrine and whole blood. Norepinephrine infusion was followed by a rise in arterial blood pressure to normal levels as above. However, despite its continued administration and the use of whole blood in amounts varying from 250 to 400 ml, blood pressure fell progressively and survival was only slightly prolonged. No animal so treated lived longer than 40 min from the time of venom injection.

Antivenin (pretreatment). Two of the three animals receiving antivenin prior to injection of 1.5 mg venom/kg survived and the third lived for 95 min. Two animals received respectively 15.7 mg of venom and 3 units of antivenin and 16.4 mg of venom and 2 units of antivenin and survived. The animal which died had received 12.2 mg of venom and 2 units of antivenin.

Antivenin after venom administration. Six animals were given antivenin following intravenous injection of 2 mg venom/kg and four survived. Two received respectively 23.6 and 24.6 mg of venom and within $2\frac{1}{2}$ min each was given 3 units of antivenin; both survived. Another animal given 14.4 mg of venom received four units of antivenin $3\frac{1}{2}$ min later and a fifth unit at 40 min and survived. Another animal survived after having received 20 mg venom and 30 min later five units of antivenin. Two died despite the fact that four units of antivenin were given to one animal (22.8 mg venom) within $1\frac{1}{2}$ min and five units to another (14.4 mg venom) within 7 min of the time of venom injection.

Norepinephrine and antivenin. Following venom injection intravenous drip of norepinephrine quickly restored blood pressure to normal and antivenin was administered intravenously. Two animals which received three and two units of antivenin $5\frac{1}{2}$ and $4\frac{1}{2}$ min after 14.4 and 15 mg of venom respectively survived. The other three animals died, after living from 106 to 271 min. These three received four, four and three units of antivenin 16, 16 and 10 min after 15.2, 12.6 and 11.1 mg of venom respectively.

Hydrocortisone (pretreatment). Three animals received 30 mg hydrocortisone/kg, intravenously and 35 to 50 min later 0.85 mg venom/kg. Two lived for 6 hr and the third died in 22 min. Eight animals received 15 to 30 mg hydrocortisone/kg 30 to 45 min before intravenous administration of 1.5 mg venom/kg. Survival time ranged from 7 to 182 min with four animals living 1 hr and one 3 hr. The remaining four lived 7, 17, 25, and 32 min.

Hydrocortisone after venom administration. Animals received a total dose of 30 to 100 mg of hydrocortisone/kg. There were no long-term survivors but life was prolonged in the majority. One animal lived only $1\frac{1}{2}$ hr but the remaining six lived 12 to 24 hr. The secondary fall in arterial pressure usually observed was greatly delayed by use of hydrocortisone.

Survival times of control animals and those treated with hydrocortisone after *N. naja* envenomation are summarized in Tables 7, 8, and 9.

TABLE 7. LENGTH OF SURVIVAL OF UNTREATED DOGS FOLLOWING INTRAVENOUS INJECTION OF *Naja naja* VENOM

Number of animals	Dosage of venom, mg/kg	Survival time
1	1	8 hr
5	1.25 to 1.62	Range 47 min to 16 hr Mean 6 hr 37 min
6	2 to 2.5	Range 42–255 min Mean 87 min
4	3	Range 42–180 min Mean 101 min

TABLE 8. TREATMENT OF LETHAL *N. naja* ENVENOMATION IN DOGS WITH HYDROCORTISONE

Dog number	Weight (kg)	Dose venom (mg/kg)	Hydrocortisone (mg/kg)	Time given	Period survival
1	9.1	2	30	45 min before venom	4 hr
2	8.2	2	30 15	30 min before venom 4 hr after venom	Survival
3	7.6	2	15 30	60 min before venom 30 min after venom	Survival
4	8.2	3	30	45 min before venom	22 min
5	7.2	2	30 20 15	30 min before venom 3 hr after venom 7 hr after venom	Survival

Untreated controls. Although all animals died, survival ranged from 47 min to 16 hr after *N. naja* venom was given intravenously in doses from 1 to 1.62 mg/kg. However no animal receiving 2 mg venom/kg or more lived longer than 255 min and the majority died within 3 hr. This dose (2 mg/kg), or greater, was chosen for the experiments with hydrocortisone as it appeared to be rapidly lethal and any improvement in survival due to treatment would be more easily determined.

Hydrocortisone (*pretreatment*). Only those three animals were survivors which received additional hydrocortisone after venom administration in addition to that given before. Pretreatment alone did not result in survival, although the doses of hydrocortisone given were very large (30 mg/kg).

TABLE 9. TREATMENT OF LETHAL *N. naja* ENVENOMATION IN DOGS WITH HYDROCORTISONE

Dog number	Weight (kg)	Dose venom (mg/kg)	Hydrocortisone (mg/kg)	Time given	Period survival
6	11.4	3	30	20 min after venom	5 hr 10 min
			15	4 hr after initial dose	
			15	20 min after 2nd dose	
7	11.8	2	30	30 min after venom	Survived
			15	4 hr after venom	
			15	8 hr after venom	
8	9.1	2	30	1 hr after venom	Survived
			15	5 hr after venom	
9	7.2	3	40	45 min after venom	5 hr 15 min
			20	4 hr after initial dose	
10	6.3	3	40	45 min after venom	26 hr
			40	4 hr after initial dose	
			40	4 hr after 2nd dose	
11	9.1	3	40	20 min after venom	20 hr
			40	4 hr after initial dose	
			40	4 hr after 2nd dose	
			30	12 hr after venom	
12	10.5	2.5	40	30 min after venom	5 hr 30 min
			30	4 hr after initial dose	
13	8.1	2.5	40	30 min after venom	Survived
			30	4 hr after initial dose	
			20	4 hr after 2nd dose	
			20	4 hr after 3rd dose	
14	9.1	2.5	40	25 min after venom	3 hr 30 min
15	9.1	2.5	40	40 min after venom	12 hr
			30	4 hr after initial dose	
			30	4 hr after 2nd dose	
16	10.5	2	40	30 min after venom	3 hr

Hydrocortisone after venom administration. Three of the eleven dogs treated survived and life of at least three others was prolonged (12, 20, and 26 hr). Two of the survivors had received 2 mg venom/kg and the third 2.5 mg/kg. None of the eleven animals lived less than 3 hr. Hydrocortisone was therefore of real value and prevented an otherwise lethal outcome in some animals.

DISCUSSION

Hemodynamic changes observed following intravenous administration of venom of *Crotalus* have been reported by Essex and Markowitz (1930) and similar effects of venom of the cobra have been studied by a number of observers including: Chapra and Iswarial (1931), Cushny and Yagi (1918), Feldberg and Kellaway (1937), and Gautrelet and Cortiggiani (1934). As shown by Essex and Markowitz changes in hematocrit and plasma volume induced by *Crotalus* venom are also well documented, but these changes in envenomation by *Naja naja* are less well known. Since Spink (1958) observed that the hemodynamic changes are somewhat similar to those which have occurred following administration of gram negative bacterial endotoxins to animals, it was of interest to determine if some of the agents such as norepinephrine and hydrocortisone which have been used clinically and experimentally for treatment of bacterial shock as reported by Lillehei and MacLean (1959) would be effective in envenomation.

Objections may be raised to use of the intravenous route for venom administration. However, since duration of survival is so variable following subcutaneous administration of venom to animals, the intravenous route provides a sharper end point for evaluation of treatment agents. Also there is good evidence that the lethality of venoms is in large measure due to systemic effects following absorption even when administered subcutaneously.

Although loss of red cells and plasma through vessel walls occurs following intravenous or topical administration of *Crotalus* venom and significant decreases in circulatory volume occur rapidly in some animals, loss of circulating blood volume alone does not account for the arterial hypotension leading to death, as rapid replacement by whole blood did not prolong life. As supportive treatment of envenomation transfusion of blood is undoubtedly of benefit, but blood replacement alone does not serve to counteract the lethal mechanism of venom.

Loss of peripheral arteriolar resistance appears to be important in the genesis of hypotension produced by venom. Norepinephrine alone or in conjunction with blood produced a prompt rise in arterial blood pressure but life of the treated animal was prolonged very little. As is often seen clinically, when this agent is used in treatment of shock from gram negative bacteremia, progressively larger doses were needed to maintain blood pressure, but life of the treated animal was prolonged very little as is often seen at even lower levels. Norepinephrine thus counteracts the hypotension due to *Crotalus* venom in only a transient and nonspecific manner.

Although the quantities of antivenin given both before and after venom daministration should have been sufficient to counteract the effects of the doses of venom given, uniform survival of animals was not obtained. Antivenin in this dosage administered intravenously will result in uniform survival of animals given as much as 8 mg *Crotalus* venom/kg subcutaneously.

Treatment by norepinephrine, then antivenin, did not result in survival of any animal if antiserum administration was delayed, although blood pressure was maintained by norepinephrine in the interim. This should have improved transport of antivenin to various parts of the circulation. No animal survived if antivenin was delayed over five minutes although blood pressure was maintained in the interim by norepinephrine. These experiments with antivenin demonstrate the rapidity with which venom is fixed at its site of action and that it is apparently not available for neutralization by antivenin thereafter.

Clinical improvement due to utlization of steroids in management of bites by *Crotalus* and other species has been reported by Benyajati *et al.* (1960), Gupta *et al.* (1960), Hoback and Green (1953), Wood *et al.* (1955), and Wig and Vaish (1960). Also, hydrocortisone in very large doses has been advocated by Lillehei and MacLean (1959) for treatment of shock due to bacterial endotoxins. This latter observation prompted our use of large doses of the drug. In addition, preliminary experiments with hydrocortisone in doses comparable to those utilized clinically showed no prolongation of survival of envenomated animals. Most dramatic effects on the arterial hypotension accompanying intravenous *Crotalus* venom administration were seen with hydrocortisone. Pretreatment resulted in prolongation of life up to 6 hr but no animal survived. When *Crotalus* venom was given and hydrocortisone administered thereafter definite improvement was noted. Arterial pressure rose and secondary decline in pressure was prevented for long periods. Then, although long term survival of animals injected with *Crotalus* venom and treated with hydrocortisone was not obtained, nevertheless the drug definitely prolonged life and appeared of benefit in maintenance of arterial blood pressure.

We have not had the opportunity to try several of the agents utilized in *Crotalus* envenomation for experimental treatment of *N. naja* envenomation. However, experiments thus far with hydrocortisone are very encouraging. Life of many animals was prolonged and survival of several animals obtained when large doses of hydrocortisone were used as exclusive treatment of *N. naja* envenomation. The value of this steroid in treatment of envenomation is established, but it must be emphasized that effective doses are much greater than those which have been usually employed clinically.

SUMMARY

Changes in plasma volume, hematocrit, arterial, portal, and inferior vena cava pressures, following intravenous injection of *C. adamanteus* and *N. naja* venom in dogs were described.

Treatment of *C. adamanteus* envenomation in dogs was carried out utilizing blood, norepinephrine, antivenin and hydrocortisone. Only the latter two appeared to be of real benefit. To be effective, antivenin must bind venom before the latter is fixed at its site of action. Hydrocortisone did not result in long term survival but appeared to counteract the arterial hypotension resulting from venom and life was prolonged.

Treatment of lethal *N. naja* for envenomation in dogs with large doses of hydrocortisone resulted in long term survival of some animals and life was prolonged in others.

ACKNOWLEDGEMENTS

This research was supported by U.S.P.H.S. Grant RG-74060-C-1.

Antivenin utilized in this study was supplied through the courtesy of Wyeth Laboratories.

REFERENCES

BENYAJATI, C., KEOPLUNG, M. and SRIBHIBHADH, R. 1960. Viper bite in Thailand: with notes on treatment. *J. Trop. Med. and Hyg.* **63**, 257.

CHAPRA, R. N. and ISWARIAL, V. 1931. An experimental investigation into the action of the venom of the Indian cobra *Naja naja tripudians*. *Indian J. Med. Res.* **18**, 1113.

CUSHNY, A. R. and YAGI, S. 1918. On the action of cobra venom. Part I. The cause of death. Part II. Action on individual organs. *Phil. Trans. Roy. Soc. Lond.* **208** (B), 1.

ESSEX, H. E. and KARKOWITZ, J. 1930. The physiologic action of rattlesnake venom (*Crotalin*). *Am. J. Physiol.* **93**, 317.

FELDBERG, W. and KELLAWAY, C. H. 1937. Circulatory effects of the venom of the Indian cobra (*Naja naji*) in dogs. *Austral. J. Exp. Biol. Med. Sci.* **15**, 441.

GAUTRELET, J. and HALPERN, N. 1934. Etude experimentale de l'action du venin de cobra sur la circulation. *C.R. Soc. Biol. Paris* **113**, 942.

GAUTRELET, J., HALPERN, N. and CORTIGGIANI, E. 1934. Ou mechanisme d'action des doses physiologiques, de venin de cobra sur la circulation, la respiration et l'excitabilité neuro-musculaire. *Arch. Inst. Physiol.* **38**, 193.

GUPTA, P. S., BHARGAVA, S. P. and SHARMA, M. L. 1960. A review of 200 cases of snake bite with special reference to the corticosteroid therapy. *J. Indian Med. Assn.* **35**, 387.

HOBACK, W. W. and GREEN, T. W. 1953. Treatment of snake venom poisoning with cortisone and corticotropin. *J.A.M.A.* **152**, 236.

LILLEHEI, R. C. and MACLEAN, L. D. 1959. Physiological approach to successful treatment of endotoxin shock in the experimental animal. *Arch. Surg.* **78**, 464.

SPINK, W. W. 1958. From endotoxin to snake venom. *J. Biol. and Med.* **30**, 355.

WOOD, J. T., HOBACK, W. W. and GREEN, T. W. 1955. Treatment of snake venom poisoning with ACTH and cortisone. *Virginia Med. Monthly* **82**, 130.

WIG, K. L. and VAISH, S. K. 1960. Snake bite and its treatment. *Indian Med. Assn. J.* **35**, 307.

THE PATHOPHYSIOLOGIC EFFECTS OF RATTLESNAKE VENOM (*CROTALUS ATROX*)

W. G. MALETTE*, J. B. FITZGERALD†, A. T. K .COCKETT‡, T. G. GLASS, JR.§, W. G. GLENN‡, and P. V. DONNELLY‡

STUDIES on the pathophysiologic effects of rattlesnake envenomation have been inconclusive to date. Recent scattered reports have indicated that physiologic changes consisting of red blood cell and plasma volume deficits occur after snake bite in mammals.

This study was formulated to determine these pathophysiologic changes in three groups of envenomed mongrel dogs. Animals were divided into 3 groups: (1) Animals envenomed but with no treatment; (2) Animals envenomed but supported by replacement of whole blood, electrolytes and plasma; and (3) A group of envenomed animals treated by intra-arterial antivenin alone. A second objective was to determine the efficacy of stock antivenin in the neutralization of venom.

METHODS AND PROCEDURES

After a 3-week quarantine period, 15 adult mongrel dogs weighing from 8 to 18 kg were divided into three groups. Splenectomy was performed 3 to 4 weeks prior to envenomation to ensure accurate blood volume determinations. Pentobarbital anesthesia, 120 mg/kg, was utilized during experimentation. Serum from each dog was tested against venom prior to envenomation. It was of interest to note that most of these serum samples reacted with venom. Thus, it was not possible to state with certainty that the majority of these dogs did not have an antivenom (antibody) level.

Lyophilized *Crotalus atrox* venom was obtained from the Ross Allen Reptile Institute (Silver Springs, Fla.), and was weighed accurately before

*Department of Surgery, U.S.A.F. Hospital Lackland, U.S.A.F. Aerospace Medical Division (A.F.S.C.), Lackland Air Force Base, Texas.

†Baylor University School of Medicine, Houston, Texas.

‡School of Aerospace Medicine, U.S.A.F. Aerospace Medical Division (A.F.S.C.), Brooks Air Force Base, Texas.

§Instructor in Surgery, University of Texas Postgraduate School of Medicine, San Antonio Division, San Antonio, Texas.

reconstitution. This pooled venom served as a source for each animal. Ya *et al.* (1960) have reported that the dosage for an LD_{100} in their dogs was 8 mg/kg. Because of an inability to determine the amount of previous immunization in the animals chosen, a super-lethal dosage of 12 mg/kg was preselected.

The antivenin used in the third group was Wyeth stock polyvalent antiserum.

Physiological data consisting of blood pressure, pulse, and the electrocardiogram were recorded continuously. Mean blood pressure was obtained by an indwelling polyethylene catheter in the femoral artery. An indwelling urinary catheter was placed per urethra in each animal, enabling continuous measurements of urine output. Plasma volume (determined by a modification of a method described by Franks and Zizza (1958), using radio-iodinated serum albumin (I^{131}) (Risa^{R})), plasma sodium and plasma potassium were determined prior to injection of venom. Plasma volumes and red cell volume measurements were also obtained 2 hr and, in most instances, either at 6 or 12 hr following envenomation. These blood samples were obtained by use of a venous catheter in the central venous system. Plasma hemoglobin determinations were made by a modification of the benzidrine method described by Crosby and his co-workers (1956 and 1954). Plasma sodium and plasma potassium concentrations were determined using the Coleman flame photometer. Urine was obtained and measured at hourly intervals by use of the indwelling Foley catheter. In all of the animals receiving venom injections, the super-lethal dose was injected subcutaneously 3 cm below the right mid-thigh on the medical aspect. Time of injection was zero time.

RESULTS

One animal was used as a control. No venom was injected and no treatment was given. This animal survived and the data (blood volume determinations, blood pressure recordings, etc.) are tabulated (see Table 3).

One group of 6 animals was envenomed as described above. No treatment was given. The second group of 4 animals was envenomed as described and blood pressure, urinary output, plasma volume and red cell volume were maintained near pre-injection levels by employing fluids, whole blood, dextran and plasma for as long as 36 hr. A third group of 4 animals was envenomed as above, and no treatment or supportive therapy was instituted other than the intra-arterial injection of antivenin at a site proximal to the injection of venom. The data are recorded in Tables 1, 2, and 2.

In the first group of 6 animals (envenomed but not treated), the striking finding was a fall in plasma volume of 36 per cent below the control volume within 6 hours post-venomization (Fig. 1). A fall of 24 per cent in red cell volume was also present (Fig. 1). Urinary output was significantly reduced 2 hr after venomization and virtually ceased after 4 to 6 hr. Blood pressure from a mean systolic pressure prior to venomization of 122 to 145 mm Hg to approximately 90 to 110 mm Hg 2 to 4 hr post-venomization.

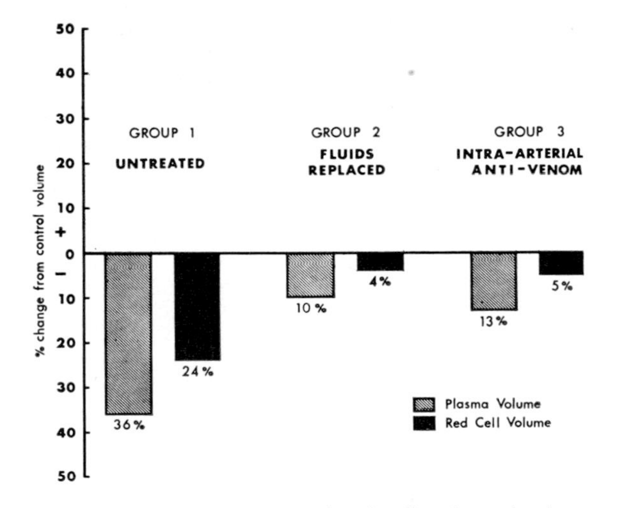

FIG. 1. Changes in plasma volume and red cell volume in three groups of dogs given injections of *Crotalus atrox* venom.

About 30 min to 1 hr prior to expiration (Fig. 2), the blood pressure was markedly reduced to levels of 50 to 70 mm Hg.

No significant changes were noted in plasma hemoblogin and plasma sodium. Plasma potassium levels were not significant. All of these 6 animals succumbed within 12 hr after the injection of the venom.

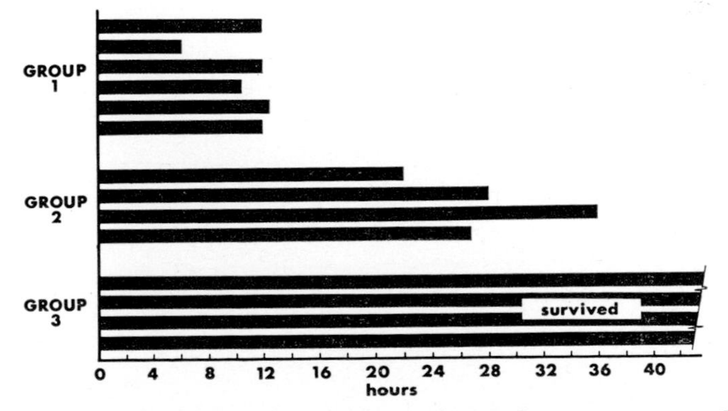

FIG. 2. Survival of dogs given injections of *Crotalus atrox* venom. Each bar represents one animal. Dogs in Group 1 were untreated. Dogs in Group 2 were treated by fluid replacement. Dogs in Group 3 were treated by intra-arterial injections of antivenin.

TABLE 1 (Group 1). PATHOPHYSIOLOGIC EFFECTS OF *Crotalus atrox* SERUM INJECTION ON DOGS RECEIVING NO TREATMENT

Dog no.	Time (hr)	Plasma	Per kg volume	Corr HCT	Blood	Per kg volume	B/P	Urine vol. (ml/hr)	Venous venom	Remarks
295	0	895	69	36	1323	102	130	15.5	None	Control
Wt 13 kg	1	—	—	—	—	—	—	8.0	found	No Rx
156 mg	2	523	40	42	902	69	120	2.0		
venom	3	—	—	—	—	—	—	0		
	4	125	—	—	—	—	—	0		
	5	—	—	—	—	—	—	0		
	6	449	35	33	670	52	110	1		Died at 12 hr
299	0	702	56	32	1114	88	127	12.5	None	Control
12.6 kg	1	—	—	—	—	—	—	6.0	found	No Rx
150 mg	2	567	45	33	915	73	119	5.0		
venom	3	—	—	—	—	—	129	3.5		
	4	—	—	—	—	—	—	0		
	5	—	—	—	—	—	107	0		
	6	847	36	38	798	63	101	0		Died at 12 hr
287	0	459	48	41	778	82	125	13.5	None	Control
9.5 kg	1	—	—	—	—	—	—	6.5	found	No Rx
114 mg	2	360	38	46	666	70	110	5.0		
venom	3	—	—	—	—	—	—	2.5		
	4	—	—	—	—	—	80	1.0		
	5	—	—	—	—	—	75	1.0		
	6	277	29	45	504	53	40	0		Died at 6 hr

TABLE 1. (*continued*).

294 8.18 kg 96 mg venom	0	415	51	30	593	72	131	10.5	None found	Control No Rx
	1	—	—	—	—	—	—	8.0		
	2	375	46	31	544	66	127	1.0		
	3	—	—	—	—	—	129	0		
	4	—	—	—	—	—	98	0		
	5	—	—	—	—	—	110	0		
	6	321	39	32	472	58	87	0		Died at 12 hr
283 18 kg 216 mg venom	0	769	43	38	1240	69	121	14.5	None found	Control No Rx
	1	—	—	—	—	—	—	11.5		
	2	636	35	41	1077	59	114	6.0		
	3	—	—	—	—	—	—	4.0		
	4	—	—	—	—	—	—	0		
	5	—	—	—	—	—	—	0		
	6	—	—	—	—	—	98	0		Died at 11 hr
325 12 kg	0	646	54	34	978	82	138	—	None found	Control No Rx
	1	—	—	—	—	—	—	—		
	2	649	54	33	968	81	138	—		
	5	125	—	—	—	—	—	—		
	12	456	38	36	713	59	110	—		Died at 12 hr

TABLE 2 (Group 2). PATHOPHYSIOLOGIC EFFECTS OF *Crotalus atrox* SERUM INJECTED ON DOGS SUPPORTED BY REPLACEMENT OF WHOLE BLOOD, ELECTROLYTES AND PLASMA

Dog no.	Time (hr)	Plasma	Per kg volume	Corr HCT	Blood	Per kg volume	B/P	Urine vol (ml/hr)	Venous volume	Remarks
293	0	432	43	33	645	65	125	20.5	None	Blood 200 ml × 2 hr
BV 10 kg	1	—	—	—	—	—	128	44.5	found	200 ml × 4 hr
Support	2	394	39	43	691	69	128	31		300 ml 5% D/W
dog.	3	—	—	—	—	—	—	18		
120 mg	4	—	—	—	—	—	132	16		
venom	5	—	—	—	—	—	131	13		
	6	362	36	47	683	68	135	25		Died at 28 hr
285	0	750	54	33	1119	80	128	18	None	Blood 10 ml kg
BV Support	1	—	—	—	—	—	132	20	found	× 2 hr
14 kg	2	782	56	37	1241	89	138	30		50 ml × 6 hr
168 mg	3	—	—	—	—	—	—	35		5 ml kg Lact & Pen
venom	4	—	—	—	—	—	133	13.5		× 6 hr
	5	—	—	—	—	—	135	10		
	6	563	40	45	1024	73	142	11		
	10	—	—	—	—	—	—	40		
	16	—	—	—	—	—	—	35		Died at 22 hr
312	0	620	52	29	873	73	160	10	None	Blood 10 ml kg × 2.5
BV Support	1	—	—	—	—	—	—	14	found	× 4 hr
12 kg	2	667	56	31	967	81	158	25		5 ml Dextrose × 6 hr
144 mg	3	—	—	—	—	—	145	8		5 ml kg Lact × 6 hr
venom	4	—	—	—	—	—	152	13		5 ml 5% D/W × 12 hr
	5	—	—	—	—	—	149	—		
	18	687	57	29	968	81	160	25		Died at 36 hr
317	0	595	43	30	821	59	152	—	None	Blood 10 ml kg × 2.5
BV Support	1	—	—	—	—	—	151	—	found	× 4 hr
14 kg	2	977	70	34	1480	106	148	—		5 ml kg Dextrose
168 mg	4	—	—	—	—	—	139	—		× 6.5 ml Lact kg
venom	5	—	—	—	—	—	147	—		× 6.5 ml 5% D/W
	18	918	66	32	1350	96	149	—		× 12 hr Died at 27 hr

TABLE 5 (Group 3 and Technical Control). PATHOPHYSIOLOGIC EFFECTS OF *Crotalus atrox* ON DOGS TREATED BY INTRA-ARTERIAL ANTIVENIN ALONE

Dog no.	Time (hr)	Plasma	Per kg volume	Corr GCT	Blood	Per kg volume	B/P	Urine vol. (ml/hr)	Venous venom	Remarks
316	0	483	41	43	847	72	159	8.5	Not	150 ml Antivenin
Wt 11.8 kg	1	—	—	—	—	—	157	10	done	Arterial Inj.
141.6 mg	2	503	43	39	831	70	160	5		
venom	3	—	—	—	—	—	—	9		
	4	—	—	—	—	—	—	14		
	6	448	38	43	786	67	153	—		Survived
321	0	558	41	39	848	65	144	10	Urticaria	150 ml Antivenin
Wt 13.6 kg	1	—	—	—	—	—	143	7		Arterial Inj.
163.2 mg	2	585	43	42	1008	74	140	12.5		
venom	3	—	—	—	—	—	135	—		
	4	—	—	—	—	—	—	9		
	5	—	—	—	—	—	139	8		
	6	427	31	42	736	54	—	7.0		Survived
344	0	526	47	38	848	76	129	9.5	Not	80 ml Antivenin
Wt 11.1 kg	1	—	—	—	—	—	—	11	done	Arterial Inj.
133.2 mg	2	—	—	—	—	—	129	8		
venom	3	—	—	—	—	—	120	—		
	4	—	—	—	—	—	126	13		
	5	—	—	—	—	—	127	11.5		
	6	541	49	38	873	78	123	12		Survived
304	0	798	62.8	39	1308	103	—	—	Not	70 ml Antivenin
Wt 12.7 kg	1	—	—	—	—	—	—	—	done	Arterial Inj.
152.4 mg	2	587	46.2	45	1067	84	—	—		
venom	3	—	—	—	—	—	—	—		
	4	—	—	—	—	—	—	—		
	5	—	—	—	—	—	—	—		
	6	—	—	—	—	—	—	—		Survived
Tech. Control										
286	0	673	41	37	1068	64	—	11.0	None	
No venom	1	—	—	—	—	—	—	10	found	
	2	701	42	39	1149	69	—	12		
	3	—	—	—	—	—	—	14		
	4	—	—	—	—	—	—	15.5		
	5	—	—	—	—	—	—	18		
	6	596	36	39	997	40	—	16		Survived

The second group of 4 animals (envenomed and given supportive therapy) survived for 22 to 36 hr (see Table 2). But, after supportive therapy ceased, all of these animals succumbed.

The third group of four animals were envenomed as described above and 70 to 150 ml of stock, reconstituted polyvalent antivenin was injected intra-arterially through a small needle in the femoral artery at a site proximal to envenomation. This injection began 30 min after the snake venom was injected and was given over a 30 to 60 min interval by slow infusion, utilizing a one-way valve constructed by Fitzgerald (1961). Plasma volumes, red cell volumes, and urinary output remained near the pre-injection level, and all of these animals survived. These animals appeared to be in good health during the following 24 to 48 hr.

In the course of this study controlled post-envenomation venous blood samples were obtained and, by sensitive immunochemical methods, no central circulating venom could be detected.

DISCUSSION

The animals used in this study were obtained locally and were inhabitants of an area infested with rattlesnakes. *The venom used in this study was obtained from rattlesnakes captured in this same area.* However, a super-lethal dose of venom was used and was, apparently, satisfactory since an "all or none" result was obtained. We would not expect any dog to survive this dose of venom, whether some degree of immunity might or might not be present.

Recently the Wyeth antivenin (pooled) has been improved and standardized to some extent. This standardization is carried out by *in vitro* neutralization technics. This presents a difficulty which is not resolved by this study, since as little as 70 ml of pooled antivenin apparently neutralized 133 mg of venom *in vivo*. The literature indicates that 1 ml of antivenin will neutralize 1 mg of venom. Further studies are indicated to resolve this problem.

The fluid from the apparently intact skin surrounding the site of venom injection was collected and injected into mice without causing death. The presence of marked edema with hemorrhage in the tissues surrounding the site of venom injection was evident.

In those animals receiving the venom and no treatment (Group 1), the blood volume fell resulting in blood pressure drop several hours later. The fall in urinary output was evident within several hours post-venomization and appeared to be an accurate index of the physiological changes taking place. Death within 12 hr was evident after envenomation. The physiological changes resemble the lesions in burns, and prompted the idea that supportive therapy alone might be the answer to the snake bite problem. Institution of supportive therapy was of some benefit to the animal; however, as supportive therapy ceased, death of the animal ensued. The question still remains as to whether or not supportive therapy maintained for longer periods might not have caused chronic survival.

The amount of antivenin, the time of injection and the period of injection were chosen arbitrarily, leaving unanswered the following questions: (1) When is the optimal time of instituting the intra-arterial antivenin injection? (2) Over how long a period of time should the injection extend? (3) How much antivenin is required per milligram of venom?

Further studies will be carried out to answer these questions.

CONCLUSIONS

1. It appeared that the rapid demise of animals receiving superlethal doses of venom (12 mg/kg) resulted from profound shock caused by losses of large amounts of fluid into the envenomed area.

2. Supportive therapy prolonged life but did not necessarily prevent the terminal event in these animals.

3. The antivenin appeared to be efficacious in the neutralization of venom *in vivo*, and caused chronic survival, eliminating the need for other therapy.

4. The results of this study, based on 100 per cent survival, were tabulated. Intra-arterial injection of antivenin in the affected limb appeared to be effective in the treatment of dogs injected with snake venom (*C. atrox*). Results obtained from injection of antivenin intra-arterially at a site proximal to the bite area suggested that this may be more efficacious than the benefit obtained from intravenous administration of antivenin with its associated dilution.

5. These results indicate that further investigation of the immunologic and physiologic effect of venom will be necessary before a clear picture can be drawn of the true nature of envenomization and a rational method of treatment developed.

ACKNOWLEDGMENT

This work was conducted at the School of Aerospace Medicine, U.S.A.F. Aerospace Medical Division (AFSC), Brooks Air Force Base, Texas.

REFERENCES

CROSBY, W. H. and FURTH, F. W. 1956. A modification of the benzidrine method for measurement of hemoglobin in plasma and urine. *Blood* **11**, 380.

CROSBY, W. H., MUNN, J. I. and FURTH, F. W. 1954. Standardizing a method for clinical hemoglobinometry. *U.S. Armed Forces Med. J.* **5**, 695.

FITZGERALD, J. B., MALETTE, W. G. and KOEGEL, EWALD. 1961. A simple device for the transfer of biologic fluids. School of Aerospace Medicine Tech. Report 61–62.

FRANKS, J. J. and ZIZZA, F. 1958. Simultaneous measurements of plasma volume in man with T-1824 and an improved I^{131} albumin method. *J. Appl. Physiol.* **13** (2), 299.

YA, P. M. and PERRY, J. B., Jr. 1960. Experimental evaluation of methods foı the early treatment of snake bite. *Surgery* **47** (6), 975.

LETHAL AND HEMORRHAGIC PROPERTIES OF SOME NORTH AMERICAN SNAKE VENOMS

JERRY A. EMERY and FINDLAY E. RUSSELL*

HEMORRHAGE as a frequent finding following bites by crotalid and viperid snakes has been reported by many workers, including Efrati and Reif (1953), and Russell (1960). In less severe cases of poisoning by these snakes the hemorrhages are usually limited to the cutaneous and subcutaneous tissues around the wound. In the more severe cases, hemorrhages may extend over the involved extremity, or may even spread to cover a large portion of the cutaneous and subcutaneous tissues of the body. In addition, hemorrhages may occur in the muscle layers adjacent to the wound. Bleeding into the heart, lungs, intestines, kidneys and other organs following severe snakebite poisoning is sometimes encountered at necropsy.

Quantitative methods for determining the amount of hemorrhage provoked by venoms, or components of venoms, have been suggested by Minton (1956), Mitsuhashi *et al.* (1959), and by Kondo *et al.* (1960). Minton studied the necrotizing effect of 11 Crotalidae venoms following their intradermal injection into the shaved belly skin of guinea pigs. As Minton points out, the areas of necrosis can only be determined in approximation as they are often irregular in shape and depth, and they present difficulties when one has to " compare deep, circumscribed necrosis with superficial, wide necrosis ". These difficulties may be overcome in part by using a large group of animals, and by measuring the area of hemorrhage on the under surface of the skin as proposed by Kondo *et al.* (1960).

The present report treats of the lethal and hemorrhagic activities of venoms of 10 species of medically important snakes found in the United States, and indicates some of the relationships between lethality and hemorrhage, and between hemorrhage on the external and under surfaces of the skin.

MATERIALS AND METHODS

The venoms used in the study were obtained from snakes milked by the authors, or supplied by Ross Allen's Reptile Institute. All venoms were dried under similar conditions, and were stored in a refrigerator until the

*Laboratory of Neurological Research, Loma Linda University, Los Angeles County Hospital, Los Angeles, California.

time of their use. The venom was dissolved in physiological saline and injected through a 27-gauge needle. The intravenous and intraperitoneal LD_{50} were determined in 15–25 g mice using methods described by Russell and Emery (1959). The local hemorrhagic effects were determined by measuring the areas of hemorrhage on the under and external surfaces of the depilate skin of the backs of 21 young adult rabbits which had received

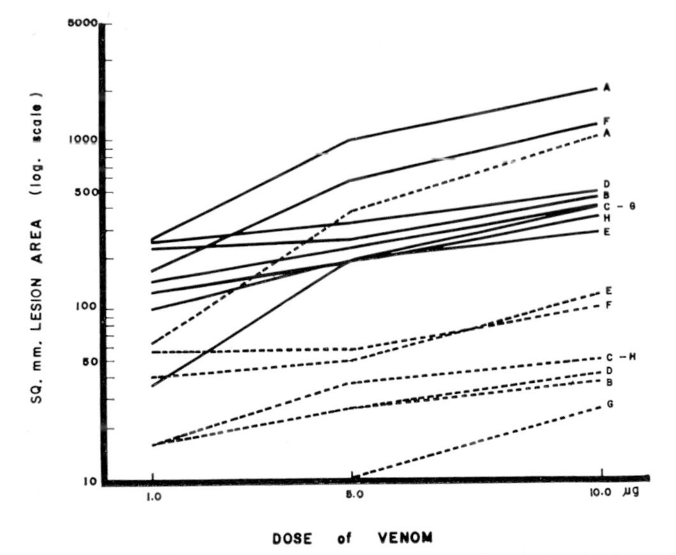

FIG. 1. Dose-hemorrhagic response on external surface of skin (- - - -) and under surface of skin (——). A, *Crotalus adamanteus*; B, *C. atrox*; C, *C. horridus*; D, *C. viridis helleri*; E, *C. ruber*; F, *C. cerastes*; G, *Agkistrodon piscivorus*; H, *A. contortrix*.

several intradermal injections of 1.0, 5.0 and 10.0 μg of one or more of the venoms. The venom was injected in 0.1 ml of saline at distances of approximately 3.5 cm. Twenty-four hours following the injections, the area of skin for study was removed from the anesthetized rabbit under aseptic conditions, smoothed out on a board but not stretched, photographed, and measurements taken of the areas of hemorrhage on both the under and external surfaces of the skin.

RESULTS

The LD_{50} for each of the 10 venoms and the median measurements of the hemorrhagic areas are shown in Table 1. It can be seen that a direct relationship between the lethality and the hemorrhagic activities of these venoms does not exist. The dose-response relationships for the hemorrhagic areas are illustrated graphically in Fig. 1. The hemorrhagic areas on the under surface of the skin were always more extensive than those on the external surface; they were also reproducible with a greater degree of consistency. Figure 2 shows the degrees of hemorrhage produced by various amounts of *A. piscivorus* venom.

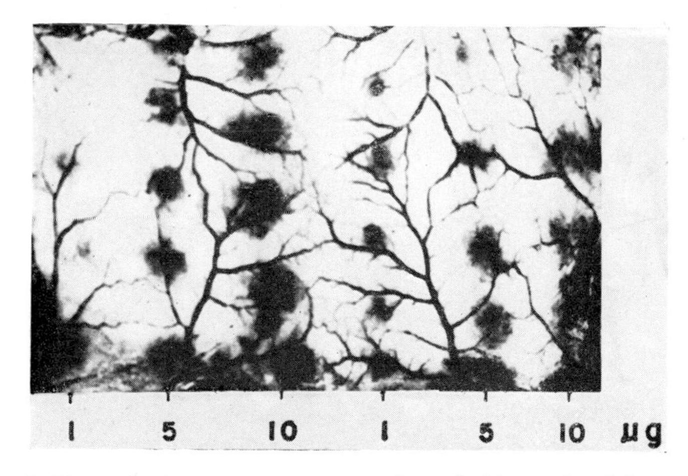

FIG. 2. Hemorrhagic areas on under surface of skin produced by various amounts of *A. piscivorus* venom.

DISCUSSION

The data indicate the advantages of using measurements from the under surface of the skin over those from the external surface when information is needed on the degree of hemorrhage produced by a venom. However, it was observed during the course of the experiments that even measurements from the under surface must be viewed critically, for the method does not permit an evaluation of the depth of the hemorrhage. The lesions produced by *C. adamanteus* were not only larger than the others but also deeper; it was not possible to measure the depth of these hemorrhages by simple photographic means. Further studies using spectrophotometric methods may permit a more reliable index of the depth of these lesions. In addition, certain venoms, particularly those of *C. adamanteus* and *C. viridis helleri*, produced lesions that spread unevenly through the tissues; thus, it was sometimes difficult to circumscribe the hemorrhagic areas. In general, however, the method is satisfactory and certainly superior to those techniques that are dependent upon measurements taken on the external surface of the skin.

The table indicates that there may be considerable differences between the responses on the under and external surfaces of the skin to specific venoms. With *C. ruber* venom, the relationship between the inner-outer responses was approximately 2 to 1, while with *A. piscivorus* venom it was approximately 24 to 1. Kondo *et al.* (1960) have indicated that the relationship

TABLE 1. LETHAL AND HEMORRHAGIC ACTIVITIES OF SNAKE VENOMS

Venom	LD_{50} mg/kg Intravenous	LD_{50} mg/kg Intraperitoneal	Area hemorrhage mm² (U)			Area hemorrhage mm² (E)		
			1	5	10	1	5	10
Crotalus adamanteus	1.68 (1.43– 1.98)	1.89 (1.63– 2.19)	256	990	1925	64	380	1080
Crotalus atrox	4.20 (3.85– 4.55)	3.71 (3.50– 3.90)	225	256	450	16	25	36
Crotalus horridus	2.63 (2.36– 2.91)	2.94 (2.72– 3.18)	36	196	400	—	36	49
Crotalus viridis helleri	1.29 (1.01– 1.44)	1.60 (1.40– 1.82)	250	324	476	16	25	40
Crotalus ruber ruber	3.70 (3.51– 3.91)	4.65 (4.22– 5.11)	100	196	289	40	49	121
Crotalus cerastes	2.60 (2.17– 3.12)	2.08 (1.76– 2.45)	169	576	1250	56	56	100
Crotalus scutulatus	0.21 (0.14– 0.29)	0.23 (0.14– 0.38)	—	—	—	—	—	—
Agkistrodon piscivorus	4.00 (3.42– 4.68)	5.11 (4.49– 5.82)	144	225	400	4	10	25
Agkistrodon contortrix	10.92 (9.58–12.45)	10.50 (9.50–11.55)	121	180	342	16	36	49
Micrurus fulvius	0.24 (0.14– 0.41)	0.33 (0.17– 0.60)	—	—	—	—	—	—

U: skin under surface measurements.

E: skin external surface measurements.

may be as high as 100–300 to 1 with the venom of *Trimeresurus flavoviridis*.

The low hemorrhagic activity found in the present study for the venoms of *C. scutulatus* and *M. fulvius* supports the clinical observations of Neill (1957), Parrish (1957), and Russell (1962). These venoms appear to produce very few hemorrhages in man, yet they are considerably more lethal than the other North American snake venoms. It is interesting to note that the last two deaths in California due to rattlesnake bites were attributed to *C. scutulatus*. Neither of the victims had evidence of serious hemorrhage at the site of the bite.

SUMMARY

The lethal and hemorrhagic activities were determined for the venoms of 10 species of medically important venomous snakes found in the United States. The relationships between lethality and hemorrhage, and between hemorrhage on the under and external surfaces of the skin are demonstrated. Certain clinical applications of these data are discussed.

ACKNOWLEDGEMENT

These studies were supported in part by Grant E–3751 of the National Institute of Allergy and Infectious Diseases.

REFERENCES

EFRATI, P. and REIF, L. 1953. Clinical and pathological observations on sixty-five cases of viper bite in Israel. *Am. J. Trop. Med. Hyg.* **2**, 1085.

KONDO, H., KONDO, S., IKEZAWA, H., MURATA, R. and OHSAKA, A. 1960. Studies of the quantitative method for determination of hemorrhagic activity of *Habu* snake venom. *Jap. J. Med. Sci. & Biol.* **13**, 43.

MINTON, S. A., Jr. 1956. Some properties of North American pit viper venoms and their correlation with phylogeny. *In Venoms*. Washington: A.A.A.S.

MITSUHASHI, S., MAENO, H., KAWAKAMI, M., HASHIMOTO, H., SAWAI, Y., MIYAZAKI, S., MAKINO, M., KOBAYASHI, M., OKONOGI, T. and YAMAGUCHI, K. 1959. Studies on *Habu* snake venom. I. Comparison of several biological activities of fresh and dried *Habu* snake venom. *Jap. J. Microb.* **3**, 95.

NEILL, W. T. 1957. Some misconceptions regarding the eastern coral snake, *Micrurus fulvius*. *Herpetologica* **13**, 111.

PARRISH, H. M. 1957. The poisonous snake bite problem in Florida. *Quart. J. Florida Acad. Sci.* **20**, 185.

RUSSELL, F. E. 1960. Rattlesnake bites in Southern California. *Am. J. Med. Sci.* **239**, 52.

RUSSELL, F. E. 1962. Snake Venom Poisoning. *In Cyclopedia of Medicine, Surgery and the Specialties*. Philadelphia: F. A. Davis.

RUSSELL, F. E. and EMERY, J. A. 1959. Use of the chick in zootoxicologic studies on venoms. *Copeia* **1**, 73.

QUANTITATIVE *IN VITRO* AND *IN VIVO* STUDIES OF RATTLESNAKE VENOM (*CROTALUS ATROX*)

W. G. GLENN*, W. G. MALETTE†, J. B. FITZGERALD‡, A. T. K. COCKETT*, and T. G. GLASS, JR.††

THESE investigations were initiated by an interest in the development of a better method of treatment for snake bite. It soon became evident that venomization and envenomization were problems that bridged several scientific disciplines and immunochemistry was considered appropriate. The initial immunochemical purpose was to follow quantitatively the *in vivo* concentration changes in *C. atrox* venom and crotalid antivenom in the circulating blood of dogs. We have not, as yet, succeeded in this facet for the elusive venom necessitated a serpentine path of observations reminiscent of the " tail wagging the dog ". This report emphasizes *C. atrox* venom characteristics and comprises diversified immunochemical observations, some of which may be considered pertinent to the original *in vivo* interests of the study.

PART I. IN VITRO *IMMUNOCHEMICAL ANALYSIS*

SOLUBILITY

When 150 mg/ml of lyophilized *C. atrox*§ venom was triturated in 0.85 per cent sodium chloride, it was only partly soluble at a final pH of 4.8. This observation extends the findings of Grasset *et al.* (1956). The precipitate was finally solubilized at pH 1.8. This partial solubility is related both to venom standardization and the lethality of the precipitate. Gel precipitin analysis in double diffusion columns, wherein the antivenin|| is separated

*School of Aerospace Medicine, U.S.A.F. Aerospace Medical Division (A.F.S.C.) Brooks Air Force Base, Texas.

†Department of Surgery, U.S.A.F. Hospital Lackland, U.S.A.F. Aerospace Medical Division (A.F.S.C.), Lackland Air Force Base, Texas.

‡Baylor University School of Medicine, Houston, Texas.

††Instructor in Surgery, University of Texas Postgraduate School of Medicine, San Antonio Division, San Antonio, Texas.

§Pooled batches from Ross Allen's Reptile Institute, Silver Springs, Fla.

||All antivenom used in this report was a pool of several batches of Anti-*Crotalidae* serum (Wyeth).

from the venom by an agar reaction arena described by Oakley and Fulthorpe (1953), was performed on the precipitate centrifuged (1000 × G, 30 min) from an original whole venom concentration of 150 mg/ml in saline. A diffuse, nondescript reaction (120 hr, 30° ± 0.01 °C) resulted from the gel diffusion analysis. Such effect could well be attributed to the low pH necessary to solubilize the precipitate, rather than a precipitin reaction *per se* and could not be considered comparable to the precipitin pattern of the whole venom (*vide infra*).

The precipitate from 840 mg/ml of whole venom was obtained, as described above. It was put into solution with one-half of the original volume of the supernate by the addition of saline adjusted to pH 1.8. This solution caused no fatalities in 24 hr when 0.1 ml was injected intraperitoneally (IP) into each of six albino male Swiss mice (20–25 g). In contrast, the supernate was lethal to 5 out of 6 mice over the same time span. On the basis of these preliminary tests, it was not considered necessary to the purposes of the investigation to further explore the composition or effect of the precipitate

LETHALITY

Two reports concerning the variations in venom potencies in the same species of snakes, and from the same snake, have been published by Minton (1953, 1957). While closer statistical scrutiny of the test data might smooth out some discrepancies, there certainly appears to be inherent variation in repeated titrations. For standardization of the pooled *C. atrox* used in this investigation, we experimentally determined and accepted an LD_{50}/24 hr IP mean dose of 0.72 μg/g ($P < 0.05$). The range of such titration in male Swiss mice (25–30 g) was 0.21 to 1.23 μg/g mouse by probit analysis. One hundred and thirty mice comprised the population. The venom used in this titration was the supernate of the saline solution and the weight of the centrifuged precipitate was subtracted.

COMPLEXITY OF VENOM

The extent of complexity of venom depends upon the concentration, the assay method, and the antivenom, if such is used in the determinations. Following the technique of double diffusion analysis in agar columns, Oakley and Fulthorpe (1953) resolved a minimum of 16 precipitin systems (120 hr, 30° ± 0.01 °C) at a whole venom concentration of 150 mg/ml when reacted with hyperimmune horse (Anti-*Crotalidae*, serum (Wyeth)) (Fig. 1). In view of the valuable contributions relative to the possibility of one antigen forming two zones by Jennings (1954) and Korngold and Van Leeuwen (1959); zone-splitting by Oakley and Fulthorpe (1953); and protein-protein interaction by Haurowitz (1958), this would not, of necessity, indicate a minimum of 16 antigens. Two of the precipitin systems could be absorbed by adding heparin to the antivenom* (Fig. 2). For those investigators interested in quantitative, double diffusion column analysis, the zones associated with heparin had a diffusivity ratio, P value as defined by Preer (1956), of 1.43 and 1.58 at 120 hr (30° ± 0.01 °C). They were, therefore, fast-diffusing molecules that formed well into the antiserum-agar area in a

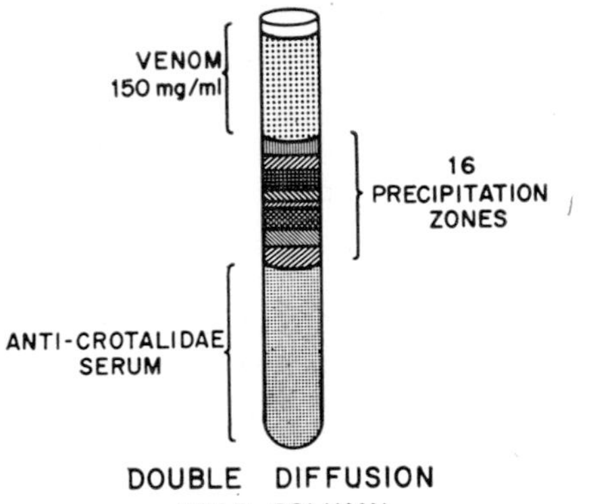

FIG. 1. Orientational schema illustrating a double diffusion column reaction between *C. atrox* whole venom and horse hyperimmune anti-*Crotalidae* serum. Some zones (not shown) actually formed well down into the antiserum-agar area. Resolution of 16 precipitin zones was obtained after 120 hr diffusion time at 30° ± 0.01 °C. (See text for clarification.)

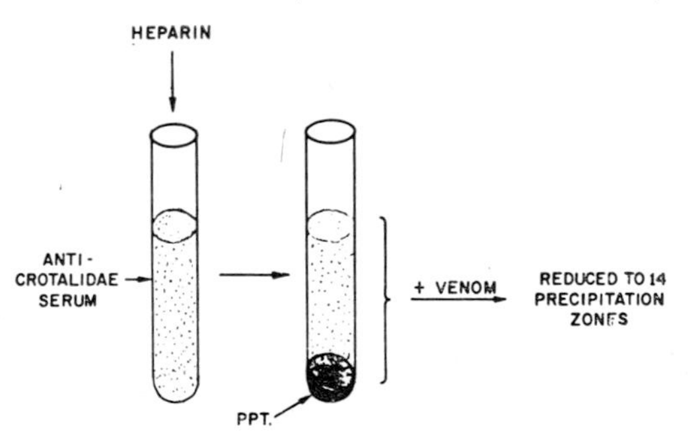

FIG. 2. Schema of the results produced when heparin was added to antivenom. The supernate, when combined with venom in a double diffusion agar column, indicated reduction of the original 16 precipitin zones to 14. Saline controls did not show such " absorption ".

double diffusion column. Absorption of precipitins by heparin indicates that either some of the venom molecules had molecular configurations similar to that of heparin—therefore, complementary antibodies were

*This observation was prompted by our prior inability to determine immunologically, with certainty, whether the pre-experimental serum or plasma samples of the dogs indicated exposure to rattlesnake venom during their roamings.

induced in the preparation of anti-venom—and/or the hyperimmunization induces non-specific, cross-reacting antibodies. An interfacial (ring) test, likewise, resulted in a precipitin reaction between whole venom and heparin. The supernate from such test was, however, still lethal for all of several mice within 24 hr (Fig. 3). These findings extend the observation of Grasset *et al.* (1956) of a coagulant-anticoagulant mechanism.

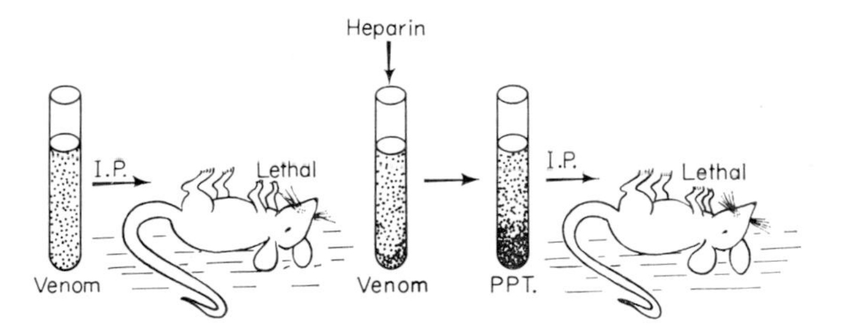

FIG. 3. The *C. atrox* whole venom-heparin reaction. (See text for details.)

VENOM ALTERATION

An unfounded belief reported by Criley (1956) and Fisher (1961) that venom contained bacteria because of the snakes' environments led Criley (1956) to treat venom with formalin before injection into horses. As Landsteiner (1947) and Kabat and Mayer (1948) have observed, there is considerable evidence that antigens treated with formaldehyde may, under certain conditions, undergo alterations in some of their characteristic specificities. To demonstrate such venom alteration, two drops of 0.5 per cent formalin and a like quantity of distilled water were each added separately to two 1-ml aliquots of *C. atrox* whole venom (48 mg/ml). This was followed by incubation at 37 °C for 24 hr. The products were then reacted independently for 96 hr (30° $\pm$ 0.01 °C) in double diffusion agar columns with Anti-*Crotalidae* serum (Wyeth). Of the six precipitin zones that were resolved, there were statistically significant ($P < 0.05$) increases in the diffusivity ratios (*P* value) of two systems in the formalin incubated sample. These systems were close to equivalence. In the four other systems, all in antigen excess, the formalin treated venom showed alteration in the combining capacities of the reactants, as illustrated by optical density scans, (Glenn, 1958), of the contrasting agar columns (Fig. 4). Such findings suggest the possibility that the antibodies produced in the altered (formolized) antigens may not reflect the characteristic specificities of the venom in its natural state.

Observations on the effect of heat on the lethality of whole venom were also made. Three saline-venom dilution series, each composed of six concentrations, were incubated at 56 °C, 80 °C, and 100 °C for 30 min. Supernates were separated by centrifugation. A control (22 °C) dilution series was run concurrently. The six concentrations in each of the four dilution series were then separately injected intraperitoneally into 42 mice at 18, 14, 12, 8, 6 and 4 μg/g mouse, for a total of 252 animals. These were randomly chosen male and female Swiss mice (20–30 g). At the 80° and 100 °C level, all of the animals survived for the first 24 hr selected as the end point. A probit analysis was done on the other two sets of data (22 °C control, 56°/30′).

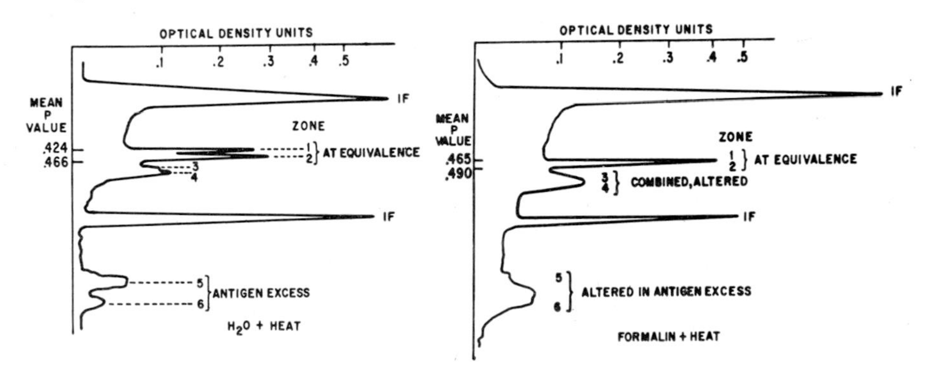

FIG. 4. Optical densities and diffusivity ratios (mean P values) of certain precipitin systems in double diffusion columns. The reactants were *C. atrox* whole venom and horse antivenom. Venom was treated either with water (control) or formalin followed by incubation 37 °C for 24 hr. Note alterations in zones 1 and 2 at equivalence, 3 and 4, and 5 and 6 in the formalin treated venom (right side). 1F indicates the junction of the venom-agar reaction arena (at the top) and the junction of the agar reaction arena-antivenom (at the bottom). Reaction time 96 hr at 30° ± 0.01 °C.

From the equation for the regression lines, estimates of the mean LD_{50}/24 hr were as follows (95 per cent confidence limits): Control, 6.9 μg/g mouse (range 4.9–8.8 μg/g); 56°/30′, 18.0 μg/g mouse (range 11.9–28.0 μg/g). The confidence interval was so large for the 56 °C temperature, the data did not cover the LD_{50} range; it was necessary, therefore, to go outside the range of the data to get an LD_{50} estimate. The partial and total lability of venom components by heat treatment, demonstrated by the above results, suggests that such components are not of the heat stable polysaccharide variety; but that whole venom depends for its action, for the most part, on protein or protein-conjugated substances.

ELECTROPHORETIC FRACTIONATION

Figure 5 diagrammatically presents the principal results of a continuous flow paper electrophoretic fractionation of *C. atrox* whole venom. The isoelectric range was assumed to be linear across the bottom of the curtain. The anodic and cathodic isoelectric reference markers were obtained by a preliminary calibration with a mixture of 3 per cent saline solutions of Cohn ethanol precipitated human plasma fractions V (albumin) and II-3 (gamma globulin). Drip points with the highest protein concentration, as determined by the Biuret reaction, were assumed to have the highest population of molecules representative of these fractions. Following the report by Albritton (1951), the mean isoelectric points of the reference substances were taken as albumin, pH 4.9, and gamma globulin, pH 6.8. After dialysis against phosphate buffered saline (Sorensen's buffer, pH 6.8–7.2) for 96 hr at 4 °C,

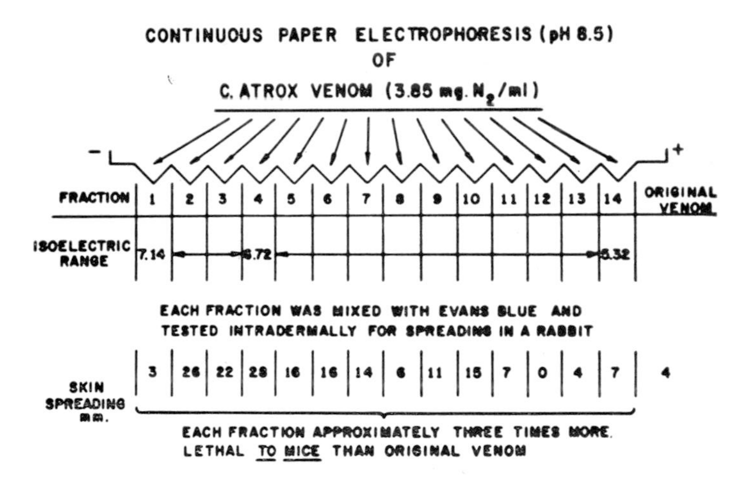

FIG. 5. Diagram of continuous flow paper electrophoretic fractionation of *C. atrox* whole venom. Sodium barbital-diethyl barbituric acid buffer at r/2 = 0.018, 40–50 mA was used for the separation. Isoelectric ranges were obtained from calibration with human plasma proteins II-3 (gamma globulin) and V (albumin). Skin spreading is the net diffusion after subtracting the spread for an intradermal injection of buffer plus 0.5 per cent Evans blue dye into a rabbit.

fractions 1 through 14 were reconstituted to one-fourteenth of the original volume of the whole venom. One-tenth ml/g mouse of each of these fractions, a similar amount of the original venom except diluted 1 : 14, and saline were separately injected IP into 16 groups of 3 male Swiss mice each (20–30 g). While $66\frac{2}{3}$ per cent of the mice injected with whole venom died in 1 hr, all but three fractions (Nos. 10, 12 and 13) killed 100 per cent of the animals in less than 30 min. So rapidly did the venom fractions act that, in most instances, death occurred in the first 13 min after injection. Even the slower acting fractions (Nos. 10, 12 and 13) produced lethality in all 3 mice in each group in 17 hr, 65 min, and 16 hr, respectively.

Fractions were also mixed separately with equal parts of 0.5 per cent solutions of Evans blue dye and 0.2 ml of each mixture was introduced intradermally into the shaven back of a rabbit. The extent of external dye spread in 90–112 min—less that spreading which resulted from the electrophoresis buffer control—is shown on the lower part of Fig. 5. Fraction 4, with an isoelectric range of pH 6.72, showed the greatest spreading effect (28 mm).

The analysis of the fractionation products so far suggests the possibility that such electrophoretic separation of the whole venom (1) either inactivated inhibitor(s) or, more likely, (2) separated paired families of molecules in which each pair is composed of an activator(s) and an inhibitor(s). It is unlikely that in such paired combinations the activator(s) and corresponding inhibibitor(s) would have the same charge-carrying capacity (by virtue of their basic and acidic groups). They would, therefore, be dissociated in an electric field. The latter hypothesis agrees with evidence presented by Grasset *et al.* (1956) of the contrasting action of venom and the heparin-venom antivenom results described above.

TABLE 1. TENTATIVE DIFFUSION COEFFICIENTS OF EIGHT COMPONENTS IN FIVE ELECTROPHORETIC FRACTIONS OF *C. atrox* VENOM REACTED WITH *antiCrotalidae* SERUM.

Data were obtained from measurement of diffusivity ratios of precipitin systems in double diffusion columns. Reaction time 72 hr at 30° ± 0.01°C

No.	Venom fraction	Position of zone at equivalence*	Mean diffusivity ratio	Mean diffusion coefficient
	Dilution		(P value)	($\times 10^{-7}$ cm^2/sec, $D_{w_{20}}$)
13	None	1	0.2620	0.227†
4	1 : 10	1	0.2902	0.301
2	1 : 40	2	0.3000	0.331
2	1 : 20	1	0.3162	0.385
9	1 : 20	1	0.3310	0.441
12	None	1	0.3315	0.443
14	None	1	0.3340	0.453
4	1 : 10	2	0.3540	0.541

*Refers to relative position of zone under consideration in relation to other zones in the agar column.

†Means sharing the same line are not statistically different from each other (multiple range test).

Preliminary approaches were made to further characterize several fractions resulting from continuous flow electrophoresis. Since this type of electrophoretic fractionation does not usually result in immunologically homogenous populations of molecules, several precipitin systems in various stages of antigen or antibody excess were evident when representative venom fractions 2, 4, 9, 13 and 14 were reacted with antivenom in double diffusion columns. Appropriate dilutions of the venom fractions resolved several systems at equivalence and mean diffusion coefficients for those systems were computed from diffusivity ratios. A total of eight precipitin zones in the five fractions were assayed by double diffusion columns and measured by semi-automatic cathetometry after 72 hr diffusion (30° $\pm$ 0.01 °C), this technique is described by Glenn (1956). A tentative range of diffusion coefficients from 0.227×10^{-7} to 0.541×10^{-7} cm^2/sec (Dw_{20}) (Table 1) was computed using 1.80×10^{-7} cm^2/sec as the constant for horse antibody (Kabat and Mayer, 1948). Although an analysis of variance on the diffusivity ratios (*P* values)—which have to one-to-one relationship with the diffusion coefficients —indicated that the diffusion coefficient values among the eight systems were statistically significant, a multiple-range test showed that the significant difference existed only for the diffusion coefficient means differing by 0.156 ($P < 0.05$). Since the quantities of materials did not permit additional physical characterizations, the diffusion coefficients presented are, at best, broad parameters for further investigation. Discounting possible protein interaction which could invalidate the diffusion coefficient data, the extremely low values suggest that the venom fractions were composed of highly globular molecules.

During the course of *in vivo* studies described later in this study, it seemed feasible to mix equal parts of whole venom with a 0.5 per cent solution of Evans blue dye in an attempt to follow the rate of venom spread after a subcutaneous injection. Fortuitously or otherwise, the experimental animal survived for a longer period than anticipated. This observation justified discontinuous paper electrophoretic analyses (Veronal buffer $\Gamma/2 = 0.05$, pH 8.6) from which it was evident that the dye did not bind to any of the migrating venom components. This does not necessarily rule out the possibility that Evans blue dye does or does not bind stationary components since the dye, as well as some venom fraction(s), did not migrate under the above conditions.

AMINO ACID ANALYSIS

After dialysis and pervaporation of the 14 venom fractions, amounts of each estimated to be approximately 1.1 mg were refluxed for 24 hr with 6 N HCl. The hydrolyzates were evaporated to dryness under partial vacuum, washed three times with distilled water and reconstituted with saline to one ml.

Each of the hydrolyzates (exclusive of Nos 2 and 18) was subjected, in duplicate, to discontinuous paper electrophoresis (Durrum cell) in two independent analyses, using potassium hydrogen phthalate buffer (pH 5.9) and acetic acid buffer (pH 1.9). With each buffer, appropriate amino acid standards were run for purposes of comparison. For both separatory conditions, 0.010 ml of the sample was applied on S&S No. 2043 filter paper strips, each run lasted 4 hr, and strips were subsequently stained with 0.2 per cent ninhydrin. For phthalate buffer, 24 mA, 500–600 V were applied; for acetic acid, 7.2 mA, 400–500 V.

The first separation (pH 5.9) showed aspartic and glutamic acid plus a neutral and alkaline group in all 14 fractions (Fig. 6). Eluates of the aspartic and glutamic acid zones, the alkaline group, and hydrolyzates of

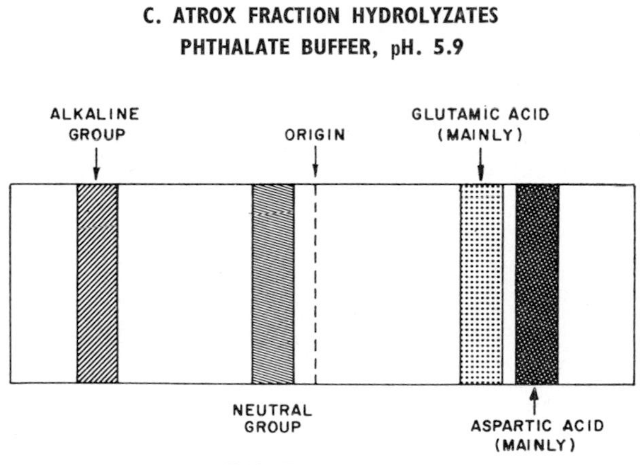

FIG. 6. Resolution of amino acid groups of *C. atrox* whole venom hydrolyzates after 4 hr separation on discontinuous paper electrophoresis at 24 mA constant current, 500–600 V. All of the 14 venom fractions showed aspartic and glutamic acids plus neutral and alkaline groups in varying concentrations.

C. atrox fractions 7 and 11 were further resolved by descending paper chromatography, using butanol–acetic acid–water (250–60–250) as the solvent following the technique of Block *et al.* (1955). Appropriate amino acid

TABLE 2. QUALITATIVE AMINO ACID COMPOSITION OF ACID HYDROLYZATES OF ELECTROPHORETICALLY SEPARATED *C. atrox* VENOM FRACTIONS

Data are from discontinuous paper electrophoresis in phthalate buffer (pH 5.9) followed by descending paper chromatography. The data represent only a partial list. Other details are given in the text (cf. Fig. 5)

Amino acid	Electrophoretic venom fraction											
	1	3	4	5	6	7	8	9	10	12	13	14
Arginine	x	x	x	x	x	x	x	x	x	x	x	x
Aspartic acid	x	x	x	x	x	x	x	x	x	x	x	x
Glutamic acid	x	x	x	x	x	x	x	x	x	x	x	x
Isoleucine	x		x									
Leucine*	x		x									
Lysine	x	x	x	x	x	x	x	x	x	x	x	x
Phenylalanine	x		x									

*Smallest amount of leucine that gave a detectable ninhydrin staining zone was 4μM.

standard solutions, prepared by the method of Block and Weiss (1956) were run concurrently. Table 2 indicates the amino acids resolved to date by combined techniques of paper electrophoresis (pH 5.9) and chromatography. The six to nine ninhydrin staining zones of each hydrolyzate which were resolved by the acetic acid buffer (pH 1.9) in paper electrophoresis were not subjected to chromatography and have not been identified.

PART II. APPROACHES TO IN VIVO *ANALYSIS*

Pre-experimental samples of serum or plasma from 25 dogs were reacted separately in an interfacial (ring) test with *C. atrox* venom (30 mg/ml) (supernate) and antivenom for 20 min at 37 °C. The antivenom reactions were all negative, but 22 animal samples showed some specific or nonspecific reaction with venom (coagulant-anticoagulant mechanism?). It was not possible, therefore, to state with certainty that some of the dogs did not have an antivenom level. This, of course, bears directly on the selection of a constant venom concentration as a definite lethal dose. No work of sufficient scope has been published to establish an LD_{50} for dogs; in view of the variability of venom potency and the difficulties with proving immunity, or lack of it, this seems like an impasse.

Several blood samples from eight dogs (each injected subcutanteously with an arbitrary *C. atrox* venom dose of 12 mg/kg) were collected at various time intervals (5 min–3 hr) after venom injection. The 12 mg/kg was the initial weight triturated into 0.85 per cent NaCl and the supernate of this concentration after centrifugation (1000 × G/30′/4 °C) was used for injection. The blood samples were obtained by catheterization at the juncture of the superior and inferior vena cavae and the sera were reacted in duplicate double diffusion columns against venom ($>$800 μg/ml), antivenom, and normal horse serum for a maximum of 96 hr. (30 ± 0.01 °C). Most results were either negative or ambiguous because of the reactions of the preinjection samples. Only samples from one animal, whose control sera did not react with the above substances, gave tenable results. In this animal, samples at 15, 45 and 63 min post-venom injection showed a diffuse precipitin system in the dog serum-antivenom reaction after 66 hr of incubation. This could, in view of the other results, be considered as suggestive of venom in the serum. There did not seem to be any indisputable method for quantitation of the amount.

Since it seemed that the necessary manipulations of the blood samples before the assay for venom may have introduced unknown factors, heparinized blood samples taken from a dog at various time intervals before and after subcutaneous venomization (−1, 5, 10, 15, 30, 45, 60 and 120 min) were injected into mice within one minute after sampling. Each of the six mice for each time interval was given 0.25 ml IP. No mice died within the first

24 hr selected as the termination time. Based on the subcutaneous dose given the dog (12 mg/kg) and considering the average blood volume per kilogram for dogs as reported by Dukes (1955), if all of the venom moved freely into the circulating blood, each mouse would have received much more than the mean LD_{50}/24 hr concentration previously determined experimentally. That no mice died neither confirms nor denies the hypothesis that venom might travel or become fixed in the lymphatic system rather than the vascular bed (Fidler *et al.*, 1940).

There does not appear to be any indisputable method for proving the efficacy of antivenin therapy unless (1) large, pooled batches of venom and antivenin are available, (2) animals that could not possibly have been accidentally exposed to snake bite are utilized, and (3) the fiducial limits of the LD_{50} dose of venom are conclusively established to give the results of the treated animals statistical significance. Lastly, the possibility exists that venom components *per se* after injection are so altered and/or bound that the two methods—reaction with antivenin or lethality in a susceptible test animal—are inapplicable and will not adequately serve as recognizing indices for quantitatively detecting *C. atrox* venom *in vivo*.

SUMMARY

The insoluble portion of *C. atrox* venom at pH 4.8 did not form a definitive precipitin system with horse antivenom when put into solution at pH 1.8 and was not lethal to mice.

C. atrox whole venom, when reacted with commercially prepared horse antivenom, showed a minimum of 16 precipitin systems in double diffusion agar columns.

Treatment with formaldehyde or heat altered the reactivity and lethality of *C. atrox* venom.

Separation of *C. atrox* whole venom into 14 fractions by continuous flow paper electrophoresis (isoelectric ranges of pH 7.14 to pH 5.32) resulted in families of venom components, each of which was highly lethal when injected intraperitoneally into mice.

Combinations of discontinuous paper electrophoresis and chromatography did demonstrate qualitative amino acid differences in certain representative *C. atrox* venom hydrolyzates.

Because of apparent coagulant-anticoagulant or other non-specific properties simultaneously present in *C. atrox* venom, it was not feasible to establish by *in vitro* tests whether dogs had been previously exposed to venom. We were also not successful in quantitatively assaying venom levels in the vascular system of dogs injected subcutaneously with venom.

The hypothesis is proposed that *C. atrox* venom consists of pairs of interacting molecules, each pair composed of an activator(s) and an inhibitor(s) which are dissociated in electrophoresis.

Certain immunochemical characteristics of *C. atrox* venom are discussed in detail.

REFERENCES

ALBRITTON, E. C. (ed.). 1951. *Standard Values in Blood.* A. F. Technical Report No. 6039. Wright Air Development Center, U.S.A.F.

BLOCK, R. J. *et al.* 1955. *A Manual of Paper Chromatography and Paper Electrophoresis.* New York: Academic Press.

BLOCK, R. J. and WEISS, K. W. 1956. *Amino Acid Handbook Methods and Results of Protein Analysis.* Springfield, Mass.: Charles C. Thomas.

CRILEY, B. R. 1956. Development of a multivalent antivenin for the family *Crotalidae. In* Buckley, E. E. and N. Porges (ed.) *Venoms.* Washington, D.C.: A.A.A.S.

DUKES, H. H. 1955. *The Physiology of Domestic Animals.* Ithaca, N.Y.: Comstock Publishing Assoc.

FIDLER, H. K. *et al.* 1940. Pathological changes produced by the subcutaneous injection of rattlesnake (*Crotalus*) venom into *Macaca mulatta* monkeys. *Am. J. Pathol.* **16**, 355.

FISCHER, F. J. *et al.* 1956. Antivenin and antitoxin in the treatment of experimental rattlesnake venom intoxication (*Crotalus adamanteus*). *Am. J. Trop. Med. and Hyg.* **10**, 75.

GLENN, W. G. 1958. *New Instrumentation for the Quantitation of Agar Precipitin Columns.* School of Aviation Medicine, U.S.A.F. Report No. 58–133.

GLENN, W. G. (1962). Quantitative analysis by diffusion column reactions. I. Variations in diffusion measurements. *J. Imm.* **88**, 535.

GRASSET, E. 1956. Comparative analysis and electrophoretic fractionations of snake venoms with special reference to *Vipera russelli* and *Vipera aspic* venoms. *In* Buckley, E. E. and N. Porges (ed.), *Venoms.* Washington, D.C.: A.A.A.S.

HAUROWITZ, F. 1958. Serological and biochemical comparisons of proteins: Summary of the conference. *In* Cole, W. H. (ed.): *Serological and Biochemical Comparisons of Proteins.* New Brunswick, N.J.: Rutgers University Press.

JENNINGS, R. K. 1954. Diffusion-precipitin studies of the complexity of antigen mixtures. II. The number of zones formed by one antigen. *J. Bact.* **67**, 565.

KABAT, E. A. and MAYER, M. M. 1948. *Experimental Immunochemistry.* Springfield, Ill.: Charles C. Thomas.

KORNGOLD, L. and LEEUWEN, G. VAN. 1959. The formation of multiple zones of precipitate by one antigen: An immunological explanation. *Int. Arch. Allergy* **15**, 278.

LANDSTEINER, K. 1947. *The Specificity of Serological Reactions.* Cambridge, Mass.: Harvard University Press.

MINTON, S. A. Jr. 1953. Variations in venom samples from copperheads (*Agkistrodon cortortrix mokeson*) and timber rattlesnakes (*Crotalus horridus horridus*). *Copeia* **4**, 212.

MINTON, S. A. Jr. 1957. Variation in yield and toxicity of venom from a rattlesnake (*C. atrox*). *Copeia* **4**, 265.

OAKLEY, C. L. and FULTHORPE, A. J. 1953. Antigenic analysis by diffusion. *J. Path. Bact.* **65**, 49.

PREER, J. R. 1956. A quantitative study of a technique of double diffusion in agar. *J. Imm.* **77**, 52.

OBSERVATIONS ON THE TREATMENT OF SNAKEBITE IN NORTH AMERICA

JOSEPH F. GENNARO, JR.*

THE ability of the poisonous snake to produce death in a spectacular manner after the infliction of what is apparently an innocuous wound has attracted the attention of scientists literally since the beginning of Science. It should be emphasized that, aside from our knowledge of the various enzymatic activities of venom and the researches done describing the effect of other factors, apparently not enzymic in nature, on the nerve fiber, neuromuscular junction, and cardiovascular system, we are still largely ignorant of the mechanism whereby snake venoms produce lethal intoxication, i.e. the role of the factors which have been isolated from venom either singly or collectively in the pathogenesis of envenomation.

In North America all the poisonous snakes, with four exceptions, are members of the family Crotalidae. The elapid exceptions are the three coral snakes, of genus *Micrurus*, and the small Sonoran coral snake of genus *Micruroides*. The North American Crotalidae are represented by at least thirty-five different species and subspecies.

A review of the properties of venoms and their effects on animals gives evidence that the venoms from the phylogenetically older snakes of the family Elapidae differ profoundly from the venoms of the more recent snakes in the family Crotalidae. The venoms of the former snakes are characteristically highly toxic, usually much more so than the venoms of the members of the latter family. Generally speaking, however, the snakes of the family Crotalidae produce venoms which are rich in enzymatic factors that cause local damage, especially hemorrhage, and digestion of the tissues at the site of the bite. In addition, the snakes of the more modern group seem to have " compensated " for the lesser degree of toxicity of their venom by an increase in the complexity of the biting apparatus and the control they employ in its use. The poison gland, apparently a specialized type of parotid salivary gland, is equipped with tendinous and muscular attachments to the bony structures of the head and jaws. These function to permit the snake great control in the release of venom during the bite.

Detailed accounts of snakebite incidents in the United States and the mortality which has occurred are not easily available. Recently, the

*Department of Anatomy, University of Florida, Gainesville, Florida.

Department of Public Health of the State of Florida has requested the physicians of that State to report hospital-treated cases. Such measures followed by a comparative study of the clinical course of each bite situation made with reference to the kind of snake and the age of the individual bitten should throw some much needed light on the epidemiology of snakebite. Though this program is still relatively new and some hospitals at which bites probably have been treated are not yet reporting regularly, over 95 bites have occurred in the first six months of 1962. Of these, thirty were bites of children and fifty-five were adults; ten were reported as known non-poisonous. Though these data are in the most preliminary stage, it appears that over one-quarter are bites caused by the Eastern diamondback rattlesnake. Three of the bites reported were caused by the coral snake. Because of the differences in the venoms, the type of bites, and the symptomatology in the envenomated individuals bitten by the crotalid and coral snakes, comments on the treatment of elapid bites will be reserved to follow the discussion on care of crotalid snakebite.

THE POISON APPARATUS AND SNAKEBITE

In this laboratory our initial concern was the function of the poison gland rather than the effect of the product of its secretion. As is common in the pit vipers, this gland is located on the side of the head between the angle of the jaw and the eye, and produces a serous secretion which passes into the base of the hollow fang by a comparatively short tubular modification of the gland at the distal end of which is located a small accessory glandular tissue, the cells of which secrete a mucous material. The anatomy and physiology of this type of mucous secreting cell was described by Gennaro *et al.* (1962). The product of the serous portion of the gland is stored in acinar spaces within the tissue while the product of the mucous secreting accessory gland is kept within the cells which produce it apparently until the moment of venom discharge. The anatomical distinction made between the sites of the formation of these two secretions and the fact that they do not mix until the critical moment provides an opportunity to speculate upon the effect of one secretion on the other. It appears, in the case of the cottonmouth moccasin, that the mucous secretion, while not toxic itself, has an enhancing effect upon the toxicity of the serous secretion.

As Gennaro *et al.* (1958) have shown, the poison gland of these snakes also functions in a manner similar to the salivary gland of the mammal in that it accumulates radioiodine administered intraperitoneally to the snake and excretes this in the venom as unbound radioiodide. This phenomenon was utilized to study the amount of venom injected by the poisonous snake in its bite and the depth to which the dose was deposited. In a series of bites performed under controlled conditions by Eastern and Western diamond-back rattlesnakes (*Crotalus adamanteus* and *Crotalus atrox*), as well as the cottonmouth moccasin (*Ancistrodon piscivorus*), it was determined that the snake can vary greatly the amount of venom injected. Western diamondback rattlesnakes consistently delivered more venom than the Eastern diamondback and the moccasin even less venom. In ten successive bites when the snakes were held, the amount of venom injected into ten pieces of meat by cottonmouth moccasins and Western diamondbacks varied by as much as two orders of magnitude. The force of the bite more than any other factor was correlated directly with the injected dose which suggests an active control of the injected volume on the part of the snake. This is confirmed by studies conducted by Gennaro, Leopold, and Merriam (1961), in which snakes were allowed to bite mice and rats and in which it was determined that the rat was consistently given a larger dose by the snakes of the three species. Though most of the snakes used in these studies were large specimens which possessed fangs long enough to penetrate to intramuscular depths, strikes into limbs of dogs under conditions as nearly approximating the natural as possible produced few injections of venom deep to the primary muscle fascia.

While it has been said that many of the crotalid snakes in North America are capable of delivering a lethal dose of venom, there is great variability in the mortality statistics of even untreated bite cases. That this is true is clearly shown in reports by Minton (1957); Githens (1935); Wood (1954); Parrish (1957a, b); Klauber (1956); and Shannon (1956). As Parrish (1959) has noted, this is probably due to the fact that for reason of circumstances surrounding the bite or because the amount of venom in the poison glands is insufficient, lethal amounts of venom are not always injected by the snake. The fact remains that, as shown by Schöttler (1951); Porges (1953); Russell (1960); and Deichman *et al.* (1958), most snakes of the family Crotalidae contain sufficient quantities of venom to deliver a lethal dose. It seems that the amount of venom injected by the Eastern diamondback rattlesnake, for example, can frequently be lethal in the adult man and usually lethal in the child. Githens (1935) stated that the bite of this snake, even after treatment, resulted in death 25 per cent of the time in 1935, though this figure must certainly be lower now. The difference in sensitivity between the adult and the child has been attributed to the difference in body mass, but may also be due to factors involving resistance in the young as compared to the older organism.

EVALUATION OF BITE SEVERITY—SYMPTOMATOLOGY

The type of treatment required in an individual case of snakebite will obviously depend upon the amount of venom injected. The evaluation of bite severity is, therefore, important in both first aid and hospital treatment. As noted by Parrish (1959), the numbers of bites by truly bona fide poisonous snakes which have not resulted in serious envenomation or envenomation at all, are an indication of the variables surrounding the snakebite incident. Undoubtedly, most of the miraculous cures effected by various means of treatment of high repute in local lore, as reviewed by Klauber (1956), are due to the fact that little or no venom was injected by the snake involved. The treatment for serious snakebite is a rigorous one; attempts to extract or neutralize the venom injected by the snake are associated with a good deal of discomfort and some danger. The course of such a treatment should not begin, therefore, unless it is surely warranted.

Symptoms of crotalid envenomation have been described in detail in many papers, including two by Russell (1960a, b) and a brochure (1961) published by Wyeth Laboratories. Wood *et al.* (1955) proposed three grades of classification of crotalid snakebite; minimal, moderate, and severe. Parrish (1959) has proposed the addition of grade 0 to the other three as a classification of the verified or suspected snakebites with the presence of fang marks or wounds, but no signs of envenomation. It has been our experience that, unless the injection of venom takes place directly into a blood vessel in which case generalized systemic symptoms such as changes in respiration and heartbeat, unconciousness and shock may occur almost immediately, the severity of the bite can be regarded as proportional to the amount of swelling in the bite area and the rapidity with which it progresses from the original site at the mark of the fang(s). The bite of a non-poisonous snake or a poisonous snake which has not injected any venom will not produce swelling. Usually, in addition to the swelling, there is pain. The bites of rattlesnakes often produce a tingling or " pins and needles " feeling of painful or uncomfortable intensity together with marked spasmodic muscular contractions, especially of the face (fasciculation). Ecchymosis, faintness or dizziness, sweating, and increase in body temperature may also be evident. As shown by Gennaro and Casey (1961), who worked with rabbits and cats, Eastern diamondback rattlesnake venom produces a pupillar constriction. This is a transient phenomenon and is apparently not directly associated with intoxication, since it disappears before the death of the animal. In the clinical situation, however, such a sign may be an indication of a serious bite.

INACTIVATION OF THE PATIENT AND IMMOBILIZATION OF THE PART

Immobilization is one of the few features of snakebite treatment about which there is some unanimity, although it is possible that its value has not been sufficiently extolled. Leopold *et al.* (1957) have demonstrated experimentally that rigorous attention paid to complete inactivation reaps dividends in the form of survival. The work of Barnes and Trueta (1941) also illustrates the value of these measures. Clinical observers of the effect of the viper bite in Israel and workers such as McCullough *et al.* (1961), investigating circumstances surrounding the bites of the crotalid snakes in the Southeastern United States, consider immobilization to be of prime importance. Muscular activity of any sort, such as moving the fingers or clenching the fists, for example, will result in an increase in the local damage produced in the tissues of the forearm by a deposition of venom there. As a matter of incidental interest, it may be observed that voluntary inactivity is almost the immediate natural response of envenomated domestic animals.

Some authorities, including Barnes and Trueta (1941), have discussed enclosing the bitten extremity in plaster as a means of better effecting immobility, however, because serious envenomation will result in considerable swelling, confinement of the limb tends to increase the ischemia which is responsible for many of the degenerative changes in the snakebitten limb. (Even without enclosure fasciotomy is occasionally required to reduce the internal pressure in an envenomated extremity.)

THE EFFECTIVENESS OF INCISION AND SUCTION AND COMMENTS ON THE USE OF EXCISION AS A MEANS OF BITE TREATMENT

In relatively recent years a controversy, at times vigorous, has existed over the relative effectiveness of the use of incision and suction in the treatment of snakebite. Actually, the use of suction with or without incision is cited as one of the earliest methods employed in the treatment of snakebite. Provera (1928) describes references to the use of this treatment in Egypt among families who treated snakebite professionally at the time of Cleopatra. In 1608, Avicennae listed methods which he recommended in the treatment of bites by venomous serpents. Included is ligature, incision, suction by mouth and cupping, excision, and amputation, and it reads very much like a modern medical directive. Still, it remained for Dudley Jackson (1929) to demonstrate that the sero-sanguineous exudate withdrawn by the incision and suction procedure was toxic and indeed removed venom. It is well to note that Jackson's motivation for his investigations into the effectiveness of this procedure was developed as a result of his estimate that the " Texas diamondback rattlesnake " (presumably *Crotalus atrox*) could inject 220 mg of venom in the average bite, and that the antivenin which he had available to him neutralized only 10 mg of venom per 10 ml vial. At that time, the administration of more than one dose of antiserum in the treatment of snakebite was considered to be contraindicated. In the published discussion following the presentation of Jackson's paper, R. H. Hutchinson, then secretary of the Antivenom Institute of America, described work in progress by Githens and his co-workers which, in retrospect, has an interesting bearing on the treatment outlined by Jackson. It was noted, for example, that dogs are extremely variable in their resistance to venom; one factor which undoubtedly, together with scantiness of data, has been responsible for a good deal of criticism of Jackson's work. The point was also made that many snakes are able to strike and inject venom to intramuscular depths and that while venom is removable by incision and suction in this circumstance, not enough is removed from the intramuscular site to save the life of the injected animal. Also noted was the fact that the toxicity of the fluid removed by suction diminished sharply with time, the material apparently having no toxicity after 5 hr, and that antivenin administered intravenously in treatment seemed much more efficacious in neutralizing venom activity than when given intramuscularly or subcutaneously. In these few short remarks, Hutchinson epitomized the value of this method of treatment. Unfortunately, his remarks were never referred to later as far as can be discerned from a thorough search of literature of this subject. His statement represents an accurate evaluation of incision and suction and, had it been more widely regarded, would have resulted in better use of these techniques in the treatment of snakebite.

Until recently, little experimental work has been done since the time of Jackson, and the decision to use or discard incision and suction as a means of treatment has largely been made on a personal preference basis. Scanning the literature, it can be seen that this is what has been done. Shannon (1956) has chosen to regard such treatment as useless because of his feeling that the venom spreads too rapidly in the tissues to be withdrawn in time. Stimson and Englehardt (1960) have chosen oppositely. Shannon's position is peculiar in that while he feels that venom is not removable by incision and suction because of its rapid spread in the tissue, he defends Jackson's work in which it was employed, noting that the latter removed enough venom to kill or seriously maim four dogs from the wound of an animal injected with four lethal doses. Jackson himself did not regard the spread of the venom into the tissues as rapid enough to seriously affect the value of the treatment. He stated in comments on his paper that venom which would kill as quickly as the first removed by immediate suction could be found in the wound even after 14 hr. Stahnke *et al.* (1957), who have advocated treatment by hypothermia as the only logical method, choose to ignore the value of incision and suction, though oddly they accept Jackson's statement regarding the duration of the venom in the bite area.

Recently, in an experimental re-evaluation of this treatment technique, the work of Merriam and Leopold (1960), using a bioassay in mice of the venom removed by suction after incision, indicated that relatively large amounts of toxin neutralizable by antivenin are removable in this way. Russell and Emery (1961), studying the zootoxicologic effects of the serosanguineous exudate removed by suction, confirm that the material removed is qualitatively similar to the venom injected and that significant amounts are removable. Merriam (1961) estimates the amount of venom removable in incision and suction to be 22 to 44 per cent of the injected venom, provided the incisions reach the level of venom deposition. This is in agreement with the studies performed in this laboratory utilizing I^{131}-labeled rattlesnake venom in which incision and suction was likewise found to be an effective method of venom removal. Amounts up to more than 50 per cent of the subcutaneously injected dose were removable when suction was started within 3 min after the injection of the venom. Much less was available from intramuscular sites through percutaneous incisions, although then the amount removed was quite variable, sometimes reaching 20 per cent of the dose. Removal was effected primarily during the first 15 min following the start of suction and not much was available after 30 min of suction. One difference apparent between our work and the work of Merriam was that even after 120 min as much as 20 or 30 per cent of the subcutaneous dose could be removed in 15 min of suction. It appears from both works, however, that longer periods of suction are of no avail, the rest of the venom injected being either systemically distributed or fixed to the tissues. No significant amounts of venom are available from suction other than at the site of the bite. Progressive proximal incision of the extremity for this purpose appears useless. Leopold and Huber (1960) have made the point that incision and suction may well disseminate the venom more rapidly. This was not confirmed in our investigation. The data from which they formed this opinion were taken from an experiment specifically designed to demonstrate that incisions which penetrate the subcutaneous tissues do accelerate venom intoxication. Such a type of incision is definitely not recommended in the treatment of snakebite, in fact, these experiments are a corroboration of the statements of Puranananda (1956) to the effect that deep incision would permit more rapid dissemination of venom. Such evidence is also an indictment against the treatment of snakebite by excision. This has been discussed by Parrish (1950, 1955, 1958). There would seem to be little doubt that exposure of fresh tissue surfaces to the venom would increase the rate of absorption of the toxin. It can be easily seen following the intramuscular injection of rattlesnake venom into the thigh of an anethestized dog that the area of necrosis will extend through the entire lateral aspect of the leg within 3 hr and that almost complete involvement of the muscle underlying the injection is effected within 1 hr. It is difficult to conceive, therefore, of complete excision of the bite area without inflicting serious permanent damage on the patient. Anything less than complete removal of the bite site would certainly increase the risk of serious envenomation.

Incision and suction, therefore, would seem to be an effective means of snakebite first-aid treatment. It should not be exclusively relied upon. Despite the fact that incision and suction is more effective when performed promptly after the bite, it is much more important to be assured that envenomation has actually occurred before incision is made. The first three to five minutes after the bite spent simply in careful observation of the bite area and the condition of the extremity would be a more profitable investment of this time. If signs of true envenomation such as swelling, pain, or fasciculation are then evident, incision through the skin and suction by means of a first-aid device or by mouth should be performed.

THE USE OF THE TOURNIQUET

The tourniquet is a difficult therapeutic measure to evaluate. Efrati and Reif (1953) say that its use does not prevent the absorption of venom and cite the work of Schreiber and Maljugin (1936) who also express the opinion that local signs appear above the tourniquet. In their experience its use does not prevent the onset of the generalized (systemic) signs of envenomation.

Our observations, experimental and clinical, are not in agreement with this view. From our work in dogs injected into the lateral aspect of the thigh with lethal doses of rattlesnake venom (subcutaneously or intramuscularly), it seems that there is an abrupt interruption of all the effects of the venom below the tourniquet when it is placed tightly about the limb proximal to the injection of venom. The erythema, inflammation, edema, and hemorrhage can be seen to end at that level. Even the histological picture shows normal muscle tissue above and hemorrhage and necrosis below the line of the occlusive tourniquet. (It may be that a tourniquet placed on the forearm or leg, however, could be negotiated via the interosseus vascular pathways in these portions of the extremities which contain *two* long bones.)

A pathognomonic sign of the bite of the Eastern diamondback rattlesnake is a tingling sensation which appears around the lips and face. In serious bites this may develop into fasciculation of the muscles of facial expression. In individuals bitten by this snake, this sensation disappears when the tourniquet is applied and reappears as the tourniquet is loosened. Such testimony would seem to indicate an interruption of the systemic distribution of at least some venom.

The Israeli workers make the statement that their experience leads them to believe that the application of a tourniquet, especially for some time, leads to a worsening of the clinical condition. Here, our experience agrees precisely.

In animals to which the tourniquet is applied, even loosely, for relatively longer periods of time (one hour or longer), there is always a great deal of local necrosis in the envenomed limb. McCollough *et al.* (1961), after a study of extremity loss due to venomous snakebite, conclude that a lightly constrictive tourniquet occluding the superficial veins and lymphatics is of probable value during the period of incision and suction. It seems that a tourniquet used at this time would delay the spread of venom proximally and increase the efficacy of the incision and suction treatment. After this treatment, which itself is of short duration, the tourniquet might well be discarded.

HYPOTHERMIA AND CRYOTHERAPY

Stahnke *et al.* (1957), emphasizing that death due to snakebites in the United States is rare and when it does occur may be due to " secondary effects arising as results of poor management ", designate the venom enzymes as the principle factors with which one must deal in the treatment of snakebite on this continent. In this work they develop the rationale that most of the deaths which might occur could certainly be avoided by the use of antivenin, death being due, they feel, to the rapid absorption of the neurotoxic factor. Further in their argument, they reject the usefulness of the tourniquet, multiple incision, and suction technique as one which is damaging as commonly practiced and therefore ineffective. They state that, in the snakebite wound, tissue destruction is the result of the enzymatic action of the venom and the action of bacteria. After these objections they advocate, for the treatment of snakebite, the ligature and cryotherapy method. Such treatment is designed to prevent the dissemination of " neurotoxic " factors as well as the action of enzymatic factors and to inactivate the principles which will operate in the destruction of tissue until they are " neutralized through natural processes ".

A great deal has been written, both pro and con, on the use of cold in the treatment of snakebite. Some individuals have spoken for the use of ice water baths, and others simple ice pack cooling. A short and straightforward examination of the facts, experimental evidence, and background is in order.

The idea that cold in any form might be useful to stop detrimental enzymatic action in the body is not a new one. Crum (1906) was the first to recommend ethyl chloride spray as a treatment for the bite of the copperhead.

Allen (1937, 1938, and 1939) retested this hypothesis with relation to the enzymatic destruction that results from tissue gangrene as well as venom. At the end of these studies he concluded that " local refrigeration is of no practical value, unless sometimes as an anaesthetic ". His later notes are favorably inclined toward refrigeration for analgesia and *temporary* arrest of enzymatic action, but later (1949) he warned that " enzymatic action can be arrested by refrigeration, but too prolonged contact with tissue may result in even greater destruction after the temperature is raised ". A discussion of this technique in the light of this work is well summarized by Shannon (1956).

In this period, Large and Heinbecker (1944a, b, c) conducted an extensive investigation of the result of refrigeration in surgical procedures on the rate and effectiveness of normal wound healing and on the normal intact extremity. Bruneau (1944), also working with Heinbecker, studied the effect of refrigeration on tissues experimentally infected with *Streptococcus hemolyticus*. In their studies they established that refrigeration, while it abolishes pain, produces ischemia and effectively isolates (especially with the application of a tight tourniquet) the extremity; it interferes with normal nerve function and produces demonstrable histologic degeneration in the nerve of the normal limb cooled to 6 °C for 96 hr; it effectively prevents any normal healing of an experimental incision in the cooled area and, subsequent to warming, causes a delay in the normal healing process; and lastly, while the cooled tissues fail to show the inflammatory response usually observed in the presence of hemolytic streptococcus organisms, a much more rapid destruction of the tissue in the cooled limb occurs than in the uncooled one after returning them to room temperature. With this background it is easy to see that: (A) No neutralization of venom enzymes will take place during the period that the limb is kept in hypothermia. This seems obvious simply because the enzyme and tissue products which would detoxify or metabolize the foreign proteins of the venom would operate best, if not entirely, at temperatures at which the venom enzymes would also find optimal. Elimination of activity of the one also eliminates activity by the other; (B) Another factor which must be considered here is the fact that some of the biologically active materials which are formed by the action of the venom enzymes on the tissues are not greatly influenced by temperature in their activity, e.g. lysolecithin, surface-active material which lyses cells at temperature close to zero with little or no difficulty; and (C) The most obvious objection is that the only real neutralization of the venom proteins, "neurotoxins" and enzymes will result after the complexing of these materials with antibodies. No experimental or clinical researches have yet been able to produce better, more effective means for the safe neutralization of venom in tissues than the immunologic one. Cooling, however, by producing serious ischemic changes within the envenomated area, effectively prevents the antiserum from reaching the venom. In studies performed in this laboratory, the amount of I^{131}-labeled antivenom (polyvalent Crotalidae-Wyeth) which collected at the sites of envenomation in the hind limb of experimental dogs was extremely reduced when the temperature of tissues was lowered in any manner. Recent experimental investigations by Russell and Emery (1961) and by Ya and Perry (1960), confirm this view and bear on the inadequacy of cold as a means of snakebite treatment. In a clinical survey of extremity loss due to venomous snakebites (McCollough *et al.* 1961), it was found that in 23 of the 27 cases which resulted in amputation, the use of cryotherapy in excess of 12 hr was reported.

The obvious conclusion to be drawn from this analysis, one which is supported by experimental research by Bata and Vukobratovic (1958), is that the application of local hypothermia and especially when combined with the application of a tight tourniquet, is an excellent method for the isolation of toxic products and the prevention of their systemic dissemination if one is prepared for amputation of the part so treated.

TREATMENT OF ENVENOMATION WITH ANTIVENIN

Far more effective than the use of cold in any form is the treatment of serious snakebite with specific or polyvalent antivenin. Recourse to the treatment of incision and suction was largely occasioned by the inefficacy of the antivenin available to Jackson. Even so, Githens (1935) regarded it as valuable and estimated that its use resulted in a great reduction in snakebite mortalities. All authorities are not of this opinion. Stimson and Engelhardt (1960) cautioned against its use (referring to the new antivenin) because of the fear of side effects. Stahnke *et al.* (1957), in their emphasis on the value of hypothermia or " cryotherapy ", mentioned that antivenin is (presumably) of little effect against the enzymes, the action of which causes local necrosis in the bite area. It is their contention that a lethal bite is not usually delivered by the North American crotalid snake and the effective use of antivenin is therefore limited. Much of the unfavorable opinion that many clinicians and snake handlers seem to have of the antivenom serum is the result of investigations such as that of Minton (1954), who found it ineffective in neutralizing the venoms from which it was produced. He mentioned that it was neither effective in preventing the lethal effect nor local necrosis (after intraparitoneal or local infiltration of the injured tissue). The manufacturer's representative (E. Buckley) stated that the antivenin employed in his work was probably the old serum. Shortly following Minton's paper, Criley (1956) described improved antivenin produced in the same year. In the hands of many authorities including Russell (1960) and Ya and Perry (1959), this new preparation seems to be quite effective in preventing death and in the general treatment of snakebite. A general review of its potency is given in a brochure published by Wyeth Laboratories (1961).

In this laboratory the new antivenin has been tested specifically not only against the lethal effect of the snake venom in the mouse, rabbit, and dog, but also the local necrotic one. It has been found to be remarkably effective against both. Our observations lead us to believe that the local hemorrhage (frequently attributed to the presence of clostridial organisms) which follows the bite of the crotalid snake is amenable to treatment by antivenin administered intravenously. As reported by Fischer *et al.* (1961), this local damage is not affected in the slightest by the administration of large quantities of tetanus antitoxin or gas gangrene antitoxin given in the same way. There is no reason to believe that all the venom proteins including the enzymes which produce hemolysis, cytolysis, or hemorrhage in the area of the bite are not antigenic in the horse. In addition, if this is so, it is quite likely that the hyperimmune serum produced against such antigens will be as effective in preventing local damage as it will the lethal effect.

Stahnke *et al.* (1957) and Stickel (1952) have expressed the belief that death following crotalid snakebites occurs due to a circulating " neurotoxin ", while necrosis is caused by proteolytic enzymes of one sort or another which are released and remain at the site of the bite. Stickle goes so far as to say that the antivenin constitutes only a supplemental measure in snakebite treatment. However, a hyperimmune serum prepared against a whole venom would be equally effective against circulating or fixed foreign protein antigens. Work in our laboratory with commercially available polyvalent antivenin (crotalid) labeled with I^{131} tracer has indicated that after intramuscular, subscapular, intraperitoneal, or intravenous administration it accumulates at the site of the bite as well as in other tissues (lung, liver, kidney) which apparently represent the systemic sites of distribution of the venom. When given prior to the administration of the venom it will prevent completely the local necrosis and when given after the administration of the venom it will drastically reduce the local effect. It is the only remedy which affects to any great extent the lethality of the venom, i.e. those factors which produce death even before much local necrosis may be evinced.

It has been our experience that the most rapid accumulation of antivenin in the bite area occurs after intravenous administration of the serum. Interstitial infusion in the venomous area is not nearly so effective in reducing local necrosis. Antivenin should be regarded as the keystone of any proper treatment. Though it is a horse serum, and can be used only with the dangers attendant upon the use of such a preparation, severe snakebite can produce alarming symptoms within 30 min (hematemesis, shock, cardiac arrhythmia, barely discernible pulse, and blood pressure). In such circumstances, and in the absence of frank allergic response, it hardly seems appropriate to concern oneself with the dangers of possible future side effects. Though high blood levels are developed much more slowly after intramuscular injection of the antivenin, its release into the blood vascular compartment from such a site is of a more sustained nature. For this reason, Russell (1960), recommended that after proper testing for sensitivity to the serum protein, half the dose be given intravenously in venoclysis and half intramuscularly in healthy muscle tissue at a site distant from the bite. Russell routinely administers the antivenin intravenously in hospital treatment of envenomation in children where the course of disease is always more grave. Under no circumstances should the injection of antivenin take place into the bite area where the swelling produced by the action of the venom proteins can be more than sufficient of itself to occasionally require fascial incision to release the internal pressure. A study by McCollough *et al.* (1961) of the morbidity following serious snakebite indicates that many of the sequelae such as serious slough are produced by the ischemia which results from the increase in internal pressure in the afflicted extremity. Administered promptly in this way, antivenin is of real value in curtailing the necrotic action of the venom at the site of the injection as well as improving the systemic condition. Our experimental work has given some indication that, perhaps as a result of secondary toxins or necrotic factors which are formed by the action of the venom on the tissues, materials for which there are no antibodies in the antivenin, the efficacy of the antiserum (especially as regards the control of local damage) is reduced with time. It is certainly true that, as the area of hemorrhage surrounding the site of injection of the venom increases in size, the antivenin will be less able to effectively contact the venom.

For this reason antivenin has been used, clinically and experimentally, with a number of agents designed to increase its penetration into the bite area which becomes almost isolated from the system. Boquet (1956) indicates that the survival times of animals envenomated with cobra venom is extended through the use of hyaluronidase administered with the antivenin. It has been our experience using hyaluronidase injected into the bite area or administered intravenously with the antivenin that in neither case does the labeled antivenin accumulate in the local area into which *Crotalus adamanteus* venom had been injected as rapidly as when the antivenin is administered alone and intravenously. Our measurements indicate that the use of hyaluronidase does not increase and perhaps inhibits the collection and complexing of the antivenin.

The rationale for the use of hyaluronidase or an enzyme which would facilitate the penetration of the antiserum into the bite area is especially appealing in the case of crotalid snakebite. Here, the hemorrhagic factors quickly produce a wide area in which, as a result of capillary destruction, there is almost complete avascularity. This results in profuse hemorrhage into the bite area and the stasis of blood in this region produces an additional obstacle which interferes with the penetration of the neutralizing antiserum. Experiments are currently underway in our laboratory to determine whether the use of streptokinase-streptodornase enzyme mixtures is any more effective in facilitating the spread of the antivenom into the bite area in the limb of the anesthetized dog after the injection of rattlesnake venom.

The dose of antivenin given must vary with the severity of the bite and can probably be said to be adequate when the progressive swelling of the bitten part is permanently inhibited. Two to five units may be customary and occasionally more are necessary. Intravenous administration, by increasing effective neutralization, will lessen the amount of serum required. A technique to curtail the undesirable side effects of serum sickness and horse serum sensitization which usually follow the administration of equine antisera in the quantities required for the proper treatment of serious envenomation with antivenin has been developed by Borden *et al.* (1961). The technique developed by these workers makes use of the fact, reported by Klauber (1956), that 98 per cent of snakebites are on the extremities and is a development in experimental animals (dogs) of a method of perfusion of the bitten limb with antivenin after heparinization and isolation. After perfusion with the antivenin solution, the isolated limb is washed with heparinized whole blood and returned to the systemic circulation. This approach to antiserum treatment, while certainly not of the " first-aid " category, can be established emergency procedure. (This procedure has been designated as routine for cases of serious envenomation in the emergency room of the Teaching Hospital of this Medical School.) Its principal value would seem to lie in the rapidity with which the antivenin would make contact with the site of venom injection and the fact that, except for " spillover ", little horse serum antibody remains unattached to antigen in the treated animal.

In a small number of experiments using I^{131}-labeled antivenin, we have determined that there is no significant difference in the rate at which antiserum reaches a site of envenomation in the thigh when administered in the artery proximal to that part or in the radial vein of the upper extremity. The significant advantage, however, of the isolation and perfusion technique should be in the reduction of side effects through the rapid and permanent elimination of excess antibody. Other work presently being projected in our laboratory has to do with the chemical treatment of the equine antivenin serum globulin to eliminate or drastically reduce its allergenicity without substantially interfering with the antigen neutralizing ability.

In general, agents which interfere with circulatory dynamics or with antigen–antibody coupling inhibit the access of antivenom to the bite area or its ability to neutralize the venom. When the limb is cooled prior to or during the administration of the antivenin, closing down of the capillary bed results in a drastic diminution of the amount of circulating iodine-labeled antivenin collected at the site of the venom injection. Corticosteroids may actually inhibit antibody neutralization of the venom though they may be valuable subsequently for treatment of reactions to the equine antivenin protein seven to ten days after its administration.

TREATMENT OF SNAKEBITE WITH ACTH, CORTICOSTEROIDS, AND ANTI-HISTAMINICS

In 1952, Stickel wrote that ACTH might " revolutionize the treatment of snakebite ". In the early years of its use, together with corticosteroid preparations and antihistaminics, several glowing reports were published by Cluxton (1951); Maier (1951); Kirsch (1952); and Hoback and Green (1953).

A very thorough investigation of these materials by Schöttler (1954), which is frequently overlooked, showed no statistical evidence of the beneficial effect of any of these substances tested in large numbers of animals. Subsequently, Wood *et al.* (1955) modified some of the original conclusions of this group regarding the effectiveness of these substances in ameliorating the deleterious effects of the snake venom.

Two experimental studies by Ganatra *et al.* (1957) and Deichmann *et al.* (1958), advocating the use of such treatment, the first performed in the mouse and the second in dogs, indicated it as valuable. Large numbers of mice tested under identical conditions in this laboratory failed to benefit from this type of treatment. There was some evidence that individuals receiving corticosteroids survived longer before death finally occurred, but in no case was there survival after a lethal dose of venom had been administered. Russell and Emery (1961) found this same situation was obtained after the injection of the venom of *Ancistrodon contortrix*, the copperhead, as well as that of the Eastern diamondback rattlesnake. These workers make the point that the corticosteroids not only do not affect absolute survival, but they do not prevent tissue damage and inflammation in the steroid treated animals, the fundamental reason for their use. Essentially, these same results have been obtained by Knowles *et al.* (1959).

It may be that the increase in survival time of animals treated with corticosteroids is the result of an increased suspension time of the circulating foreign protein (venom) produced by the cortisone. At present, there seems to be little doubt that these measures have no effect on the lethality of the venom or on the local necrosis which frequently follows in the bite sequence. Studies with I^{131}-labeled antivenin indicate that their use in conjunction with the antiserum seriously interferes with the neutralization of the venom antigen by the antibody. Their value would seem to be restricted to a suppression of the foreign protein reaction to the antivenin 7 to 10 days after the bite.

THE USES OF OTHER ANTISERA AND ANTIBIOTICS—SUPPORTIVE THERAPY

The rapidly developing necrotic lesion which follows a serious crotalid snakebite has often been mistaken for gangrene. Almost without exception, case reports which discuss gangrenous changes in limbs soon after snakebite fail to take into account the short time (minutes or hours) in which such a state would have been required to develop. In few of these cases has positive evidence of gangrene been found in the wound as shown by laboratory tests. The result of work in our laboratory, by Fischer *et al.* (1961), has shown us that this " gangrenous appearance " of the bite area is completely unaffected by the administration of polyvalent gas gangrene or tetanus antitoxins. Repeated references are made by several investigators, including Criley (1956); Stahnke *et al.* (1957); and Jackson (1944), to conditions of filth which exist in the mouth of the snake, and to pathogenic anaerobes which can be cultured from dry venom preparations. As a matter of fact, the work of Williams *et al.* (1934), who studied samplings of the microfloral populations of the mouths of the snakes in the wild and those recently collected, indicates that such is remarkably small. The results of the study by Parrish *et al.* (1956), which are so frequently quoted to show that clostridial organisms can be found in the mouths of snakes, actually showed only one anaerobe—nonpathogenic to man. Fischer *et al.* have shown that the flora which develops in the mouths of the snakes of this country shortly after captivity and which rapidly increase in quantity in carelessly handled animals to such an extent that it may be impossible for the mouth to close, does not include organisms of the anaerobic type.

General consideration of the venom apparatus makes it clear that the poisonous secretion is not usually situated in the mouth of a snake, at any rate, but is conducted through it to the object bitten. Fresh venom, like most body fluids, is free of micro-organisms. It may be true, as reported by Boys *et al.* (1960); Kellaway and Williams (1933); and Prevat (1951), that clostridial organisms have been demonstrated in venom preparations. The hypothesis suggests itself that contamination has occurred during the drying. This is to some extent substantiated by the investigation of Williams *et al.* (1958), whose study showed that dried venom contamination increases as preparation procedures are prolonged. While it is advisable, in view of the gravity of the disease, to administer tetanus prophylaxis in cases of snakebite, it does not seem wise to increase the foreign protein burden of the body by the administration of large quantities of additional antiserum required for passive immunization without specific evidence of its need as, for example, from a positive culture of the snakebite wound.

The fact that fresh venom from a snake in the wild is relatively clean, however, does not guarantee the cleanliness of the bite wound, especially after incision performed with a pocket knife, and oral suction. The tissue digests produced by the enzymatic action of the venom make an extremely rich culture medium for bacteria, especially since there is almost no blood flow as a result of the destruction of the capillaries and arterioles in the path of the venom spread. The warmth, hydrolysed protein produced by the venom, and anaerobic condition in an area to which the phagocytic defenses of the body have little access all represent conditions which predispose to infection. For this reason antibiotic therapy should generally support the specific means of treatment. In a case of serious envenomation, depending upon the circumstances and the individual,* 200 to 800 mg of oxytetracycline administered orally and one to two million units of penicillin given parenterally each 24-hr period would not be excessive.

Fidler *et al.* (1940) observed renal and hepatic lesions produced experi-

*Contraindicated when symptoms include nausea.

mentally by injection of crotalid venom. Extensive vascular damage was also observed by Taube and Essex (1937). For these reasons the serum electrolyte levels and the hematocrit should be checked as soon as possible in a serious bite and frequently from then on until the critical period is past. The opportunity to type and cross match the blood should be taken at this time. In cases of massive envenomation, especially in children, this may be difficult to do later. If the hematocrit and hemoglobin values drop greatly, whole blood should be administered as necessary. At the time of maximum hemorrhage, there is frequently an abrupt rise in the serum potassium level, perhaps the result of lysis of the pooled red cells in the tissues. Frequent ion exchange resin enemas may reduce this hyperkalemia, although peritoneal dialysis can also be performed if necessary.

Care should be taken to prevent contracture in the envenomated extremity and physiotherapy should be instituted as soon as possible to maintain motor and sensory function in the affected area.

THE BITE OF THE NORTH AMERICAN CORAL SNAKE

Even in papers such as those by Merriam (1961) and Ya and Perry (1960) dealing with ophidiasis in North America, the coral snakes of genus *Micrurus* have largely been ignored. Even accounts such as those by Wood (1954) and Parrish (1957a, b), which deal exclusively with areas inhabited by the coral snake, fail to mention, or only mention briefly, these elapids on grounds that they are " not commonly encountered " or cause few deaths " as a result of less aggressive (than the pit viper) nature ". As a result, a great deal of confusion, misapprehension, and ignorance exists concerning these snakes, the nature of their venom, and especially, the method of treatment of an individual bitten by them.

Neil (1957) has catalogued some common misconceptions about the habits of this snake and the nature of its venom, together with 20 case histories of coral snake bites recorded from 1934 to 1956. Neil and also Minton (1957) estimate the incidence of lethality in humans to be 20 per cent of the bites, only about half that of the mortality rate of Eastern diamondback rattlesnake bites which occurred between 1930 and 1950. Data still being compiled by the Florida State Board of Health, indicate that seven coral snake bites have occurred in Florida in 1962, though none of these have been fatal.

While these incidents are not frequent they are of serious consequence. Shannon (1956) points out that " It is incumbent upon the physician to acquaint himself with the general nature of the poisonous snakes in the region where he is practising medicine." It is to be hoped, also, that even without detailed knowledge of the nature of the venom involved, he will be acquainted with the fundamentals of proper treatment.

Venoms are heterogeneous mixtures of enzymes and toxins probably protein in nature. Elaborately developed through the history of the species, they are composed of a mosaic of factors which both kill the prey and partially digest it. These have been classified neatly into descriptive compartments by names like " neurotoxins ", " hemotoxins ", " cytolysins ", " cardiotoxins ", etc. As our knowledge of the venom increases and our insight into some of the mechanisms whereby these potent biologically active materials exert their effect increases, these terms are ever less apt. Jimenez-Porras (1961) has pointed out that the complexity of such enzymatic organization is extremely important in the physiology of the reptile. The end product of one reaction may be a substrate for another enzyme present in the same venom. In like manner, the substrate produced as an end-product in an enzyme reaction may be a " secondary " toxin in the tissues of the envenomated animal. There are some indications, in papers by Gennaro *et al.* (1962) and Russell and Long (1960), that the " unfolding " of the venom complex and the successive activities of the venom in tissues may be controlled by the concentration of metal ion co-factors necessary for optimal reactivity of both enzymes and (what are apparently) non-enzymic factors. Russell and Long (1960) emphasize that, in such complexity of organization, the so-called " neurotoxins " may have hemolytic activity and cardiotoxins may have " neurotoxic " activity, etc.

The venom of the coral snake is primarily distinguished from that of the pit viper by the *absence* of the hemorrhagic principles, two in number, which have been found in the venom of crotalid snakes, as reported by Ohsaka *et al.* (1960), and by the presence of extremely potent toxic material(s) which produce a much different effect in the envenomated individual than the venom of the pit viper. Barnes and Trueta (1941) noted that " venom molecules " of the elapids are much smaller in size than those of the crotalids, and therefore, are much more rapidly disseminated through the tissues of the bitten individual.

While it is true that potent toxins are separable from cobra venom, for example, by dialysis, which would indicate their small size, powerful hemolytic material remains within the dialysis membrane, too large to pass through. Toxic factors of small size have also been described to exist in the venom of the crotalid snakes (crotamine-*C. terrificus* venom), however, and so it may simply be that the elapid venoms contain more lower molecular weight components than do the crotalid ones. This may mean that incision and suction could be of some value in the treatment of the bite of the larger elapid snakes, but this possibility should be carefully evaluated experimentally before it is attempted clinically.

The amount of venom the North American coral snake can be made to deliver if it is held and carefully " milked " into a container is so small that the fact that it can produce such serious consequences in the adult human seems incredible. The fangs of this snake are not retractable like those of the pit viper, but remain erect at the front of the mouth. If the mouth is forced open they are observable as small projections on the underside of the upper jaw. The fangs are so small that, while it is possible for them to bite through the thin skin of the ear of a mouse or the dorsum of a bare foot, they could not possibly penetrate the thick callus of a workman's palm or even the scaly tail of the same mouse whose ear proved so easy to penetrate.

Envenomation following coral snake bite manifests itself almost always by the onset of systemic discomfort accompanied by little or no swelling at the site of the puncture which may be only a slight abrasion of the skin. A warm or cold sensation may be experienced which generally is followed by a drowsiness, pleasant, but potentially of serious consequence. At this time, there is thickening of speech with slurring of the words and drooping (ptosis) of the eyelids. The general impression of motor dysfunction is remarkably similar to inebriation.

The most successful method for the treatment of coral snake envenomation is by *intravenous* administration of the antivenin (Soro Antielapidico-Instituto Butantan), available as a solution of precipitated horse globulin antibodies made in response to venom of *Micrurus corallinus*, the Brazilian coral snake; the antivenin which Keegan *et al.* (1961) have shown neutralizes the venom of the North American coral snake. *One should not assume, according to Raynolds* (1959), *that because cobra venom is " neurotoxic ", an antivenin made from it will be effective in treating coral snake bites because coral snake venom is also " neurotoxic "*. Until the work of Keegan and his associates, even the effectiveness of South American coral snake antivenin in treatment of North American coral snake bite was questioned by Shannon (1953).

Coral snake envenomation results in respiratory embarassment or failure. For this reason a positive pressure respirator is a good supportive consideration. In the bites of the crotalid snakes of North America many of the symptoms of envenomation show spectacular remission after the administration of crotalid antivenin. This does not seem to be so in the treatment of elapid venom intoxication. Here, the progressive damage seems irreversible.* Some success has been obtained in the treatment of seriously intoxicated experimental animals with the use of a chelating agent administered intravenously (EDTA-Sodium). Russell (personal comments) informed the writer that this type of therapy was attempted in a child suffering from a black widow spider bite and produced remarkable improvement after administration of the antiserum had no effect. Laboratory evidence produced by Gennaro *et al.* (1962) seems to indicate that intravenous administration of certain buffered sulfhydryl drugs (glutathione, cysteine) would also be effective in this situation.

*RAMSEY, G. F. and KLICKSTEIN, G. D. 1962. *J.A.M.A.* **182**, 949, provide a notable exception to this general impression.

It may be that better understanding of the mechanisms of venom toxicity will enable future workers to revise completely the methods of bite treatment and discard many disadvantages presently necessary.

ACKNOWLEDGEMENTS

These investigations were supported by Public Health Service grants NIH RG 7024(C1): (C2).

The assistance and advice of the many coworkers who participated in the experimental background of this work is gratefully acknowledged as is the help of the members of the staff of the Library of the College of Medicine.

Appreciation for heroic efforts in the preparation of the manuscript under adverse conditions of time must be expressed to Beverly Turner Sites.

REFERENCES

ALLEN, F. M. 1937. Local asphyxia and temperature change in relation to gangrene and other surgical problems. *Trans. Assoc. Am. Phys.* **52**, 189.

ALLEN, F. M. 1938. The tourniquet and local asphyxia. *Am. J. Surg.* **41**, 192.

ALLEN, F. M. 1939. Observation on local measures in the treatment of snakebite. *Am. J. Trop. Med.* **19**, 393.

ALLEN, F. M. 1949. Venomous bites and stings. *J. Am. Med. Assn.* **139**, 616.

Antivenin, Brochure on crotalid snakes, treatment of their bite, and the use of polyvalent antivenin (Crotalidae). 1961. Wyeth Laboratories, Div. of Am. Home Products Corp., N.Y.

AVICENNAE. 1608. Du regimine modisionis universari, et de curatione mordications serpentum et specibus curum. *Cannon Medicinae Ex Geradi Cremonensis Verzione*, Fol. II, libri IV, fen 6, tract 3 Venetrus.

BARNES, J. M. and TRUETA, J. 1941. Absorption of bacteria, toxins and snake venom from the tissues. *Lancet* **240**, 623.

BATA, A. and VUKOBRATOVIC, S. 1958. Effet et application de l'hypothermie dans les morsures de serpents venimeux. *Bull. Soc. Path. Exot.* **51**, 998.

BOQUET, P. 1956. Effect of hyaluronidase on the therapeutic activity of antivenoms. *Venoms*, p. 387. Publ. No. 44. AAAS, Wash., D.C.

BORDEN, J., FONKALSRUD, E. W., NEWCOMER, V., LONGMIRE, W. P., Jr. and ROCHLIN, D. B. 1961. Snakebite: Treatment by isolation perfusion technique. *Surg.* **49**, 303.

BOYS, F., BEAMER, P. and SMITH, H. 1960. Antibiotics in tests for toxicity of snake venom. *J. Am. Med. Assn.* **174**, 306.

BRUNEAU, J. and HEINBECKER, P. L. 1944. Effects of cooling of experimentally infected tissues. *Annals. of Surg.* **120**, 716.

BUCKLEY, E. Personal communication.

CLUXTON, H. E., Jr. 1951. Treatment of black widow spider bite and copperhead snake bite with ACTH. Proc. 2d ACTH Conf. Vol. II; *Therapeutics*. J. R. Mote, Ed., N.Y.: The Blakiston Co.

CRILEY, B. 1956. Development of a multivalent antivenin for the family Crotalidae. *Venoms*, p. 373. Publ. No. 44. AAAS, Wash., D.C.

CRUM, C. W. R. 1906. Treatment of the bites of copperhead snakes. *J. Am. Med. Assn.* **46**, 1433.

DEICHMANN, W. B., RADOMSKI, J. L., FARRELL, J. J., MACDONALD, W. E. and KEPLINGER, M. L. 1958. Acute toxicity and treatment of intoxications due to Crotalus adamanteus (rattlesnake venom). *Am. J. Med. Sci.* **326**, 204.

EFRATI, P. and REIF, L. 1953. Clinical and pathological observations on 65 cases of viper bite in Israel. *Am. J. Trop. Med. and Hyg.* **2**, 1085.

EMERY, J. A. and RUSSELL, F. E. 1961. Studies with cooling measures following injection of *Crotalus* venom. *Copeia* (3), 322.

FIDLER, H. K., GLASGOW, R. D. and CARMICHAEL, E. B. 1940. Pathological changes produced by the subcutaneous injection of rattlesnake (*Crotalus*) venom into *Matcaca mulata* monkeys. *Am. J. of Path.* **16**, 355.

FISCHER, F. J., RAMSEY, H. W., SIMON, J. and GENNARO, J. F. Jr. 1961. Antivenin and antitoxin in the treatment of experimental rattlesnake venom intoxication (*Crotalus adamanteus*). *Am. J. Trop. Med. Hyg.* **10**, 75.

GANATRA, R. D., DHOPESHWARKAR, G. A., SHETH, U. K. and LEWIS, R. A. 1957. The use of hydrocortisone in experimental viper venom poisoning in mice. *Indian J. Med. Sci. Bombay*, **11**, 493.

GENNARO, J. F., CALLAHAN, W. P. and LORINCZ, A. E. 1962. In press. Symp. on Mucous Secretion, N.Y. Acad. of Sci. The anatomy and biochemistry of a mucous secreting cell type present in the poison apparatus of the pit viper *Ancistrodon piscivorus piscivorus.*

GENNARO, J. F., SQUICCIARINI, P. J. and ROHAN, N. J. 1958. The accumulation of radioiodine by the poison gland of the cottonmouth moccasin (*Ancistrodon piscivorus piscivorus*). *Anat. Rec.* **130**, 304.

GENNARO, J. F., LEOPOLD, R. S. and MERRIAM, T. W. 1961. Observations on the actual quantity of venom introduced by several species of crotalid snakes in their bite. *Anat. Rec.* **139**, 303.

GENNARO, J. F. and CASEY, E. R. 1961. Central parasympathetic stimulation of the mammalian eye after intravenous injection of rattlesnake (*Crotalus adamanteus*) venom. *Anat. Rec.* **139**, 230.

GENNARO, J. F., MORRIS, R., BREWSTER, H. B. and DEVITT. H. P. 1962. Sulfhydryl inactivation of the toxicity and hemolytic activity of snake venom and the mechanism of its action. *Fed. Proc.* **21**, 36D.

GITHENS, T. S. 1935. Snakebite in the United States. *Sci. Monthly* **41**, 163.

HOBACK, W. W. and GREEN, T. W. 1953. Treatment of snake venom poisoning with cortisone and corticotropin. *J. Am. Med. Assn.* **152**, 236.

JACKSON, D. 1929. Treatment of snakebite. *Southern Med. J.* **22**, 605.

JACKSON, D. 1944. Management of snakebite. *Clin. Trop. Med.* Bercovitz, Ed., Paul Hoeber, Inc. N.Y.

JIMENEZ-PORRAS, J. M. 1961. Biochemical studies on the venom of the rattlesnake, *Crotalus atrox atrox. J. E. Z.*, **148** (3), 251.

KEEGAN, H. L., WHITTEMORE, F. W., Jr. and FLANIGAN, J. F. 1961. Heterologous antivenin in neutralization of North American coral snake venom. *Pub. Health Rep.* **76**, 540.

KELLAWAY, C. H. and WILLIAMS, F. E. 1933. Investigation of the toxicity and sterility of commercial preparations containing modified snake venom. *Med. J. Australia* **1**, 581.

KIRSCH, R. 1952. Uber Kreuzotterbissverletzungen. *Zentralbl. chir.* **77**, 198.

KLAUBER, L. M. 1956. *Rattlesnakes, Their Habits, Life Histories, and Influence on Mankind.* Univ. of Calif. Press. Berkeley.

KNOWLES, R. P., SNYDER, C. C., with the technical assistance of HAAST, W. 1959. Observations on experimental snake venom poisoning and immunity. From an address delivered at the meeting of the Fla. State Vet. Med. Assn.

LARGE, A. and HEINBECKER, P. L. 1944a. Refrigeration in clinical surgery. *Annals Surg.* **120**, 707.

LARGE, A. and HEINBECKER, P. L. 1944b. Effect of cooling on wound healing. *Annals Surg.* **120**, 727.

LARGE, A. and HEINBECKER, P. L. 1944c. Nerve degeneration following prolonged cooling of an extremity. *Annals Surg.* **120**, 742.

LEOPOLD, R. S., HUBER, G. S. and KATHAN, R. H. 1957. An evaluation of the mechanical treatment of snakebite. *Military Med.* **120**, 414.

LEOPOLD, R. S. and HUBER, G. S. 1960. Ineffectiveness of suction in removing snake venom from open wounds. *U.S. Armed Forces M. J.* **11**, 682.

MAIER, H. K. 1951. Benadryl hydrochloride in the treatment of snakebite in dogs. *Vet. Med.* **46**, 463.

McCOLLOUGH, N. C., GRIMES, D. W. and GENNARO, J. F. 1961. An evaluation of extremity loss due to venomous snakebite in the State of Florida. *J. Bone and Joint Surg.* **43-A**, 597.

MERRIAM, T. W. and LEOPOLD, R. S. 1960. Evaluation of incision and suction in venom removal. *Clin. Res.* **8**, 258.

MERRIAM, T. W. 1961. Current concepts in the management of snakebite. *Military Med.* **126**, 526.

MINTON, S. A., Jr. 1954. Polyvalent antivenin in the treatment of experimental snake venom poisoning. *Am. J. Trop. Med. and Hyg.* **3**, 1077.

MINTON, S. A., Jr. 1957. Snakebite. *Scientific Am.* **196**, 114.

NEIL, W. T. 1957. Some misconceptions regarding the Eastern coral snake, *Micrurus fulvius*. *Herpetologica* **13**, 111.

OHSAKA, A., IKEZAWA, H., KONDO, H., KONDO, S. and UCHIDA, N. 1960. Haemorrhagic activities of habu snake venom and their relations to lethal toxicity, proteolytic activities and other pathological activities. *Brit. J. Exp. Path.* **41**, 478.

PARRISH, H. M. 1960. Treatment of poisonous snakebites: present status of incision and suction. *J. Ind. State Med. Assn.* **53**, 1879.

PARRISH, H. M. 1955. Early excision and suction of snakebite wounds in dogs. *N. Carol. Med. J.* **16**, 93.

PARRISH, H. M. 1957a. The poisonous snakebite problem in Florida. *Quarterly J. Fla. Acad. Sci.* **20**, 185.

PARRISH, H. M. 1957b. On the incidence of poisonous snakebite in Florida: an analysis of 241 cases occurring during 1954–1955. *Am. J. Trop. Med. and Hyg.* **6**, 761.

PARRISH, H. M. 1958. The nature of poisonous snakebites epidemiology, diagnosis and treatment. *Vet. Med.* **53**, 197.

PARRISH, H. M. 1959. Poisonous snakebite resulting in lack of venom poisoning. *Virginia Med. Monthly* **86**, 396.

PARRISH, H. M., MACLAURIN, A. W. and TUTTLE, R. L. 1956. North American pit vipers, bacterial flora of the mouths and venom glands. *Virginia Med. Monthly* **83**, 383.

POLLARD, C. B. 1954. Developments in the field of venoms, antivenoms, and snakebite treatment. *Am. J. Med. Tech.* **20**, 239.

PORGES, N. 1953. Snake venoms, their biochemistry and mode of action. *Science* **117**, 47.

PREVOT, A. R. 1951. Recherches sur la pollution des venins de serpent par les anaerobies et leur sterilisation. *Ann. de l'Institute Pasteur* **81**, 665.

PROVERS, G. 1928. Ancient and Modern Therapy. *Med. Ital.* **9**, 337.

PURANANANDA, C. 1956. Treatment of snakebite cases in Bangkok. *Venoms*, p. 353. Publ. No. 44, AAAS, Wash., D.C.

RAYNOLDS, A. H. 1959. Treatment of snakebite Questions and Answers. *J. Am. Med. Assn.* **169**, 782.

RUSSELL, F. E. 1960. Rattlesnake bites in Southern California. *Am. J. Med. Sci.* **239**, 51.

RUSSELL, F. E. 1960. Snake venom poisoning in Southern California. *Calif. Med.* **93**, 347.

RUSSELL, F. E. Personal communication.

RUSSELL, F. E. and LONG, T. E. 1960. Effects of venoms on neuromuscular transmission. *Myasthenia Gravis*. Henry R. Viets, Ed. Charles C. Thomas, Publ. Springfield, Ill.

RUSSELL, F. E. and EMERY, J. A. 1961. Effects of corticosteroids on lethality of *Ancistrodon contortrix* venom. *Am. J. Med. Sci.* **241**, 507.

RUSSELL, F. E. and EMERY, J. A. 1961. Incision and suction following injection of rattlesnake venom. *Am. J. Med. Sci.* **241**, 160.

SCHREIBER, M. S. and MALJUGIN, T. A. 1936. Clinical observations on the problem of snakebite. *Vestnik khirurgii.* **47**.

SHANNON, F. A. 1953. Comments on the treatment of reptile poisoning in the southwest. *Southwest. Med.* **34**, 367.

SHANNON, F. A. 1956. Comments on the treatment of reptile poisoning. *Venoms.* E. Buckley and N. Porges, Ed., Publ. No. 44. Am. Assn. for the Adv. of Sci., Wash., D.C.

SCHÖTTLER, W. H. A. 1951. Toxicity of principal snake venoms of Brazil. *Am. J. Trop. Med. and Hyg.* **31**, 489.

SCHÖTTLER, W. H. A. 1954. Antihistamines, ACTH, cortisone, hydrocortisone, and anaesthetics in snakebite. *Am. J. Trop. Med. and Hyg.* **3**. 1083.

STAHNKE, H. L., ALLEN, F. M., HORAN, R. V. and TENERY, J. H. 1957. The treatment of snakebite. *Am. J. Trop. Med. and Hyg.* **6**, 323.

STICKEL, W. H. 1952. Venomous snakes of the United States and treatment of their bites. Dept. of Interior Wildlife Leaflet, No. 339.

STIMSON, A. C. and ENGELHARDT, H. T. 1960. The treatment of snakebite. *J. Occ. Med.* **2**, 163.

TAUBE, H. N. and ESSEX, H. E. 1937. Pathologic changes in the tissues of the dog following injection of rattlesnake venom. *A.M.A. Arch. Path.* **24**, 43.

WILLIAMS, F. E., FREEMAN, M. and KENNEDY, E. 1934. The bacterial flora of the mouths of the Australian venomous snakes in captivity. *Med. J. Australia* **2**, 190.

WOOD, J. T. 1954. A survey of 200 cases of snakebite in Virginia. *Am. J. Trop. Med. and Hyg.* **3**, 936.

WOOD, J. T., HOBACK, W. W. and GREEN, T. W. 1955. Treatment of snake venom poisoning with ACTH and cortisone. *Virg. Med. Monthly* **82**, 130.

YA, P. M. and PERRY, J. F., Jr. 1960. Experimental evaluation of methods for the early treatment of snakebite. *Surg.* **47**, 975.

AUTHOR INDEX